# THE GENERAL POINT PROCESS

Applications to
Structural Fatigue
Bioscience, and
Medical Research

## APPLIED MATHEMATICS AND COMPUTATION

A Series of Graduate Textbooks, Monographs, Reference Works
Series Editor: ROBERT KALABA, University of Southern California

No. 1 MELVIN R. SCOTT
*Invariant Imbedding and its Applications to Ordinary Differential Equations: An Introduction, 1973*

No. 2 JOHN CASTI and ROBERT KALABA
*Imbedding Methods in Applied Mathematics, 1973*

No. 3 DONALD GREENSPAN
*Discrete Models, 1973*

No. 4 HARRIET H. KAGIWADA
*System Identification: Methods and Applications, 1974*

No. 5 V. K. MURTHY
*The General Point Process: Applications to Structural Fatigue, Bioscience, and Medical Research, 1974*

No. 6 HARRIET H. KAGIWADA and ROBERT KALABA
*Integral Equations Via Imbedding Methods, 1974*

No. 7 J. T. TOU and R. C. GONZALEZ
*Pattern Recognition Principles, 1974*

# THE GENERAL POINT PROCESS

## Applications to Structural Fatigue Bioscience, and Medical Research

V. K. Murthy
University of California, Los Angeles
and University of Southern California

1974

**Addison-Wesley Publishing Company**
Advanced Book Program
Reading, Massachusetts

London · Amsterdam · Don Mills, Ontario · Sydney · Tokyo

CODEN: APMCC

Library of Congress Cataloging in Publication Data

Murthy, V. K.
The general point process.

(Applied mathematicas and computation, v.5)
Bibliography: p.
1. P processes. I. Title.
QA274.42.M86 519.5'3 74-16382
ISBN 0-201-04892-0
ISBN 0-201-04893-0 (pbk.)

Reproduced by Addison-Wesley Publishing Company, Inc., Advanced Book Program, Reading, Massachusetts, from camera-ready copy prepared by the author.

American Mathematical Society (MOS) Subject Classification Scheme (1970): 60G35, 60K05, 60K10, 62P10, 73M10, 73P05, 92–02, 92A05, 92A15



Manufactured in the United States of America

ABCDEFGHIJ-MA-7987654

To:

Suramma, Philippa, and Sujata

CONTENTS

## SERIES EDITOR'S FOREWORD

Execution times of modern digital computers are measured in nanoseconds. They can solve hundreds of simultaneous ordinary differential equations with speed and accuracy. But what does this immense capability imply with regard to solving the scientific, engineering, economic, and social problems confronting mankind? Clearly, much effort has to be expended in finding answers to that question.

In some fields, it is not yet possible to write mathematical equations which accurately describe processes of interest. Here, the computer may be used simply to simulate a process and, perhaps, to observe the efficacy of different control processes. In others, a mathematical description may be available, but the equations are frequently difficult to solve numerically. In such cases, the difficulties may be faced squarely and possibly overcome; alternatively, formulations may be sought which are more compatible with the inherent capabilities of computers. Mathematics itself nourishes and is nourished by such developments.

Each order of magnitude increase in speed and memory

size of computers requires a reexamination of computational techniques and an assessment of the new problems which may be brought within the realm of solution. Volumes in this series will provide indications of current thinking regarding problem formulations, mathematical analysis, and computational treatment.

ROBERT KALABA

# PREFACE

The word "event" or "point," as used in this book, stands for the happening of a situation. Examples of this are: a pedestrian being knocked down by a car, an aeroplane experiencing sudden accelerations due to turbulence or maneuvering procedures, a person suffering an acute myocardial infarction, or a woman suffering a miscarriage or delivering a stillborn child, etc. The lapses in time between points, when time is counted arbitrarily, i.e., not at the beginning of the happening of an event, is called a General Point Process. The Ordinary Point Process, or Renewal Process as it is called, is a particular case when time is counted with the occurrence of an event.

The prime object of this book is two-fold. Firstly, to develop the theory involving the distribution of the events by any specified time for a General Point Process. Secondly, to bring together as many fields of applications of this theory, certainly not in an exhaustive way, but only with the fond hope that the readers realize the interdisciplinary nature of this work.

Rightfully so, the author has incorporated the

related work of his former students, Mr. Sheldon Geller and Mr. Leonard Chessler; his colleague William Warren and teacher Walter Smith; and finally, his co-author on many related applications, Boyd Swartz. Last, but not least, the work of the man who indirectly inspired me to put together this book, Dr. Edward Perrin, by his basic contributions to theoretical biology using the General Point Process.

I am grateful to Dr. John M. Weiner for his kindness and generosity which he showed in so many ways and which helped in the finishing of this book.

Finally, this book would never have seen the light of day, but for the patient understanding and tireless efforts of Mrs. Ruth Goldstein, who literally is responsible for the typing and organization of this work.

V. K. Murthy
University of California
and
University of Southern California

# LIST OF ABBREVIATIONS

| | |
|---|---|
| BAN | Best asymptotically normal |
| B.V. | Bounded variation |
| DHR | Decreasing hazard rate |
| DMR | Decreasing mean residual life |
| GHR | General hazard rate |
| G.P.P. | General Point Process |
| IHR | Increasing hazard rate |
| IHRA | Increasing hazard rate average |
| L.T. | Laplace Transform |
| L.-S.T | Laplace-Stieltjes Transform |
| P.P. | Point process |
| psd | Power spectral density |
| ref | Reliability function |
| r.v. | Random variable |
| w.r.t | With respect to |

# CHAPTER 1. PRELIMINARIES

## 1.1. Introduction, Notation and Preliminary Results

In this chapter the results on the Cumulants of a General Point Process (GPP) are obtained. These results are actually generalizations of those Smith [196] has obtained for ordinary point processes. After establishing the asymptotic representation theorems for the $\varphi$-moments and $\psi$-cumulants of a General Point Process (the definition of the $\varphi$-moments and the $\psi$-cumulants are given in the next section ) the table of the first eight cumulants of an ordinary point process has been extended to the case of a General Point Process. A theorem is proved leading to a check on the calculations. As a particular case of the General Point Process, the cumulants of the "Equilibrium Process" are obtained. We will now develop the necessary notation and preliminary results.

## 1.2. Notation and Preliminary Results

Let $\{x_i\}$, $i = 1,\ldots,n,\ldots,$ be an infinite sequence of independent, nonnegative, identically distributed random variables which are not all zero with probability one and let their distribution function be $F(x)$. Unless otherwise stated it is assumed that $F(x)$ is such that for some $K$ its $K^{th}$ convolution has an absolutely continuous component. Let $\mu_r = E(x_i^r)$, if this moment exists. Such a sequence of r.v.'s is called a point process (P.P.). Further, let $x_0$ be a nonnegative, r.v. independent of $x_i$ $(i \geq 1)$ with distribution function $K(x)$, where $K(x)$ is not necessarily identical with $F(x)$ and let $\nu_r = E(x_0^r)$, if this moment exists. Then the augmented sequence $\{x_i\}$, $i = 0,1,\ldots$ is called a General Point Process (G.P.P.).

Let $S_k = x_1 + \cdots + x_k$. $N_t$ is defined as the maximum suffix $k$ for which $S_k \leq t$, subject to the condition $N_t = 0$, if $x_1 > t$. In the obvious renewal application, the $x_i$ represent the lifetimes of articles being renewed and $N_t$ is the number of renewals made by time $t$, subject to the original object having been installed at time $t = 0$. On the other hand, one considers a G.P.P. when the initial installation was not known to be at $t = 0$, but only to be at some point chosen on the positive semiaxis of the time scale, in accordance with a certain probability distribution. In particular, $x_0$ of the G.P.P. might be the "residual lifetime" of the article in use at the arbitrary chosen origin $t = 0$.

For a G.P.P., let $\tilde{S}_{-1} = 0$; $\tilde{S}_k = x_0 + x_1 + \cdots + x_k$,

$k = 0.1, \ldots,$ and for all $t \geq 0$, define the random variable $\tilde{N}_t$ as the greatest integer $k$ such that $\tilde{S}_{k-1} \leq t$.

The random variable $\tilde{N}_t$ associated with a G.P.P. is studied following the lines of study by Smith [196] of the random variable $N_t$ associated with a P.P. We deal only with a continuous G.P.P., that is, we suppose there is no $\omega > 0$ such that with probability one, every $x_n$ is divisible by $\omega$. It will be convenient to introduce another random variable $N'_t$ defined as the maximum suffix $k$, such that $\tilde{S}_k \leq t$, for $t \geq 0$. It will be seen in Lemma 2, that the study of $\tilde{N}_t$ and $N'_t$ are equivalent and we therefore concentrate on $N'_t$ rather than $\tilde{N}_t$, as its study is less complicated. Let us introduce some moment formulae with respect to the random variable $N_t$; when these moments involve either $\tilde{N}_t$ or $N'_t$ instead on $N_t$, the corresponding symbol ~ or ' is put on the moments. Let $m_r(t)$ and $\kappa_r(t)$ denote, respectively, the $r^{th}$ conventional moment and cumulant of $N_t$. Let

$$\varphi_k(t) = E(N_t + 1)(N_t + 2) \cdots (N_t + k)$$

be the $\varphi$-moment of order $k$ with generating function

$$\Phi_t(\zeta) = E \frac{1}{(1 - \zeta)^{N_t+1}} .$$

The corresponding $\psi$-cumulant of order $k$ is obtained by a formal power series expansion of the cumulant generating function

$$\Psi_t(\zeta) = \log \varphi_t(\zeta) \quad .$$

Let $M_t(z) = E\, e^{zN_t}$ and let $K_t(z) = \log M_t(z)$. Then it can be shown (Smith [1]) that

$$M_t(z) = E\, e^{zN_t} = e^{-z}\, \Phi_t(1 - e^{-z}) \quad ,$$

and hence that

$$K_t(z) = - z + \Psi_t(1 - e^{-z}) \quad ,$$

and

$$\Psi_t(\zeta) = \log (1 - \zeta) + K_t(- \log \overline{1 - \zeta}) \quad .$$

By these formulae, the $\psi$-cumulants of $N_t$ can be expressed in terms of the conventional cumulants and vice versa.

In what follows we will assume that the functions we are dealing with vanish identically for negative values of their argument. If $\Omega(t)$ is any function of bounded variation (B.V.) in every finite interval, then we write

$$\Omega^*(s) = \int_0^\infty e^{-st}\, d\Omega(t) \quad ,$$

for the Laplace-Stieltjes transform (L-S.T.) of $\Omega(t)$. If $\Omega(t)$ is any function which is integrable in every finite interval then we write

$$\Omega^0(s) = \int_0^\infty e^{-st}\,\Omega(t)dt \quad ,$$

for the Laplace transform (L.T.) of $\Omega(t)$. All the transforms that arise in this chapter will exist for $\Re e(s) > 0$. Also, when $\Omega(t)$ has both an L-S.T. and an L.T., then

$$\Omega*(x) = s\Omega^0(s) \quad .$$

We will make repeated use of the following lemma of Smith [171].

LEMMA A: <u>A necessary and sufficient condition for the distribution function</u> $F(x)$ <u>of a nonnegative r.v. to have its first</u> $k$ <u>moments finite is that there exists another distribution function</u> $F_{(k)}(x)$ <u>such that</u>

$$F*(s) = 1 - \mu_1 s + \mu_2 \frac{s^2}{2!} - \cdots + \mu_{k-1}\frac{(-s)^{k-1}}{(k-1)!} + \mu_k \frac{(-s)^k}{k!} F^*_{(k)}(s) \quad .$$

Let $\gamma_n$ and $\gamma'_n$ stand for finite rational functions of $\mu_1, \mu_2, \ldots, \mu_n$ and $\nu_1, \nu_2, \ldots, \nu_n$, respectively, and let $\gamma_{ij}$ denote a rational function in $\mu_1, \mu_2, \ldots, \mu_i$ and $\nu_1, \nu_2, \ldots, \nu_j$. If $\mu_n < \infty$, and

$$K^*_n(s) = \frac{1 - F^*_{(n)}(s)}{1 - F^*(s)} \quad , \qquad n \geq 1 \quad ,$$

then $K_n(x)$ is a function of bounded variation, (Smith

[196]). Let $M_w^{*d}$ stand for any multinomial expression in $K_1^*, K_2^*, \ldots, K_w^*$, with coefficients $\gamma_w$ and with maximum degree of any term not greater than d.

We shall now prove

LEMMA 1: $$\varphi_n^*(s) = K^*(s)\, \varphi_n^*(s) \quad .$$

<u>Proof</u>: By definition

$$\varphi_n'(t) = E(N_t' + 1)\,(N_t' + 2) \cdots (N_t' + n) \quad ,$$

where $N_t'$ is the maximum k such that $\tilde{S}_k \leq t$. Therefore

$$\begin{aligned} \Pr\,[N_t' = k] &= \Pr\,[\tilde{S}_k < t < \tilde{S}_{k+1}] \\ &= K(t) * F_k(t) - K(t) * F_{k+1}(t) \quad , \end{aligned}$$

where $F_j(t)$ denotes the $j^{th}$ convolution of $F(x)$, and $*$ represents the Stieltjes convolution. Therefore

$$\varphi_n'(t) = \sum_{k=0}^{\infty} (k + 1)(k + 2) \cdots (k + n)$$

$$\times\, [K(t) * F_k(t) - K(t) * F_{k+1}(t)] \quad .$$

Taking the Laplace-Stieltjes transform on both sides we get

$$\varphi_n'^*(s) = \sum_{k=0}^{\infty} (k+1)(k+2) \cdots (k+n)\; K^*(s)[F^*(s)]^k[1 - F^*(s)]$$

$$= K^*(s) \sum_{k=0}^{\infty} (k+1) \cdots (k+n)[F^*(s)]^k [1-F^*(s)] \quad .$$

But Smith [ ] has shown that

$$\varphi_n^*(s) = \sum_{k=0}^{\infty} (k+1) \quad (k+n)[F^*(s)]^k [1-F^*(s)]$$

$$= \frac{n!}{[1-F^*(s)]^n} \quad .$$

Hence the lemma is proved.

LEMMA 2: $\dfrac{\tilde{\varphi}_n(t)}{n!} = 1 + \displaystyle\sum_{j=1}^{n} \dfrac{\varphi_j'(t)}{j!}$ .

Proof: By definition

$$\tilde{\varphi}_n(t) = E(\tilde{N}_t+1)(\tilde{N}_t+2) \cdots (\tilde{N}_t+n) = n![1-K(t)]$$

$$+ \sum_{k=1}^{\infty} (k+1)(k+2) \quad (k+n)\ K^*(s)[F^*(s)]^{k-1}[1-F^*(s)]$$

$$= n![1-K^*(s)] + K^*(s)[1-F^*(s)]$$

$$\times \left[ (n+1)! + \frac{(n+2)!}{2!} F^* + \frac{(n+3)!}{3!} F^* + \cdots \right] =$$

$$= n![1 - K^*(s)] + \frac{(n+1)!}{(n+1)} \frac{K^*(s)}{F^*(s)} [1 - F^*(s)]$$

$$\cdot \left[(n+1)F^* + \frac{(n+1)(n+2)}{2} F^* + \cdots\right]$$

$$= n!\left[1 - K^*(s)\right] + \frac{n!K^*(s)}{F^*(s)} \left[1 - F^*(s)\right]\left[\{1 - F^*(s)\}^{-(n+1)} - 1\right] .$$

Therefore

$$\frac{\tilde{\varphi}_n^*(s)}{n!} = 1 - K^*(s) + \frac{K^*(s)}{F^*(s)} \left[\frac{1}{[1 - F^*(s)]^n} - (1 - F^*(s))\right]$$

$$= 1 - K^*(s) + \left[1 + (1 - F^*(s)) + (1 - F^*(s))^2 + \cdots + (1 - F^*(s))^n\right] \frac{K^*(s)}{[1 - F^*(s)]^n}$$

$$= 1 - K^*(s) + K^*(s)\left[1 + \varphi_1^*(s) + \frac{\varphi_2^*(s)}{2!} + \cdots + \frac{\varphi_n^*(s)}{n!}\right]$$

$$= 1 + \sum_{j=1}^{n} \frac{\varphi_j^*(s)\, K^*(s)}{j!} = 1 + \sum_{j=1}^{n} \frac{\varphi_n'^*}{j!} ,$$

by Lemma 1. Therefore

$$\frac{\tilde{\varphi}_n(t)}{n!} = 1 + \sum_{j=1}^{n} \frac{\varphi_j'(t)}{j!} .$$

The importance of the above result is that it shows that the asymptotic behavior of the moments $\tilde{\varphi}_n(t)$ can easily be inferred from the asymptotic behavior of the moments $\varphi_n'(t)$.

## 1.3. The asymptotic form of $\tilde{\varphi}_n(t)$

We shall first obtain the asymptotic form of $\varphi_n'(t)$ and then, by using Lemma 2, the asymptotic form of $\tilde{\varphi}_n(t)$ can be written down immediately.

From Lemma 1, we have

$$(1.3.1) \qquad \varphi_n'^{*}(s) = K^{*}(s)\,\varphi_n^{*}(s) \quad ,$$

and we have, therefore,

$$(1.3.2) \qquad \varphi_n'(t) = \int_0^t \varphi_n(t-x)\,dK(x) \quad .$$

If $\mu_{n+1} < \infty$, we have from Theorem 1 of Smith [196], that

$$(1.3.3) \quad \varphi_n(t) = \gamma_1 t^n + \gamma_2 t^{n-1} + \cdots + \gamma_n t + M_n^n(t) \quad ,$$

where

$$M_n^n(t) - \gamma_{n+1} \in B \quad ,$$

$B$ being the class of functions $\lambda(t)$ which are of bounded variation, tend to zero as $t \to +\infty$ and are such that

$$\lambda(t) - \lambda(t-\alpha) = O\left(\frac{1}{t}\right) \quad \text{as} \quad t \to \infty \quad ,$$

for every $\alpha > 0$. Substituting from (1.3.3) in (1.3.2) we get

$$(1.3.4) \qquad \varphi_n'(t) = \int_0^t \sum_{j=1}^{n} \gamma_n (t-x)^{n+1-j} \, dK(x) + \int_0^t M_n^n(t-x) \, dK(x) \quad .$$

Taking the L-S.T. on both sides of (1.3.4), we get

$$(1.3.5) \qquad \varphi_n'^{*}(s) = \sum_{j=1}^{n} \frac{\gamma_j}{s^{(n+1-j)}} K^*(s) + M_n^{n*}(s) \, K^*(s) \quad .$$

From (1.3.5) it is evident that we should assume $\nu_n < \infty$ in order to account for the entire polynomial part of $\varphi_n'(t)$.

But, from Lemma A, for $\nu_n < \infty$, it is both necessary and sufficient that

(1.3.6)

$$K^*(s) = 1 + \gamma_1' s + \gamma_2' s^2 + \cdots + \gamma_{n-1}' s^{n-1} + \gamma_n' K_{(n)}^*(s) s^n$$

where $K_n(t)$ is a distribution function. Now

(1.3.7)

$$\varphi_n'^{*}(s) = \frac{\gamma_n}{s} K^*(s) + \frac{\gamma_{n-1}}{s^2} K^*(s) + \cdots + \frac{\gamma_{n+1-j}}{s^j} K^*(s) + \cdots + \frac{\gamma_1}{s^n} K^*(s) + M_n^{n*}(s) \, K^*(s)$$

$$= \frac{\gamma_n}{s} [1 + \gamma_1' s \, K_{(1)}^*(s)] + \frac{\gamma_{n-1}}{s^2} [1 + \gamma_1' s + \gamma_2' s^2 \, K_{(2)}^*(s)] +$$

$$+ \cdots + \frac{\gamma_{n+1-j}}{s^j}\left[1 + \gamma_1' s + \cdots + \gamma_{j-1} s^{j-1} + \gamma_j' s^j K^*_{(j)}(s)\right]$$

$$+ \cdots + \frac{\gamma_1}{s^n}\; 1 + \gamma_1' s + \cdots + \gamma_{n-1}' s^{n-1} + \gamma_n' s^n K^*_{(n)}(s)$$

$$+ M_n^{n*}(s)\, K^*(s)$$

$$= \frac{1}{s}\left[\sum_{j=1}^{n} \gamma_{j-1}' \gamma_{n+1-j}\right] + \frac{1}{s^2}\left[\sum_{j=1}^{n-1} \gamma_{j-1}' \gamma_{n-j}\right]$$

$$+ \cdots + \frac{1}{s^k}\left[\sum_{j=1}^{n+1-k} \gamma_{n-1} \gamma_{n+2-k-j}\right]$$

$$+ \cdots + \frac{1}{s^{n-1}}\left[\sum_{j=1}^{2} \gamma_{j-1}' \gamma_{3-j}\right] + \frac{\gamma_1}{s^n} + \sum_{j=1}^{n} \gamma_j \gamma_{n+1-j}$$

$$\cdot K^*_{(j)}(s) + M_n^{n*}(s)\, K^*(s)$$

$$= \frac{\gamma_{n,n-1}}{s} + \frac{\gamma_{n-1,n-2}}{s^2} + \frac{\gamma_{n+1-k,n-k}}{s^k}$$

$$+ \cdots + \frac{\gamma_{2,1}}{s^{n-1}} + \frac{\gamma_1}{s^n} + \gamma_{n,1} K^*_{(1)}(s) + \gamma_{n-1,2} K^*_{(2)}(s)$$

$$+ \cdots + \gamma_{1,n} K^*_{(n)}(s) + M_n^{n*}(s)\, K^*(s) \quad .$$

Hence

(1.3.8)

$$\varphi_n'(t) = \gamma_1 t^n + \gamma_{2,1} t^{n-1} + \qquad + \gamma_{n-1,n-2} t^2 + \gamma_{n,n-1} t + \omega'(t) ,$$

where

(1.3.9)

$$\omega'(t) = \gamma_{n,1} K_{(1)}(t) + \gamma_{n-1,2} K_{(2)}(t) + \cdots + \gamma_{1,n} K_{(n)}(t) + \int_0^t M_n^n(t - x)\, dK(x) \quad .$$

We will now prove that $\omega'(t) - \gamma_{n+1,n}$ belongs to the class B if we further assume $\nu_{n+1} < \infty$.

LEMMA 3: <u>If the first moment of a distribution function</u> $F(x)$ <u>is finite, then</u> $(F(x) - 1)$ <u>belongs to the class</u> B.

<u>Proof</u>: Clearly $F(x) - 1$ is of bounded variation and tends to zero as $x \to \infty$.

To prove $x[F(x) - F(x - \alpha)]$ tends to zero as $x \to \infty$ for every $\alpha > 0$, we notice that

$$\begin{aligned} x[F(x) - F(x - \alpha)] & \\ &< x[1 - F(x - \alpha)] \\ &= x \int_{x-\alpha}^{\infty} dF(x) \\ &= (x - \alpha) \int_{x-\alpha}^{\infty} dF(x) + \alpha \int_{x-\alpha}^{\infty} dF(x) \\ &< \int_{x-\alpha}^{\infty} t\, dF(t) + \alpha \int_{x-\alpha}^{\infty} dF(t) \quad . \end{aligned}$$

The right-hand side tends to zero as $x \to \infty$ and the left-hand side is always nonnegative. Hence

$$\lim_{x \to \infty} x[F(x) - f(x - \alpha)] = 0 \quad ,$$

and our lemma is proved.

In fact, if $\mu_n < \infty$, $\lim_{x \to \infty} x^n[F(x) - F(x - \alpha)] = 0$ for $\alpha > 0$; this result is a straightforward generalization of the above lemma.

Since $\nu_n < \infty$, the means of $K_{(1)}(t), \ldots, K_{(n-1)}(t)$ are all finite and if we further assume $\nu_{n+1} < \infty$, the mean of $K_{(n)}(t)$ is finite and applying Lemma 3 we have

(1.3.10)

$$\gamma_{n,1} K_{(1)}(t) + \gamma_{n-1,2} K_{(2)}(t) + \ldots + \gamma_{1,n} K_{(n)}(t) - \gamma_{n,n} \in B \quad .$$

Smith [196] has proved that if $\mu_{n+1} < \infty$

(1.3.11) $$M_n^n(t) - \gamma_{n+1} = \lambda(t) \quad ,$$

where $\lambda(t) \in B$.

Using (1.3.11) we discover that if

$$\varphi(t) = \int_0^t M_n^n(t - x)\, dK(x) = \gamma_{n+1} K(t) + \int_0^t \lambda(t - x)\, dK(x) \; ,$$

then

$$(1.3.12)\quad t[\varphi(t) - \varphi(t-\alpha)] = t\,\gamma_{n+1}[K(t) - K(t-\alpha)] + \int_0^t t[\lambda(t-x) - \lambda(t-\alpha-x)]\,dK(x) + t\int_{t-\alpha}^t \lambda(t-\alpha-x)\,dK(x) \;.$$

It is not difficult to show that every term on the right-hand side of (1.3.12) tends to zero as $t \to \infty$. Therefore

$$(1.3.13)\qquad \varphi(t) - \gamma_{n+1} \;\epsilon\; B \;.$$

Combining (1.3.10) and (1.3.13) we obtain that if $\mu_{n+1} < \infty$, $\nu_{n+1} < \infty$, then

$$\omega'(t) - \gamma_{n,n} - \gamma_{n+1} = \omega'(t) - \gamma_{n+1,n} \;\epsilon\; B \;;$$

and we have therefore proved the following theorem:

THEOREM 1: <u>If</u> $\mu_{n+1} < \infty$, $\nu_{n+1} < \infty$, <u>then as</u> $t \to \infty$

$$\varphi_n'(t) = \gamma_1 t^n + \gamma_{2,1}t^{n-1} + \cdots + \gamma_{n-1,n-2}t^2 + \gamma_{n,n-1}t + \gamma_{n+1,n} + \omega(t) \;,$$

<u>where</u> $\omega(t)$ <u>belongs to the class</u> B.

The corresponding theorem for $\tilde{\varphi}_n(t)$ of a G.P.P.

follows from Lemma 2 and the closure property of B under linear combinations. Notice that, in all three of the moments $\varphi_n(t)$, $\varphi'_n(t)$ and $\tilde{\varphi}_n(t)$ the coefficient of $t^n$ is the same $\gamma_1$; it is, in fact $n!/\mu_1^n$ (where $\mu_1$ is the first moment of the distribution).

Now, for a discussion of the asymptotic behavior of the cumulants of a G.P.P., we need additional information concerning the remainder term in Theorem 1. We will achieve this by putting additional restrictions on the $\mu$'s and $\nu$'s.

We have from (1.3.7) that

$$(1.3.14)\quad \varphi_n^*(s) = \frac{\gamma_1}{s^n} + \frac{\gamma_{2,1}}{s^{n-1}} + \cdots + \frac{\gamma_{n-1,n-2}}{s^2} + \frac{\gamma_{n,n-1}}{s} + \gamma_{n,1} K^*_{(1)}(s) + \gamma_{n-1,2} K^*_{(2)}(s) + \cdots + \gamma_{1,n} K^*_{(n)}(s) + M_n^{*n}(s) K^*(s) .$$

Therefore, we have for the Laplace transform of $\varphi'_n(t)$,

$$(1.3.15)\quad \varphi_n'^{\,0}(t) = \frac{\gamma_1}{s^{n+1}} + \frac{\gamma_{2,1}}{s^n} + \cdots + \frac{\gamma_{n,n-1}}{s^2} + \gamma_{n,1}\frac{K^*_{(1)}(s)}{s} + \gamma_{n-1,2}\frac{K^*_{(2)}(s)}{s} + \cdots + \gamma_{1,n}\frac{K^*_{(n)}(s)}{s} + \frac{M_n^{*n}(s) K^*(s)}{s}.$$

We will now prove the following basic lemma.

LEMMA 4: If $\mu_{n+p+1} < \infty$, $\nu_{n+p} < \infty$, and $p > 0$, then

$$(-1)^p \varphi_n^{0(p)}(s) = \frac{\gamma_1}{s^{n+p+1}} + \frac{\gamma_{2,1}}{s^{n+p}} + \cdots + \frac{\gamma_{n,n-1}}{s^{p+2}} + \frac{\gamma_{n+1,n}}{s^{p+1}} + O\left(\frac{1}{s}\right), \quad \text{as } s \to 0+ .$$

Proof: Differentiating (1.3.15) $p$ times on both sides, we get

$$(1.3.16) \quad \left(\frac{-d}{ds}\right)^p \varphi_n'^{0}(s) = \frac{\gamma_1}{s^{n+p+1}} + \frac{\gamma_{2,1}}{s^{n+p}} + \cdots + \frac{\gamma_{n,n-1}}{s^{p+2}} + \gamma_{n,1}\left(\frac{-d}{ds}\right)^p \left[\frac{K^*_{(1)}(s)}{s}\right] + \gamma_{n-1,2}\left(\frac{-d}{ds}\right)^p \left[\frac{K^*_{(2)}}{s}\right] + \cdots + \gamma_{1,n}\left(\frac{-d}{ds}\right)^p \left[\frac{K^*_{(n)}}{s}\right] + \left(\frac{-d}{ds}\right)^p \left[\frac{M_n^{*n} K^*}{s}\right] .$$

We show that if the first $p$ moments of any distribution function $F(x)$ of a nonnegative random variable are finite then

$$(1.3.17) \quad \left(\frac{-d}{ds}\right)^p \frac{F^*(s)}{s} = \frac{1}{s^{p+1}} + O\left(\frac{1}{s}\right) .$$

To begin with, we remark that since the first $p$ moments of the distribution function $F(x)$ are finite, we have from Lemma A,

$$\frac{F^*(s)}{s} = \frac{1}{s} + \gamma_1 + \gamma_2 s + \gamma_3 s^2 + \cdots + \gamma_{p-1} s^{p-2} + \gamma_p s^{p-1} F^*_{(p)}(s) ,$$

where $F_{(p)}(t)$ is a distribution function.

Differentiating $p$ times on both sides of this equation yields

$$(1.3.18) \quad \left( \frac{-d}{ds} \right)^p \frac{F^*_{(p)}}{s} = \frac{1}{s^{p+1}} + \gamma_p \left( \frac{-d}{ds} \right)^p [s^{p-1} F^*_{(p)}(s)] .$$

But for any function $\Omega(t)$ of bounded variation, it follows from Smith [196] that

$$(1.3.19a) \quad \Omega^{*(p)}(s) = O\left( \frac{1}{s^p} \right) \quad \text{as} \quad s \to 0+ ,$$

$$(1.3.19b) \quad \left( \frac{-d}{ds} \right)^p [s^{p-1} \Omega^{*(p)}(s)] = O\left( \frac{1}{s} \right) .$$

From (1.3.18) and (1.3.19b) above, (1.3.17) follows.

If we now apply (1.3.17) to all the terms

$$\frac{K^*_{(1)}}{s} , \quad \frac{K^*_{(2)}}{s} , \ldots, \quad \text{and} \quad \frac{K^*_{(n)}}{s}$$

and use the fact that $K^*_{(2)}$ and other $K^*$'s have their first $p$ moments finite (in view of $\nu_{n+p} < \infty$), then we find

(1.3.20)

$$\gamma_{n,1}\left(\frac{-d}{ds}\right)^p\left[\frac{K^*_{(1)}(s)}{s}\right] + \cdots + \gamma_{1,n}\left(\frac{-d}{ds}\right)^p\left[\frac{K^*_{(n)}(s)}{s}\right]$$

$$= \frac{\gamma_{n,n}}{s^{p+1}} + O\left(\frac{1}{s}\right) .$$

But, if $\mu_{n+p+1} < \gamma$, then $M_n^{*n}$ can be written as

$$M_n^{*n}(s) = \gamma_{n+1} + \gamma_{n+2}s + \gamma_{n+3}s^2 + \cdots + \gamma_{n+p}s^{p-1} + s^p M_{n+p}^{*n} ,$$

where $M_{n+p}^{*n}$ is B.V., and hence

(1.3.21)

$$\frac{M_n^{*n}(s)\, K^*(s)}{s} = \frac{\gamma_{n+1}\, K^*}{s} + \gamma_{n+2}\, K^* + \gamma_{n+3}s\, K^*$$

$$+ \cdots + \gamma_{n+p}s^{p-2}\, K^* + s^{p-1}\, K^*\, M^*_{n+p} .$$

Upon differentiating (1.3.21) w.r.t. s, p times, and using (1.3.17) and (1.3.19), we find

$$(1.3.22)\qquad \left(\frac{-d}{ds}\right)^p\left[\frac{M_n^{*n}\, K^*}{s}\right] = \frac{\gamma_{n+1}}{s^{p+1}} + O\left(\frac{1}{s}\right) ,$$

and on combining (1.3.20) and (1.3.22) we discover that

$$(1.3.23)\qquad \gamma_{n,1}\left(\frac{-d}{ds}\right)^p\left[\frac{K^*_{(1)}(s)}{s}\right]$$

$$+ \cdots + \gamma_{1,n}\left(\frac{-d}{ds}\right)^p\left[\frac{K^*_{(n)}(s)}{s}\right] +$$

$$+ \left( \frac{-d}{ds} \right)^p \left[ \frac{M_n^{*n} \; K^*}{s} \right] = \frac{\gamma_{n+1,n}}{s^{p+1}} + O\left( \frac{1}{s} \right) .$$

The lemma is therefore proved.

From Lemma 1 we have that

$$(1.3.24) \qquad \varphi_n'^{*}(s) = K^*(s) \, \varphi_n^*(s) .$$

If we divide both sides by $s$ we find that

$$(1.3.25) \qquad \varphi'^{0}_n(s) = K^*(s) \; \varphi_n^0(s) ,$$

and hence that

$$(1.3.26) \quad \varphi_n'^{0(p)}(s)$$

$$= \varphi_n^{0(p)}(s) \, K^*(s) + \binom{p}{1} \varphi_n^{0(p-1)}(s) \, K^{*(1)}(s)$$

$$+ \cdots + \binom{p}{r} \varphi_n^{0(p-r)}(s) \, K^{*(r)}(s)$$

$$+ \cdots + \varphi_n^0(s) \, K^{*(p)}(s) .$$

Let us write

$$(1.3.27) \quad K^{*[p]}(s) = (-1)^p \frac{K^{*(p)}(s)}{\nu_p} = \gamma_p \, K^{*(p)} .$$

Then, if $K(t)$ has its first $n+p$ moments finite, the first $n$ moments of $K^{*[p]}$ are finite, and upon using (1.3.27), (1.3.26) can be written as

$$(1.3.28)\quad \varphi_n'^{0(p)} = \varphi_n^{0(p)} K^* + \gamma_1' \varphi_n^{0(p-1)} K^{*[1]} + \cdots + \gamma_r' \varphi_n^{0(p-r)} K^{*[r]} + \gamma_p' \varphi_n^{0} K^{*[p]}$$

where $K^{*[r]}$, $r = 0,1,\ldots,p$, has its first $n+p+r$ moments finite. Now, we have from Smith [196] that if $\mu_{n+p+1} < \infty$, $n > 0$, $p > 0$, then

$$(1.3.29)\quad (-1)^p \varphi_n^{0(p)} = \frac{\gamma_1}{s^{n+p+1}} + \frac{\gamma_2}{s^{n+p}} + \cdots + \frac{\gamma_{n+1}}{s^{p+1}} + \Omega^0(s),$$

Where $\Omega^0$ is the Laplace transform of a function which belongs both to the class $B$ and to the class $L$ ($L$ is the class of functions $\lambda(t)$ such that $\lambda(t)/(1+t)$ belongs to $L_1(0,\infty)$). We denote the intersection $B \cap L$ by $R$.

Applying (1.3.29) repeatedly in (1.3.28), and using the fact that

$$\varphi_n^0 = \frac{\gamma_1}{s^{n+1}} + \frac{\gamma_2}{s^n} + \cdots + \frac{\gamma_n}{s^2} + M_n^{0n},$$

we obtain

$$(1.3.30)\quad (-1)^{(p)} \varphi_n'^{0(p)}(s)$$

$$= \left[\frac{\gamma_1}{s^{n+p+1}} + \frac{\gamma_2}{s^{n+p}} + \cdots + \frac{\gamma_{n+1}}{s^{p+1}} + \Omega_1^0\right] K^* +$$

$$+ \left[\frac{\gamma_1}{s^{n+p}} + \frac{\gamma_2}{s^{n+p-1}} + \cdots + \frac{\gamma_{n+1}}{s^p} + \Omega_2^0 \quad \gamma_1' \, K^{*[1]}\right.$$

$$+ \cdots + \left[\frac{\gamma_1}{s^{n+2}} + \frac{\gamma_2}{s^{n+1}} + \cdots + \frac{\gamma_{n+1}}{s^2} + \Omega_p^0\right] \gamma_{p-1}' \, K^{*[p-1]}$$

$$+ \left[\frac{\gamma_1}{s^{n+1}} + \frac{\gamma_2}{s^{n+2}} + \cdots + \frac{\gamma_n}{s^2} + M_n^{On}\right] \gamma_p' \, K^{*[p]} \quad .$$

Comparing (1.3.30) with Lemma 3 and using Lemma A, we get

$$(1.3.31) \qquad (-1)^p \, \varphi_n'^{\,0(p)} = \frac{\gamma_1}{s^{n+p+1}} + \frac{\gamma_2}{s^{n+p}} + \cdots + \frac{\gamma_{n,n-1}}{s^{p+2}} + \frac{\gamma_{n+1,n}}{s^{p+1}} + \tilde{\Omega}^0 \quad ,$$

where

$$(1.3.32) \quad \tilde{\Omega}^0 = \sum_{\ell=0}^{p-1} \sum_{j=1}^{n+1} \gamma_{n,n+p+1-j-\ell} \, K^{0[\ell]}_{(n+p+1-j-\ell)} + \sum_{j=1}^{n} \gamma_j \, K^{0[p]}_{(n+1-j)} + \Omega_1^0 \, K^* + \Omega_2^0 \, K^{*[1]} + \cdots + \Omega_p^0 \, K^{*[p-1]} + M_n^{0n} \, K^{*[p]} \quad .$$

It is clear from (1.3.32) that $\tilde{\Omega}_p^0$ is the Laplace transform of a function of bounded variation.

But Lemma 3 leads to

$$\tilde{\Omega}^0 = 0\left(\frac{1}{s}\right)$$

i.e.,

$$\text{(1.3.33)} \quad \lim_{s \to 0} s\tilde{\Omega}^0 = \lim_{t \to \infty} \tilde{\Omega}(t) = \tilde{\Omega}(\infty) = 0 .$$

Noticing the fact that $(-1)^p \varphi'^{0(p)}$ is the Laplace transform of $t^p \varphi_n'(t)$, we get from (1.3.31) that

$$\text{(1.3.34)} \quad \varphi_n'(t) = \gamma_1 t^n + \gamma_{2,1} t^{n-1} + \cdots + \gamma_{n,n-1} t + \gamma_{n+1,n} + \frac{\tilde{\Omega}(t)}{t^p} ,$$

where $\tilde{\Omega}(t)$ is of bounded variation and tends to zero at $\infty$. Also, in view of Theorem 1, since $\tilde{\Omega}(t)/t^p$ must be bounded, we can equivalently write $\tilde{\Omega}(t)/t^p$ as $\lambda'(t)/(1+t)^p$, where $\lambda'(t)$ is B.V. and tends to zero at $+\infty$.

From (1.3.32) we get

$$\text{(1.3.35)} \quad \tilde{\Omega}(t) = \sum_{\ell=0}^{p-1} \sum_{j=1}^{n+1} \gamma_{j,n+p+1-j-\ell} K_{(n+p+1-j-\ell)}^{[\ell]}(t) + \sum_{j=1}^{n} \gamma_j K_{(n+1-j)}^{[p]}(t) + \int_0^t \Omega_1(t-x)\, dK(x) + \int_0^t \Omega_p(t-x)\, dK^{[p-1]}(x) + \gamma_{n+1} K^{[p]}(t) +$$

$$+ \int_0^t \lambda(t - x)\, dK^{[p]}(x) \quad ,$$

where

$$M_n^n(t) - \gamma_{n+1} = \lambda(t) \in B \; .$$

Since $\tilde{\Omega}(t) \to 0$ as $t \to \infty$, the right-hand side of (1.3.35) must also tend to zero and hence (1.3.35) can also be written as

$$(1.3.36) \quad \Omega(t) = \sum_{\ell=0}^{p-1} \sum_{j=1}^{n+1} \gamma_{n,n+p+1-j-\ell} \left[ K^{[\ell]}_{(n+p+1-j-\ell}(t) - 1 \right]$$

$$+ \sum_{j-1}^{n} \gamma_j \left[ K^{[p]}_{(n+1-j)}(t) - 1 \right]$$

$$+ \int_0^t \Omega_1(t - x)\, dK(x) + \cdots$$

$$+ \int_0^t \Omega_p(t - x)\, dK^{[p-1]}(x) + {}_{n+1}\left[ K^{[p]}(t) - 1 \right]$$

$$+ \int_0^t \lambda(t - x)\, dK^{[p]}(x) \quad .$$

The terms in (1.3.36) whose first moments are not finite in accordance with the assumptions made so far are $K_{(n+p)}$, $K^{[p-1]}_{(n+1)}$ and $K^{[p]}_{(n)}$ and all these have their means finite if we further assume that $\nu_{n+p+1} < \infty$. Also, if

$F(x)$ is a distribution function with a finite mean $\mu_1$, then $F(x) - 1 \in L_1(0,\infty)$ as is seen from the fact that

$$\int_0^\infty |F(x) - 1| dx = \mu_1 .$$

In view of Lemma 3,

$$\sum_{\ell=0}^{p-1} \sum_{j=1}^{n+1} \gamma_{j,n+p+1-j-\ell} \left[ K^{[\ell]}(t) - 1 \right] + \sum_{j=1}^{n} \gamma_j \left[ K^{[p]}_{(n+1-j)}(t) - 1 \right] + \gamma_{n+1} \left[ K^{[p]}(t) - 1 \right]$$

belongs to both B and to $L_1(0,\infty)$.

Now $\Omega_1^0, \Omega_2^0, \ldots, \Omega_p^0$ are Laplace transforms of functions which belong to B. Also, $\Omega_2(t), \ldots, \Omega_p(t)$ belong to the class $L_1(0,\infty)$ and $\Omega_1(t)$ belongs to $L_1(0,\infty)$, as shown by Smith [196]. If, in addition, $\mu_{n+p+2} < \infty$, the function $\lambda(t) = M_n^n(t) - \gamma_{n+1}$ belongs to B and it can also be seen to belong to $L_1(0,\infty)$ by noticing that $\lambda^* = M_n^{*n} - \gamma_{n+1}$ and so $\lambda^0 = M_{n+1}^{*n}$ Where $M_{n+1}^{*n}$ is B.V., since $\mu_{n+1} < \infty$. If $\lambda(t) \in R$, we have shown in (1.3.12) that

$$\mu(t) = \int_0^t \lambda(t - x)\, dK(x) \in B .$$

Further, if $\lambda(t) \in L_1(0,\infty)$, then $\mu(t)$ also belongs to

$L_1(0,\infty)$. We have thus proved

(A) If $\mu_{n+p+1} < \infty$, $\nu_{n+p+1} < \infty$, $n > 0$, $p > 0$ then

$$\varphi_n'(t) = \gamma_1 t^n + \gamma_{2,1} t^{n-1} + \cdots + \gamma_{n,n-1} t + \gamma_{n+1,n} + \frac{\tilde{\Omega}(t)}{t^p}, \tag{1.3.37}$$

where $\tilde{\Omega}(t) \in B$, and

(B) If $\mu_{n+p+1} < \infty$, $\nu_{n+p+1} < \infty$, $n > 0$, $p > 0$ then

$$\varphi_n'(t) = \gamma_1 t^n + \gamma_{2,1} t^{n-1} + \cdots + \gamma_{n,n-1} t + \gamma_{n+1,n} + \frac{\Omega(t)}{t^{p-1}}, \tag{1.3.38}$$

where $\Omega(t) \in B$ and also to $L_1(0,\infty)$. Comparing (A) and (B) we must have

$$\frac{\tilde{\Omega}(t)}{t} = \Omega(t) \in L_1(0,\infty),$$

and therefore as

$$\frac{\tilde{\Omega}(t)}{t} \quad \text{or, equivalently as} \quad \frac{\lambda'(t)}{1+t} \in L. \tag{1.3.39}$$

Combining (1.3.37) and (1.3.39) we have proved

THEOREM 2: <u>If</u> $\mu_{n+p+1} < \infty$, $\nu_{n+p+1} < \infty$, $p > 0$,

$n > 0$, <u>then</u>

$$\varphi_n'(t) = \gamma_1 t^n + \gamma_{2,1} t^{n-1} + \dots + \gamma_{n,n-1} t + \gamma_{n+1,n} + \frac{\lambda'(t)}{(1+t)^p}$$

<u>where</u> $\lambda'(t) \in R$.

Let us now recall the relationship (Lemma 2)

$$(1.3.40) \qquad \frac{\tilde{\varphi}_n(t)}{n!} = 1 + \sum_{j=1}^{n} \frac{\varphi_j'(t)}{j!} ,$$

between $\varphi_n'(t)$ and $\tilde{\varphi}_n(t)$ of the General Point Process.

In view of the additive property of the class $R$ and (1.3.40), the result corresponding to Theorem 2 for a G.P.P. may be stated as

THEOREM 2': <u>If</u> $\mu_{n+p+1} < \infty$, $\nu_{n+p+1} < \infty$, $p > 0$, $n > 0$, <u>then</u>

$$(1.3.41) \quad \tilde{\varphi}_n(t) = \gamma_1 t^n + \gamma_{2,1} t^{n-1} + \dots + \gamma_{n,n-1} t + \gamma_{n+1,n} + \frac{\lambda(t)}{(1+t)^p} ,$$

<u>where</u> $\lambda(t) \in R$.

## 1.4. <u>The Asymptotic Behavior of the</u> $\psi$-<u>Cumulants</u>

$\tilde{\psi}_n(t)$ is a linear combination with numerical weights of a finite number of terms like

$$\tilde{\varphi}_{p_1}(t)\, \tilde{\varphi}_{p_2}(t) \cdots \tilde{\varphi}_{p_r}(t)$$

(1.4.1) where

$$p_1 + p_2 + \cdots + p_r = n \ .$$

Using (1.3.41) in the individual terms of (1.4.1) and also the property that, if $\lambda_1(t) \in B$, $\lambda_2(t) \in R$, then $\lambda_1(t)\, \lambda_2(t) \in R$, we get

$$(1.4.2) \quad \tilde{\psi}_n(t) = \gamma_1 t^n + \gamma_{2,1} t^{n-1} + \cdots + \gamma_{n,n-1} t + \gamma_{n+1,n} + \frac{\lambda(t)}{(1+t)^p} ,$$

where $\lambda(t) \in R$.

In the corresponding representation for $\psi_n(t)$ of the Renewal Process, Smith has shown that all the coefficients of the nonlinear terms in $t$ vanish identically. Before establishing that the same thing is true for $\tilde{\psi}_n(t)$ of the General Point Process, we will demonstrate the truth by computing the first of three $\tilde{\psi}$'s of a General Point Process.

In what follows, the finiteness of the appropriate moments is assumed, the remainder term omitted, and the sign " $\sim$ " is used to represent the "approximation" sign.

$\tilde{\psi}_1(t)$: Assumption: $\mu_2 < \infty$, $\nu_1 < \infty$ .

We have, by definition,

$$\tilde{\psi}_1(t) = \tilde{\varphi}_1(t) = 1 + \varphi_1'(t) .$$

Taking the L-S.T. on both sides,

$$\tilde{\varphi}_1^* = 1 + \varphi_1'^* .$$

But $\tilde{\varphi}_2(t) = 2 + 2\tilde{\varphi}_1'(t) + \varphi_2'(t)$. Now

$$\varphi_2'^* = K^* \varphi_2^* = \frac{2!\,K^*}{(1 - F^*)^2} = \frac{2!\left[1 - \nu_1 s + \frac{\nu_2 s^2}{2!} \cdots\right]}{\left[\mu_1 s - \frac{\mu_2}{2!} s^2 + \frac{\mu_3}{3!} s^3 \cdots\right]^2}$$

$$= \frac{2!}{\mu_1^2 s^2}\left[1 - \frac{\mu_2}{2!\mu_1} s + \frac{\mu_3}{3!\mu_1} s^2 \cdots\right]^2 \left[1 - \nu_1 s + \frac{\nu_2}{2!} s^2 \cdots\right]$$

$$= 2!\left[\frac{1}{\mu_1^2 s^2} + \left(\frac{\mu_2}{\mu_1^3} - \frac{\nu_1}{\mu_1^2}\right)\frac{1}{s} + \left(\frac{3\mu_2^2}{4\mu_1^4} - \frac{\mu_3}{3\mu_1^3} - \frac{\nu_1\mu_1}{\mu_1^3} - \frac{\nu_2}{2!\,\mu_1^2}\right)\right] + \cdots$$

therefore,

$$\varphi_2'(t) \sim \frac{t^2}{\mu_1^2} + 2\left(\frac{\mu_2}{\mu_1^3} - \frac{\nu_1}{\mu_1^2}\right)t + \left(\frac{3\mu_2^2}{2\mu_1^4} - \frac{2\mu_3}{3\mu_1^3} - \frac{2\nu_1\mu_2}{\mu_1^3} + \frac{\nu_2}{\mu_1^2}\right) .$$

Substituting for $\varphi_2'(t)$ and $\varphi_1'(t)$ in $\tilde{\varphi}_2(t)$, we get

$$\tilde{\varphi}_2(t) \sim \frac{t^2}{\mu_1^2} + \left( \frac{2}{\mu_1} + \frac{2\mu_2}{\mu_1^3} - \frac{2\nu_1}{\mu_1^2} \right) t$$

$$+ \left( 2 + \frac{3\mu_2^2}{2\mu_1^4} - \frac{2\mu_3}{3\mu_1^3} - \frac{2\nu_1}{\mu_1} - \frac{2\nu_1\mu_2}{\mu_1^3} + \frac{\nu_2}{\mu_1^2} \right) .$$

But

$$\frac{\tilde{\varphi}_3(t)}{3!} = 1 + \varphi_1'(t) + \frac{\varphi_2'(t)}{2!} + \frac{\varphi_3'(t)}{3!} .$$

Therefore

$$\tilde{\varphi}_3(t) = \frac{t^3}{\mu_1^3} + \left( \frac{9\mu_2 + 6\mu_1^2 - 2\mu_1\nu_1}{2\mu_1^4} \right) t^2 + \frac{t}{\mu_1^5}$$

$$\cdot \left[ 6\mu_1^4 + 6\mu_1^2\mu_2 + 9\mu_2^2 - 3\mu_1\mu_3 - 9\nu_1\mu_1\mu_2 + 3\mu_1^2\nu_2 - 6\mu_1^3\nu_1 \right]$$

$$+ \frac{1}{10\mu_1^6} \left[ 60\mu_1^6 + 30\mu_1^4\mu_2 + 45\mu_1^4\mu_2^2 - 20\mu_1^3\mu_3 + 90\mu_2^3 + 9\mu_1^2\mu_4 \right.$$

$$- 72\mu_1\mu_2\mu_3 - 108\mu_1\mu_2^2\mu_3\nu_1 + 54\mu_1^2\mu_2\nu_2$$

$$\left. - 12\mu_1^3\nu_3 - 60\mu_1^5\nu_1 - 60\mu_1^3\mu_2\nu_1 + 30\mu_1^4\nu_2 \right] .$$

We find in $\tilde{\Psi}_3(t)$:

$$\text{Coefficient of } t^3 = \frac{1}{\mu_1^3}(1 - 3 + 2) \equiv 0 ,$$

$$\text{Coefficient of } t^2 = -\frac{6\mu_1^2 + 6\mu_2 - 6\nu_1\mu_1}{\mu_1^4} - \frac{6\mu_1^2 + 3\mu_2 + 6\nu_1\mu_1}{2\mu_1^4} + \frac{6\mu_1^2 + 3\mu_2 - 6\nu_1\mu_1}{\mu_1^4} + \frac{9\mu_2 + 6\mu_1^2 - 6\nu_1\mu_1}{2\mu_1^4} \equiv 0.$$

Also, as in the case of $\tilde{\psi}_1(t)$ and $\tilde{\psi}_2(t)$ we find for the contribution due to $K(x)$, to the coefficient of $t$ in $\tilde{\psi}_3(t)$, to be

$$\frac{3\mu_1^2\nu_2 - 6\mu_1^3\nu_1 - 9\nu_1\mu_1\mu_2}{\mu_1^5} - \frac{3\mu_1^2\nu_2 - 6\mu_1^3\nu_1 - 6\mu_1\mu_2\nu_1}{\mu_1^5} - \frac{3[2\mu_1^2 + \mu_2 - 2\nu_1\mu_1]^2 - 6\nu_1\mu_1\mu_2}{2\mu_1^5} + \frac{3[2\mu_1^2 + \mu_2 - 2\nu_1\mu_1]^2}{2\mu_1^5} \equiv 0 .$$

We will now prove that the above observations are true for $\tilde{\psi}_n(t)$ of a G.P.P. We will also show that the coefficient of $t$ in the asymptotic representation of $\tilde{\psi}_n(t)$ does not involve the moments of $K(x)$ and, finally, that the contribution to the constant term due to $K(x)$ is by way of an additive function of the $\mu$'s and $\nu$'s. From Lemma 2

$$\frac{\tilde{\varphi}^*_r}{r!} = 1 + \varphi_1^{*'} + \frac{\varphi_2^{*'}}{2!} + \quad + \frac{\varphi_r^{*'}}{r!} . \tag{1.4.3}$$

Therefore

$$\frac{\tilde{\varphi}^*_{r+1}}{(r+1)!} - \frac{\tilde{\varphi}^*_r}{r!} = \frac{\varphi'^*_{r+1}}{(r+1)!} \quad . \tag{1.4.4}$$

Multiplying both sides of (1.4.4) by $z^{r+1}$ and summing w.r.t., $r$ from $0$ to $\infty$, we get

$$(1 - z)\,\tilde{\Phi}^*_s(z) = \Phi'^*_s(z) \quad .$$

But

$$\Phi'^*_s(z) = 1 + \varphi'^*_1(s)z + \varphi'^*_2(s)\frac{z^2}{2!} + \cdots$$

$$= 1 + K^*\,\varphi^*_1 z + K^*\,\varphi^*_2\frac{z^2}{2!} + \cdots$$

$$= 1 - K^* + K^*[1 + \varphi^*_1(s)z + \varphi^*_2(s)\frac{z^2}{2!} + \cdots$$

$$= 1 - K^* + K^*\,\Phi^*_s(z) \quad . \tag{1.4.5}$$

Substituting from (1.4.5) in (1.4.4), we obtain

$$\tilde{\Phi}^*_s(z) = \frac{1 - K^*(s)}{1 - z} + \frac{K^*(s)\,\Phi^*_s(z)}{1 - z} \quad . \tag{1.4.6}$$

Furthermore, from (1.4.3) we find

$$\frac{\tilde{\varphi}^*_j}{j!} = K^*\left[1 + \varphi^*_1 + \frac{\varphi^*_2}{2!} + \quad + \frac{\varphi^*_j}{j!}\right] + 1 - K^* \quad . \tag{1.4.7}$$

If we now let $Q = 1 - F^*$, and express $K^*$ in the form

$$(1.4.8) \qquad K^* = 1 + \lambda_1 Q + \lambda_3 Q^2 + \cdots$$

then, on substituting from (1.4.8) into (1.4.7) we discover that

$$(1.4.9) \qquad \frac{\tilde{\varphi}_n^*}{n!} = (1 + \lambda_1 + \lambda_2 + \cdots + \lambda_n) + (1 + \lambda_1 + \cdots + \lambda_{n-1}) \frac{1}{Q} + (1 + \lambda_1 + \cdots + \lambda_{n-2}) \frac{1}{Q^2} + \cdots + \frac{1}{Q^n} + R^*(s) \quad ,$$

where

$$(1.4.10) \qquad R^*(s) = \sum_{j=1}^{\infty} \lambda_j \sum_{k=1}^{j} Q^k + \sum_{j=1}^{\infty} \lambda_j Q^j \quad .$$

Now

$$\sum_{k=1}^{j} Q^k = Q \frac{1 - Q^j}{1 - Q}$$

and substituting in $R^*(s)$ we get

$$R^*(s) = \frac{Q}{1 - Q} \sum_{j=1}^{\infty} \lambda_n [1 - Q^j] + \sum_{j=1}^{\infty} \lambda_j Q^j$$

$$= \frac{Q}{1 - Q} \sum_{j=1}^{\infty} \lambda_j + \sum_{j=1}^{\infty} \lambda_j Q^j \left[ \frac{1 - 2Q}{1 - Q} \right] \quad .$$

Thus, since $\Sigma \lambda_i = -1$,

$$R^*(s) = \frac{1-2Q}{1-Q} \sum_{j=0}^{\infty} \lambda_j Q^j - \frac{1-2Q}{1-Q} - \frac{Q}{1-Q}$$

$$= K^* \frac{1-2Q}{1-Q} - 1$$

$$(1.4.11) \qquad = \frac{K^*}{F^*} (2F^* - 1) - 1 \quad .$$

Thus, we have

$$(1.4.12) \quad \frac{\tilde{\varphi}_n(t)}{n!} = (1+\lambda_1 + \cdots + \lambda_n) + (1+\lambda_1 + \cdots + \lambda_{n-1}) \cdot \varphi_1(t) + (1+\lambda_1 + \cdots + \lambda_{n-2}) \frac{\varphi_2(t)}{2!} + \cdots + (1+\lambda_1) \frac{\varphi_{n-1}(t)}{(n-1)!} + \frac{\varphi_n(t)}{n!} + R(t) \quad ,$$

where, in view of (1.4.11)

$$\lim_{s \to 0} R^*(s) = \lim_{t \to \infty} R(t) = 0 \quad .$$

From (1.4.9) we derive

$$(1.4.13) \quad \frac{\tilde{\varphi}^*_{n+1}}{(n+1)!} - \frac{\tilde{\varphi}^*_n}{n!} = \lambda_{n+1} + \lambda_n \varphi^*_1 + \lambda_{n-1} \frac{\varphi^*_2}{2!} + \cdots + \lambda_1 \frac{\varphi^*_n}{n!} + \frac{\varphi^*_{n+1}}{(n+1)!}$$

Multiplying both sides of (1.4.13) by $z^{n+1}$ and summing for $n$ from $0$ to $\infty$, leads to

$$(1.4.14) \qquad (1-z)\, \tilde{\Phi}^*_s(s) = \Lambda(z)\, \Phi^*_s(z) \quad ,$$

so that

$$(1.4.15) \qquad (1 - z)\tilde{\Phi}_t(z) = \Lambda(z)\Phi_t(z) \quad ,$$

where

$$(1.4.16) \qquad \Lambda(z) = 1 + \lambda_1 z + \lambda_2 z^2 + \cdots \quad .$$

Upon taking logarithms on both sides of (1.4.15), we find

$$(1.4.17) \qquad \tilde{\Psi}_t(z) = \Psi_t(z) + \log \Lambda(z) - \log (1 - z) \quad ,$$

where

$\tilde{\Psi}_t(z)$ is the $\tilde{\psi}$-cumulant generating function of the General Point Process, and

$\Psi_t(z)$ is the $\psi$-cumulant generating function of the Point Process.

Let $\gamma_{j,j}$ denote the coefficient of $z^j/j!$ in the power series expansion of $\log \Lambda(z) - \log (1 - z)$.

Then, from (1.4.17) we obtain

$$(1.4.18) \qquad \tilde{\psi}_n(t) = \psi_n(t) + \gamma_{n,n} \quad .$$

Smith [196] has shown that if $\mu_{n+p+1} < \infty$, $p > 0$, then

$$(1.4.19) \qquad \psi_n(t) = \gamma_n t + \gamma_{n+1} + \frac{\lambda(t)}{(1 + t)^p} \quad ,$$

where $\lambda(t) \in R$ .

Substituting (1.4.19) in (1.4.18) we find

$$(1.4.20) \qquad \tilde{\psi}_n(t) = \gamma_n t + \gamma_{n+1} + \gamma_{n,n} + \frac{\lambda(t)}{(1+t)^p} ,$$

where $\lambda(t) \in R$ .

Comparing (1.4.20) and (1.4.2), we see that the rational functions $\gamma_1, \gamma_{2,1}, \ldots, \gamma_{n-1,n-2}$ vanish identically and that $\gamma_{n,n-1}$ is a $\gamma_n$, which means that the coefficient of $t$ in $\tilde{\psi}_n(t)$ of the General Point Process does not involve any moments of $K(x)$, and finally, that

$$(1.4.21) \qquad \gamma_{n+1,n} = \gamma_{n+1} + \gamma_{n,n} .$$

This shows that the contribution due to being a General Point Process is by way of an addition of a $\gamma_{n,n}$ to the constant term in the asymptotic representation of the $\psi_n$-cumulant. We have thus proved that

THEOREM 3: <u>If</u> $\mu_{n+p+1} < \infty$, $\nu_{n+p+1} < \infty$, $n > 0$, $p > 0$, <u>then</u>

$$(1.4.22) \qquad \tilde{\psi}_n(t) = \gamma_n t + \gamma_{n+1} + \gamma_{n,n} + \frac{\lambda(t)}{(1+t)^p}$$

<u>where</u> $\lambda(t) \in R$ .

## 1.5. The Formal Calculations

Assuming $\mu_1 = 1$, Smith has tabulated the first eight $\gamma_n$ and $\gamma_{n+1}$ of (1.4.22). To complete Smith's table for a General Point Process, in other words, to extend the table of the $\psi$-cumulants to the G.P.P., the first eight $\gamma_{n,n}, n = 1,2,\ldots,8$ need to be tabulated under the assumption $\mu_1 = 1$. The method of calculating the $\gamma_{n,n}$'s will be briefly outlined here, and for the actual calculations, the reader is referred to the author's Doctoral Dissertation [ ].

We have that $\lambda_1, \lambda_2, \ldots, \lambda_n, \ldots$ are the coefficients of $(1-F^*), (1-F^*)^2, \ldots, (1-F^*)^n, \ldots,$ in the following power series representation of $K^*$,

$$(1.5.1) \qquad K^* = 1 + \lambda_1(1 - F^*) + \lambda_2(1 - F^*)^2 + \cdots \quad .$$

Denoting the moments about the origin of the distribution $K(x)$ by $\nu$'s and the corresponding moments of $F(x)$ by $\mu$'s, and setting $\mu_1 = 1$, we can solve for the first eight $\lambda$'s in terms of the $\mu$'s and $\nu$'s by solving the equations obtained by equating the coefficients of the first eight powers of $s$ on either side of the relation (1.5.1). The first eight $a_n$, $n = 1,2,\ldots,8$, where

$a_n$ is the coefficient of $z^n/n!$ in the power series expansion of $\log \Lambda(z)$ can be solved in terms of the first eight $\lambda$'s. Now, substituting for the $\lambda$'s, their values in terms of $\mu$'s and $\nu$'s, we finally express the $a_n$, $n = 1,2,\ldots,8$, in terms of $\mu$'s and $\nu$'s.

Bearing in mind the relation

$$\gamma_{n,n} = a_n + (n-1)! \quad , \tag{1.5.2}$$

and substituting the values for $a_n$, $n = 1,2,\ldots,8$, in terms of $\mu$'s and $\nu$'s calculated previously, we finally express $\gamma_{n,n}$, $n = 1,2,\ldots,8$, in terms of the moments of $F(x)$ and $K(x)$.

## 1.6. Check on the Formal Calculations of the Cumulants of the General Point Process

In the work so far, apart from the assumption of the finiteness of the appropriate moments, it has been implicitly assumed that the distribution function $F(x)$ is such that, for some $k$, its convolution $F_k(x)$ has an absolutely continuous component.

Let $G_n$ be the class of functions $F(x)$, which can be written as

$$1 - \frac{1}{n}\left[e^{-x/\nu_1} + e^{-x/\nu_2} + \cdots + e^{-x/\nu_n}\right], \qquad x \geq 0$$

and the $\nu_i'$'s are real and positive, and let

$$G = U_n G_n .$$

Smith [196] has shown that if $F(x) \epsilon G$, then

(i) $F^*(s)$ is analytic in some open neighborhood of $s = 0$, and

(ii) there is a unique function $z_1(s)$ defined on this neighborhood, vanishing at $s = 0$ and satisfying the relation

$$s - 1 = F^*(z_1(s)) , \tag{1.6.1}$$

and, further

$$z_1(s) = \sum_1^\infty \frac{\alpha_n}{n!} s^n , \tag{1.6.2}$$

where $\alpha_n = \gamma_n$ of (1.4.22).

We will now prove that, if $F(x) \epsilon G$, $\gamma_{n,n}$ can be expressed in terms of $\gamma_n$ $(= \alpha_n)$ and the cumulants of $K(x)$, and this relationship provides a check on the calculations of the previous section. We prove

THEOREM 4: <u>If</u> $F(x) \epsilon G$, <u>then</u>

$$\sum_{n=1}^\infty \frac{\kappa_n}{n!} (-1)^n \left[ \sum_{m=1}^\infty \frac{\alpha_m}{m!} s^m \right]^n =$$

$$= \sum_{n=1}^{\infty} \frac{a_n}{n!} s^n .$$

<u>Proof</u>: We have

$$K^*(s) = \sum_{n=0}^{\infty} \lambda_n [Q(s)]^n = \Lambda|Q(s)| ,$$

where

$$\Lambda(z) = 1 + \lambda_1 z + \lambda_2 z^2 + \cdots .$$

Also

$$\log \Lambda(Q) = \sum_{n=1}^{\infty} a_n \frac{[Q(s)]^n}{n!}$$

but

$$\log K^*(s) = \sum_{n=1}^{\infty} (-1)^n \frac{\kappa_n}{n!} s^n ,$$

where $\kappa_n$ is the $n^{th}$ cumulant of $K(x)$. Therefore,

$$\sum_{n=1}^{\infty} (-1)^n \frac{\kappa_n}{n!} s^n \equiv \sum_{n=1}^{\infty} \frac{a_n}{n!} [Q(s)]^n$$

$$\equiv \sum_{n=1}^{\infty} \frac{a_n}{n!} [1 - F^*(s)]^n .$$

Putting $s = z_1(s)$ in the above formula and making use of (1.6.1) and (1.6.2), we get

$$(1.6.3) \qquad \sum_{n=1}^{\infty} \frac{\kappa_n}{n!} (-1)^n \left[ \sum_{m=1}^{\infty} \frac{\gamma_m}{m!} s^m \right]^n = \sum_{n=1}^{\infty} \frac{a_n}{n!} s^n .$$

Comparing the coefficients of the first eight powers of $s$ on either side of (1.6.3), we get

$$(1.6.4) \quad a_1 = -\kappa_1$$

$$a_2 = -\kappa_1\alpha_2 + \kappa_2$$

$$a_3 = -\kappa_1\alpha_3 + 3\alpha_2\kappa_2 - \kappa_3$$

$$a_4 = -\kappa_1\alpha_4 + \kappa_2(3\alpha_2^2 + 4\alpha_3) - 6\alpha_2\kappa_3 + \kappa_4$$

$$a_5 = -\kappa_1\alpha_5 + \kappa_2(5\alpha_4 + 10\alpha_2\alpha_3) - \kappa_3(15\alpha_2^2 + 10\alpha_3) + 10\kappa_4\alpha_2 - \kappa_5$$

$$a_6 = -\kappa_1\alpha_6 + \kappa_2(10\alpha_3^2 + 6\alpha_5 + 15\alpha_2\alpha_4) - \kappa_3(15\alpha_4 + 60\alpha_2\alpha_3 + 15\alpha_2^3) + \kappa_4(45\alpha_2^2 + 20\alpha_3) - 15\kappa_5\alpha_2 + \kappa_6$$

$$a_7 = -\kappa_1\alpha_7 + \kappa_2(7\alpha_6 + 21\alpha_2\alpha_5 + 35\alpha_3\alpha_4)$$
$$- \kappa_3(70\alpha_3^2 + 21\alpha_5 + 105\alpha_2\alpha_4 + 105\alpha_3\alpha_2^2)$$
$$+ \kappa_4(35\alpha_4 + 105\alpha_2^3 + 210\alpha_2\alpha_3) - \kappa_5(105\alpha_2^2 + 35\alpha_3)$$
$$+ 21\kappa_6\alpha_2 - \kappa_7 .$$

$$a_8 = -\kappa_1\alpha_8 + \kappa_2(35\alpha_4^2 + 8\alpha_7 + 28\alpha_2\alpha_6 + 56\alpha_3\alpha_5)$$
$$- \kappa_3(28\alpha_6 + 168\alpha_2\alpha_5 + 280\alpha_3\alpha_4 + 280\alpha_3^2\alpha_2 + 210\alpha_2^2\alpha_4)$$
$$+ \kappa_4(105\alpha_2^4 + 280\alpha_3^2 + 840\alpha_2^2\alpha_3 + 420\alpha_2\alpha_4 + 56\alpha_5)$$
$$- \kappa_5(70\alpha_4 + 560\alpha_2\alpha_3 + 420\alpha_2^3) + \kappa_6(210\alpha_2^2 + 56\alpha_3)$$
$$- \kappa_7(28\alpha_2) + \kappa_8 .$$

Now

$$\gamma_{n,n} = a_n + (n-1)! .$$

Smith [196] has tabulated the first eight $\kappa$'s and Kendall [120] has tabulated the cumulants. Using these two tables, all the individual terms in $\gamma_{n,n}$ tabulated in the previous section for $n = 1,2,\ldots,8$ are checked and they all pass the check. Another obvious check is that $\gamma_{n,n} \equiv 0$, when $F(x) = K(x)$, which is verified in the case of $\gamma'_{n,n}$'s.

## 1.7 The Cumulants of an Ordinary Point Process

In (1.4.18) we have discovered that the $\tilde{\psi}$-cumulants of a General Point Process are obtained by adding to the $\psi$-cumulants of an Ordinary Point Process, obtained earlier by Smith [196] a quantity represented by $\gamma_{n,n}$ where $\psi_n$ is given by

$$(1.7.1) \qquad \psi_n = \gamma_n t + \gamma_{n+1} + \frac{\lambda(t)}{(1+t)^p}$$

where, as usual, $\lambda(t) \in R$ and $\mu_{n+p+1} < \infty$, $p > 0$. Smith tabulated in [196] the first eight $\gamma$'s of (1.7.1), assuming the common mean of the point process $\mu_1 \equiv 1$.

In Section 1.5 we have obtained the first eight $\gamma'_{n,n}$'s given by (1.5.2) in order to complete the table. The table of the first eight $\tilde{\psi}$-cumulants of a General Point Process given by

$$(1.7.2) \qquad \tilde{\psi}_n(t) = \psi_n(t) + \gamma_{n,n} \; .$$

Equation (1.7.1) can also be written as

$$\psi_n = \alpha_n t + \beta_n + r_n(t)$$

where the remainder term, $r_n(t)$ goes to 0 as n goes to infinity. Also,

$$\alpha_n = \alpha_n(\mu_1, \mu_2, \ldots, \mu_n) \quad \text{and} \quad \beta_n = \beta_n(\mu_1, \mu_2, \ldots, \mu_{n+1})$$

are respectively given by the following tables. We only give the tables for $n = 1$ through 8, as one needs at most the first eight cumulants, or equivalently, the moment of the renewal random variable $N_t$ of the Ordinary Point Process in terms of the moments of the common distribution, $F(x)$. If $\mu_k$ denotes the $k^{th}$ moment about the origin of $F(x)$, and assuming $\mu_1 = 1$, we have from Smith [196] the following two tables for $\alpha$'s and $\beta$'s:

Table for $\alpha$'s

$$\alpha_2 = \mu_2$$

$$\alpha_3 = -\mu_3 + 3\mu_2^2$$

$$\alpha_4 = \mu_4 - 10\mu_2\mu_3 + 15\mu_2^3$$

$$\alpha_5 = -\mu_5 + 15\mu_2\mu_4 + 10\mu_3^2 - 105\mu_2^2\mu_3 + 105\mu_2^4$$

$$\alpha_6 = \mu_6 + 21\mu_2\mu_5 - 35\mu_3\mu_5 + 210\mu_2^2\mu_4 + 280\mu_2\mu_3^2 - 1260\mu_2^3\mu_3 + 945\mu_2^5$$

$$\alpha_7 = -\mu_7 + 28\mu_2\mu_6 + 56\mu_3\mu_5 - 378\mu_2^2\mu_5 + 35\mu_4^2 - 1260\mu_2\mu_3\mu_4 + 3150\mu_2^3\mu_4 - 280\mu_3^3 + 6300\mu_2^2\mu_3^2 - 17{,}325\mu_2^4\mu_3 + 10395\mu_2^6$$

$$\alpha_8 = \mu_3 - 36\mu_2\mu_7 - 84\mu_3\mu_6 + 630\mu_2^2\mu_6 - 126\mu_4\mu_5$$
$$+ 2520\mu_2\mu_3\mu_5 - 6930\mu_2^3\mu_5 + 1575\mu_2\mu_4^2 + 2100\mu_3^2\mu_4$$
$$- 34650\mu_2^2\mu_3\mu_4 + 51975\mu_2^4\mu_4 - 15400\mu_2\mu_3^3$$
$$+ 138600\mu_2^3\mu_3^2 - 270270\mu_2^5\mu_3 + 135135\mu_2^7 \ .$$

<u>Table for β's</u>

$$\beta_1 = \frac{1}{2}\mu_2$$

$$\beta_2 = -\frac{2}{3}\mu_3 + \frac{5}{4}\mu_2^2$$

$$\beta_3 = \frac{3}{4}\mu_4 - 5\mu_2\mu_3 + \frac{11}{2}\mu_2^3$$

$$\beta_4 = -\frac{4}{5}\mu_5 + \frac{17}{2}\mu_2\mu_4 + \frac{16}{3}\mu_3^2 - 44\mu_2^2\mu_3 + \frac{279}{8}\mu_2^4$$

$$\beta_5 = \frac{5}{6}\mu_6 - 13\mu_2\mu_5 - 20\mu_3\mu_4 + \frac{395}{4}\mu_2^2\mu_4 + 125\mu_2\mu_3^2$$
$$- 465\mu_2^3\mu_3 + \frac{579}{2}\mu_2^5$$

$$\beta_6 = -\frac{6}{7}\mu_7 + \frac{37}{2}\mu_2\mu_6 + 34\mu_3\mu_5 - 195\mu_2^2\mu_5 + \frac{165}{8}\mu_2\mu_3\mu_4$$
$$- 605\mu_2\mu_3\mu_4 + 1290\mu_2^3\mu_4 - \frac{1160}{9}\mu_3^3$$
$$+ 2465\mu_2^2\mu_3^2 - 5790\mu_2^4\mu_3 + \left(\frac{11895}{4}\right)\mu_2^6$$

$$\beta_7 = \frac{7}{8}\mu_8 - 25\mu_2\mu_7 - \frac{161}{3}\mu_3\mu_6 + 350\mu_2^2\mu_6 - 77\mu_4\mu_5$$
$$+ 1295\mu_2\mu_3\mu_5 - 3108\mu_2^3\mu_5 + \frac{1575}{2}\mu_2\mu_4^2 + 1015\mu_3^2\mu_4$$
$$- 14560\mu_2^2\mu_3\mu_4 + \left(\frac{76335}{4}\right)\mu_2^4\mu_4 - 6230\mu_2\mu_3^3$$
$$+ 6230\mu_2\mu_3^3 + 48860\mu_2^3\mu_3^2 - 83265\mu_2^5\mu_3 +$$

$$+ \left( \frac{72855}{2} \right) \mu_2$$

$$\begin{aligned}
\beta_8 = & -\frac{8}{9}\mu_9 + \frac{65}{2}\mu_2\mu_8 + 80\mu_3\mu_7 - 584\mu_2^2\mu_7 + 133\mu_4\mu_6 \\
& - 2520\mu_2\mu_3\mu_6 + 6713\mu_2^3\mu_6 + \frac{392}{5}\mu_5^2 - 3626\mu_2\mu_4\mu_5 \\
& - 2352\mu_3^2\mu_5 + 37464\mu_2^2\mu_3\mu_5 - 54138\mu_2^4\mu_5 - 2870\mu_3\mu_4^2 \\
& + \left( \frac{91315}{4} \right)\mu_2^2\mu_4^2 + 59010\mu_2\mu_3^2\mu_4 - 339990\mu_2^3\mu_3\mu_4 \\
& + \left( \frac{634935}{2} \right)\mu_2^5\mu_4 + \left( \frac{19040}{3} \right)\mu_3^4 - 218960\mu_2^2\mu_3^3 \\
& + 1019970\mu_2^4\mu_3^2 - 1359960\mu_2^6\mu_3 + \left( \frac{8294895}{16} \right)\mu_2^8 .
\end{aligned}$$

## 1.8 Cumulants of the "Equilibrium" Point Process

Consider a point process which has been in progress for a long time. Fix a point $t$ on the time axis (it is not a matter of necessity that the event $\mathcal{E}$ of the point process happen at the arbitrarily chosen point $t$ on the time axis). Let us denote by $Y(t)$, the time that elapses from $t$ on to the next succeeding event of the point process. Let $K_t(x)$ denote the distribution function of $Y(t)$. What we now observe from the instant $t$ onwards, is a General Point Process whose "residual lifetime" distribution is $K_t(x)$; the intervals between events being independently, identically distributed random variables with the same distribution function $F(x)$. Cox and Smith [44] have shown that

$$
(1.8.1) \qquad \lim_{t \to \infty} K_t(x) = \frac{1}{\mu_1} \int_0^x [1 - F(y)]dy = K(x), \text{ say.}
$$

In other words, if a point process with a distribution function $F(x)$ of the intervals between successive events, has been in progress a long time since, and if observations are made, starting from an arbitrary origin $t$, then what we are actually observing is a General Point Process whose "residual Lifetime" distribution is given by the $K(x)$ of (1.8.1) This particular General Point Process is called the "equilibrium process." We can now write down the cumulants of the "equilibrium process" as a particular case of the General Point Process. We put small $e$ on $\gamma_{n,n}$ to stand for the "equilibrium process."

We have that

$$
(1.8.2) \qquad \gamma^e_{n,n} = a^e_n + (n - 1)! \quad ,
$$

where $a^e_n$ (1.6.4) with the modification that the $\kappa$'s should be replaced by $\kappa^e$. We will tabulate the first eight $\kappa^e$'s of $K(x)$ as given by (1.8.1) assuming that

$\mu_1 = 1.$

(1.8.3)

$$\kappa_1^e = \frac{\mu_2}{2}$$

$$\kappa_2^e = \frac{\mu_3}{3} - \frac{\mu_2^2}{4}$$

$$\kappa_3^e = \frac{\mu_4}{4} - \frac{\mu_2\mu_3}{2} + \frac{\mu_2^3}{4}$$

$$\kappa_4^e = \frac{\mu_5}{5} - \frac{\mu_2\mu_4}{2} - \frac{\mu_3^2}{3} + \mu_2^2\mu_3 - \frac{3\mu_2^4}{8}$$

$$\kappa_5^e = \frac{\mu_6}{6} - \frac{\mu_2\mu_5}{2} - \frac{5}{6}\mu_3\mu_4 + \frac{5}{4}\mu_2^2\mu_4 + \frac{5}{3}\mu_2\mu_3^2 - \frac{5}{2}\mu_2^3\mu_3 + \frac{3}{4}\mu_2^5$$

$$\kappa_6^e = \frac{1}{7}\mu_7 - \frac{1}{2}\mu_2\mu_6 - \mu_3\mu_5 + \frac{3}{2}\mu_2^2\mu_5 - \frac{5}{8}\mu_4^2 + 5\mu_2\mu_3\mu_4$$
$$- \frac{15}{4}\mu_2^3\mu_4 + \frac{10}{9}\mu_3^3 - \frac{15}{2}\mu_2^2\mu_3^2 + \frac{15}{2}\mu_2^4\mu_3 - \frac{15}{8}\mu_2^3$$

$$\kappa_7^e = \frac{1}{8}\mu_8 - \frac{1}{2}\mu_2\mu_7 - \frac{7}{6}\mu_3\mu_6 - \frac{7}{4}\mu_4\mu_5 + \frac{7}{4}\mu_4\mu_5 + 7\mu_2\mu_3\mu_5$$
$$- \frac{21}{4}\mu_2^3\mu_5 + \frac{35}{8}\mu_2\mu_4^2 + \frac{35}{6}\mu_3^2\mu_4 - \frac{105}{4}\mu_2^2\mu_3\mu_4$$
$$+ \frac{105}{8}\mu_2^4\mu_4 - \frac{35}{3}\mu_2\mu_3^3 + 35\mu_2^3\mu_3^2 - \frac{105}{4}\mu_2^5\mu_3 + \frac{45}{8}\mu_2^7$$

$$\kappa_8^e = \frac{1}{9}\mu_9 - \frac{1}{2}\mu_2\mu_8 - \frac{4}{3}\mu_3\mu_7 + 2\mu_2^2\mu_7 - \frac{7}{3}\mu_4\mu_6 + \frac{28}{3}\mu_2\mu_3\mu_6$$
$$- 7\mu_2^3\mu_6 - \frac{7}{5}\mu_5^2 + 14\mu_2\mu_3\mu_5 + \frac{28}{3}\mu_3^2\mu_5 - 42\mu_2^2\mu_3\mu_5$$
$$+ 21\mu_2^4\mu_5 + \frac{35}{3}\mu_3\mu_4^2 - \frac{105}{4}\mu_2^2\mu_4^2 - 70\mu_2\mu_3^2\mu_4$$
$$+ 140\mu_2^3\mu_3\mu_4 - \frac{70}{9}\mu_3^4 + \frac{280}{3}\mu_2^2\mu_3^3 - 175\mu_2^4\mu_3^2$$
$$+ 105\mu_2^6\mu_3 - \frac{315}{16}\mu_2^8 \quad .$$

Substituting (1.8.3) in (1.6.4) and (1.6.4) in (1.8.2), we obtain for the first four $\gamma^e_{n,n}$ the following:

$$
(1.8.4)\quad \begin{cases}
\gamma^e_{11} = 1 - \dfrac{\mu_2}{2} \\[2ex]
\gamma^e_{22} = \dfrac{1}{3}\mu_3 - \dfrac{3}{4}\mu_2^2 + 1 \\[2ex]
\gamma^e_{33} = 2\mu_2\mu_3 - \dfrac{\mu_4}{4} - \dfrac{5}{2}\mu_2^3 + 2 \\[2ex]
\gamma^e_{44} = \dfrac{1}{5}\mu_5 - \dfrac{5}{2}\mu_2\mu_4 + 15\mu_2^2\mu_3 - \dfrac{105}{8}\mu_2^4 \\
\qquad\qquad - \dfrac{5}{3}\mu_3^2 + 6 \ .
\end{cases}
$$

# CHAPTER 2. ESTIMATION

## 2.1. The Variance-Time Curve of a Point Process (V-T-Curve)

Empirical investigations on the estimation of the variance-time curve (V-T-curve) of a Point Process were carried out earlier by Cox and Smith [44]. In this chapter a statistic is proposed as an estimate of the variance-time curve at a given point on the time-axis, based on observations in a given interval of a point process. "Equilibrium" is assumed for the calculations. Sampling properties are derived when the basic point process is arbitrary and the difficulties in the derivations for the general case are pointed out. Under the Null Hypothesis that the underlying point process is purely random (Poisson Process), the consistency and asymptotic normality of the statistic are established; the later result, incidentally, provides a test of significance for randomness of the underlying point process. Some difficulties involved in certain non-null distributions of the statistic are discussed. The concept of "estimability" within the framework of our derivations is introduced and certain non-estimability results are proved. In a later chapter the extension of these concepts to the multidimensional case are obtained.

## 2.2. The Statistic for Estimating the (V-T)-Curve

The variance-time curve is the graph of the variance of $N_t$, the number of events up to time $t$ of a Point Process, plotted against $t$, the time parameter. Neglecting the remainder, which tends to zero as $t \to \infty$, the explicit expression for the variance-time curve in terms of the moments of the underlying point process is given, assuming equilibrium, i.e., the process has been in progress a long time since,

$$(2.2.1) \qquad V(t) = \text{Var}\,(N_t) = \alpha t + \beta' ,$$

where

$$\alpha = \frac{\mu_2 - \mu_1^2}{\mu_1^3}, \quad \text{and}$$

$$(2.2.2) \qquad \beta' = \frac{3\mu_2^2 - 2\mu_1\mu_3}{6\mu_1^4} .$$

Suppose observations on the process are made in the interval $(0,T)$. We propose as an estimate of $V(\tau)$, $0 < \tau < T$, the statistic $\hat{V}(\tau)$, defined thus:

$$(2.2.3) \quad \hat{V}(\tau) = \frac{1}{T - \tau} \int_0^{T-\tau} (N(t + \tau, t))^2 \, dt - \frac{\tau^2}{T^2} (N(0,T))^2 ,$$

where $N(t + \tau, t)$ denotes the number of events in the interval $(t, t + \tau)$ and $N(0,T)$, the number of events in $(0,T)$.

## 2.3. The General Properties of the Statistic

Let $N_t^e$ denote the number of events of an equilibrium process in $(0,t)$. Taking expectations on both sides of (2.2.3), we obtain

$$\begin{aligned} E(\hat{V}(\tau)) &= \frac{1}{T-\tau} \int_0^{T-\tau} E(N(t+\tau,t))^2 \, dt - \frac{\tau^2}{T^2} E(N(0,T))^2 \\ &= \frac{1}{T-\tau} \int_0^{T-\tau} E(N_\tau^e)^2 \, dt - \frac{\tau^2}{T^2} E(N_T^e)^2 \\ &= E(N_\tau^e)^2 - \frac{\tau^2}{T^2} E(N_T^e)^2 \\ &= E(N_\tau^e)^2 - \frac{\tau^2}{T^2} [\alpha T + \beta' + \alpha'^2 T^2 + o(1)] , \end{aligned}$$

as $T \to \infty$, where $\alpha' = 1/\mu_1$. Thus

$$(2.3.1)\quad E(\hat{V}(\tau)) = E(N_\tau^e)^2 - \tau^2 \alpha'^2 + O(1), \quad \text{as } T \to \infty$$

$$= E(N_\tau^e)^2 - E^2(N_\tau^e) + \frac{\tau^2}{\mu_1^2} + O(1) .$$

But we have from Chapter 1 that $E(N_t) = \varphi_1'(t)$, and

$$\varphi_1'^*(s) = K^* \varphi_1^* = \frac{K^*}{1 - F^*} .$$

However, assuming equilibrium,

$$K^* = \frac{1 - F^*}{\mu_1 s}$$

and so

$$\varphi_1'^{*e}(s) = \frac{1}{\mu_1 s} .$$

Hence

$$E(N_t^e) = \frac{t}{\mu_1} ,$$

exactly, and thus

$$E^2(N_\tau^e) - \frac{\tau^2}{\mu_1^2} \equiv 0 .$$

We have, therefore, that

$$(2.3.3) \qquad E(\hat{V}(\tau)) = V(\tau) + O(1), \quad \text{as} \quad T \to \infty .$$

In other words, $\hat{V}(\tau)$ is an asymptotically unbiased estimate of $V(\tau)$, for any arbitrary underlying point process.

## 2.4. The Asymptotic Normality Statistic When the Underlying Point Process is Poisson

In the particular case when the underlying point process is Poisson, with parameter $\lambda$, we obtain

$$
\begin{aligned}
(2.4.1) \qquad E(\hat{V}(\tau)) &= E(N_\tau^e)^2 - \frac{\tau^2}{T^2} E(N_T^e)^2 \\
&= \lambda\tau + \lambda^2\tau^2 - \frac{\tau^2}{T^2}(\lambda T + \lambda^2 T^2) \\
&= \lambda\tau + \lambda^2\tau^2 - \frac{\tau^2\lambda}{T} - \lambda^2\tau^2 \\
&= \lambda\tau\left(1 - \frac{\tau}{T}\right) .
\end{aligned}
$$

It is evident from (2.4.1) that $(T/(T-\tau))\,\hat{V}(\tau)$ is an exactly unbiased estimate of $V(\tau)$ in this case and that this estimator is also asymptotically unbiased in the general case.

Evidently,

$$(2.4.2)\quad \text{Cov}\,(\hat{V}(\tau),\hat{V}(\tau+h)) = E\,(\hat{V}(\tau) - E\,\hat{V}(\tau))\,(\hat{V}(\tau+h) - E\,\hat{V}(\tau+h))$$

for arbitrary $h$. However,

$$V(\tau) - E\,V(\tau) = \frac{1}{T-\tau}\int_0^{T-\tau} (N^2(t+\tau,t) - E\,N^2(t+\tau,t))dt$$

$$= \frac{\tau^2}{T^2}\;(N^2(0,T) - E\,N^2(0,T)) \quad ,$$

and if we write

$$\Delta N^2(t+\tau,t) = N^2(t+\tau,t) - E\,N^2(t+\tau,t) \quad ,$$

$$\Delta N^2(T) = N^2(0,T) - E\,N^2(0,T) \quad ,$$

then, we have that

$$(2.4.3)\quad (\hat{V}(\tau) - E\,\hat{V}(\tau))\,(\hat{V}(\tau+h) - E\,\hat{V}(\tau+h))$$

$$= \frac{1}{T-\tau}\left[\int_0^{T-\tau} \Delta N^2(t+\tau,t)dt - \frac{\tau^2}{T^2}\Delta N^2(T)\right]$$

$$\times \left[\frac{1}{T-\tau-h}\int_0^{T-\tau-h} \Delta N^2(t+\tau+h,t)dt - \frac{(\tau+h)^2}{T^2}\;\Delta N^2(T)\right]$$

$$= I_1 - I_2 - I_3 + I_4 \quad ,$$

say, where

(2.4.4)

$$I_1 = \frac{1}{(T-\tau)(T-\tau-h)} \int_{t=0}^{t=T-\tau} \int_{t'=0}^{t'=T-\tau-h}$$

$$\times\ \Delta N^2(t+\tau,t)\ \Delta N^2(t'+\tau,t')dt\ dt' \quad ,$$

$$I_2 = \frac{t^2}{T^2(T-\tau-h)} \int_0^{T-\tau-h} \Delta N^2(T)\ \Delta N^2(t+\tau+h,t)dt \quad ,$$

$$I_3 = \frac{(\tau+h)^2}{T^2(T-\tau)} \int_0^{T-\tau} \Delta N^2(T)\ \Delta N^2(t+\tau,t)dt \quad ,$$

$$I_4 = \frac{\tau^2(\tau+h)^2}{T^4} (\Delta N^2(T))^2 \quad .$$

Upon taking expectations on both sides of (2.4.3), we discover that

(2.4.5) $\mathrm{Cov}\ (\hat{V}(\tau),\hat{V}(\tau+h))$

$$= E(I_1) - E(I_2) - E(I_3) + E(I_4) \quad .$$

We will evaluate $E(I_2)$, $E(I_3)$ and $E(I_4)$ first, and then obtain the more complicated $E(I_1)$. Clearly,

(2.4.6)

$$E(I_2) = \frac{\tau^2}{T^2(T-\tau-h)} E \int_0^{T-\tau-h} \Delta N^2(T)\ \Delta N^2(t+\tau+h,t)dt$$

$$= \frac{\tau^2}{T^2(T-\tau-h)} \int_0^{T-\tau-h} \mathrm{Cov}\ (N^2(T),N^2(t+\tau+h,t))dt \ .$$

Consider the diagram below:

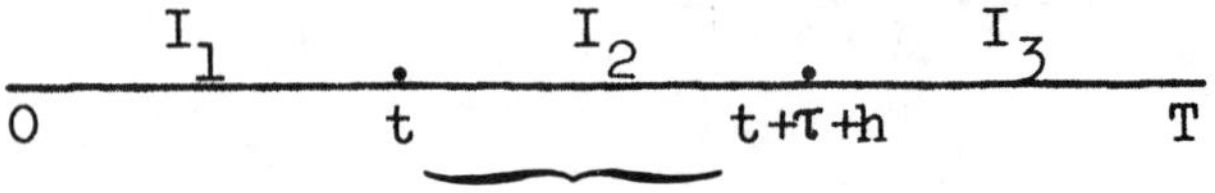


In this figure

$$I_1 \equiv (0,t] \qquad ,$$

$$I_2 \equiv (t, t+\tau+h] \ ,$$

and

$$I_3 \equiv (t+\tau+h, T] \ .$$

Let $N_I$ stand for the observed number of events in the interval I. Then

$$\text{(2.4.7)} \quad \text{Cov}\,(N^2(T), N^2(t+\tau+h, t))$$

$$= \text{Cov}\,(N^2_{I_2}, (N_{I_1} + N_{I_2} + N_{I_3})^2)$$

$$= \text{Cov}\,(N^2_{I_2}, N^2_{I_1}) + \text{Var}\,(N^2_{I_2}) + \text{Cov}\,(N^2_{I_2}, N^2_{I_3})$$

$$+ 2\,\text{Cov}\,(N^2_{I_2}, N_{I_1}N_{I_2}) + 2\,\text{Cov}\,(N^2_{I_2}, N_{I_1}N_{I_3})$$

$$+ 2\,\text{Cov}\,(N^2_{I_2}, N_{I_2}N_{I_3}) \ .$$

So far, we do not know how to evaluate expressions like $E\,(N^2_{I_1} N^2_{I_2})$ for an arbitrary underlying point process. However, when the underlying point process is purely random

(Poisson), since events in disjoint intervals are independent, we can evaluate the terms of the right-hand side of (2.4.7).

Thus, when the underlying process is Poisson, (2.4.7) reduces to

$$(2.4.8)\qquad \operatorname{Cov}\,(N^2(T), N^2(t+\tau+h,t)) = \operatorname{Var}\,(N^2_{I_2}) = \operatorname{Var}\,(N^2_{\tau+h}) ,$$

and so

$$(2.4.9)\quad E(I_2) = \frac{\tau^2}{T^2(T-\tau-h)}\,(T-\tau-h)\operatorname{Var}\,(N^2_{\tau+h}) = \frac{\tau^2}{T^2}\operatorname{Var}\,(N^2_{\tau+h}) .$$

Similarly, when the underlying process is Poisson, we find

$$(2.4.10)\qquad E(I_3) = \frac{(\tau+h)^2}{T^2}\operatorname{Var}\,(N^2_t) ,$$

$$(2.4.11)\qquad E(I_4) = \frac{\tau^2(\tau+h)^2}{T^4}\operatorname{Var}\,(N^2_T) .$$

On putting $\lambda t = \mu$, we have, for a Poisson process,

$$(2.4.12)\quad \begin{cases} E(N_t) = \mu , \\ E(N_t^2) = \mu + \mu^2 , \\ E(N_t^3) = \mu + 3\mu^2 + \mu^3 , \\ E(N_t^4) = \mu + 7\mu^2 + 6\mu^3 + \mu^4 . \end{cases}$$

Thus

$$\begin{aligned} \operatorname{Var}(N_T^2) &= E(N_T^4) - E^2(N_T^2) \\ &= \mu + 6\mu^2 + 4\mu^3 \\ &= \lambda T + 6\lambda^2 T^2 + 4\lambda^3 T^3 . \end{aligned}$$

From this it follows that

$$(2.4.13)\quad E(I_4) = \frac{4\lambda^3\tau^2(\tau + h)^2}{T} + \frac{6\lambda^2\tau^2(\tau + h)^2}{T^2} + \frac{\lambda\tau^2(\tau + h)^2}{T^3} .$$

Before we calculate the more complicated expression $\operatorname{Cov}(\hat{V}(\tau), \hat{V}(\tau + h))$, we will obtain $\operatorname{Var}(\hat{V}(\tau))$. The only quantity still to be calculated for obtaining $\operatorname{Var}(\hat{V}(\tau))$ is $E(I_1)$ when $h = 0$. We have

$$(2.4.14)\qquad E(I_1) = \frac{1}{(T - \tau)^2} \int_0^{T-\tau} \int_0^{T-\tau} \times$$

$$\times \quad \text{Cov}\, N^2(t + \tau, t), N^2(t' + \tau, t')\,dt\,dt' \quad ,$$

<u>CASE I</u>: $t > t'$:

a) $t > t' + \tau$:

In this case we evidently have

$$\text{Cov}\,(N^2(t + \tau, t), N^2(t' + \tau, t')) = 0 \quad .$$

b) $t' < t < t' + \tau$:

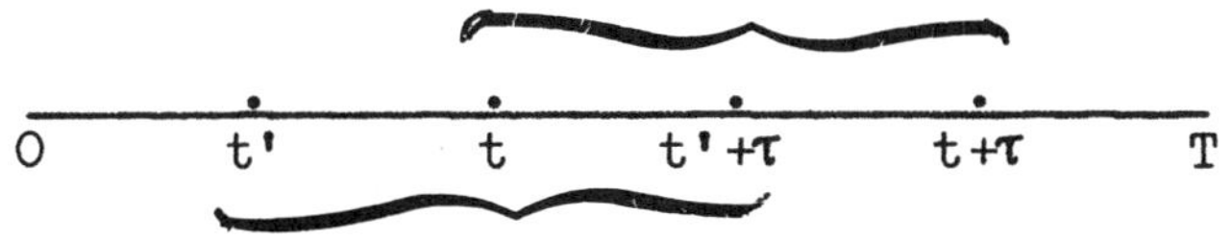


Let

$$I_1 \equiv (t', t] \quad ,$$

$$I_2 \equiv (t, t' + \tau] \quad ,$$

$$I_3 \equiv (t' + \tau, t + \tau] \quad .$$

Then

$$N(t + \tau, t) = N_{I_2} + N_{I_3} \quad ,$$

$$N(t' + \tau, t') = N_{I_1} + N_{I_2} \quad .$$

Therefore,

$$\text{Cov}\,(N^2(t+\tau,t),N^2(t'+\tau,t'))$$

$$= \text{Cov}\,(N^2_{I_2} + N^2_{I_3} + 2N_{I_2}N_{I_3}, N^2_{I_1} + N^2_{I_2} + 2N_{I_1}N_{I_2})$$

$$= \text{Var}\,(N^2_{I_2}) \quad ,$$

when the underlying process is Poisson, and therefore, is equal to $\text{Var}(N^2_{t'-t+\tau})$.

<u>CASE</u> <u>II</u>: $t' > t$.

a) $t' > t + \tau$:

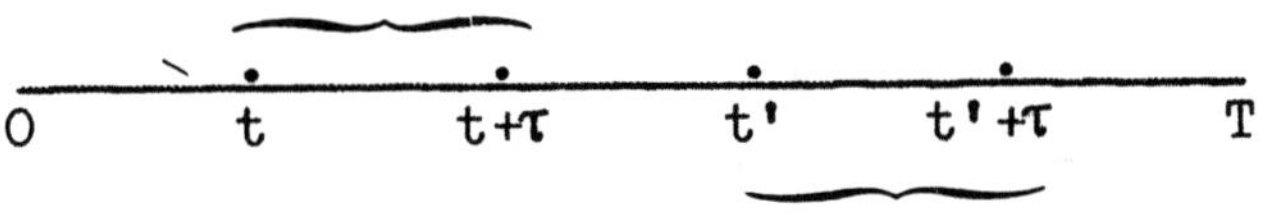


In this case

$$\text{Cov}\,(N^2(t+\tau,t),N^2(t'+\tau,t')) \equiv 0 \quad .$$

b) $t < t' < t + \tau$:

In this case one obtains, as before,

$$\text{Cov}\,(N^2(t+\tau,t),N^2(t'+\tau,t'))$$

$$= \text{Var}\,(N^2_{t-t'+\tau}) \quad .$$

Figure 1 below is an illustration of the domain of integration.

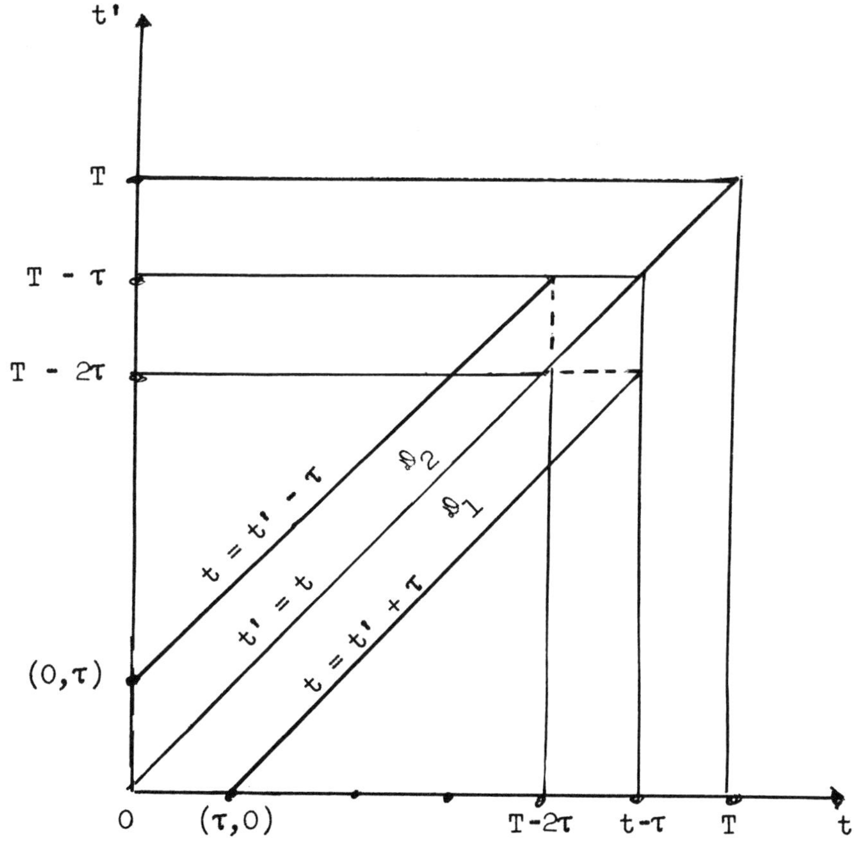


FIGURE 1

THE DOMAIN OF INTEGRATION

Now

(2.4.14)

$$\int_0^{T-\tau}\int_0^{T-\tau} \text{Cov}\,(N^2(t+\tau,t),N^2(t'+\tau,t'))dt\,dt'$$

$$= \int_{\mathcal{D}_1} \text{Var}\,N^2_{t'-t+\tau}\,dt\,dt' + \int_{\mathcal{D}_2} \text{Var}\,N^2_{t-t'+\tau}\,dt\,dt' \quad .$$

By symmetry, we discover that

(2.4.15)

$$\int_0^{T-\tau}\int_0^{T-\tau} \operatorname{Cov}\,(N^2(t+\tau,t),N^2(t'+\tau,t'))dt\,dt'$$

$$= 2\int_{t'=0}^{t'=T-2\tau}\int_{t=t'}^{t=t'+\tau} (\operatorname{Var} N^2_{t'-t+\tau})dt\,dt'$$

$$+ \ 2\int_{t'=T-2\tau}^{t'=T-\tau}\int_{t=t'}^{t=T-\tau} \operatorname{Var}\,(N^2_{t'-t+\tau})dt\,dt' \ .$$

If we write

$$\varphi(t,t') = \operatorname{Var}\,(N^2_{t'-t+\tau}) \ ,$$

then

$$\varphi(t,t') = \lambda(t'-t+\tau) + 6\lambda^2(t'-t+\tau)^2 + 4\lambda^3(t'-t+\tau)^3$$

$$= A + Bt' + Ct'^2 + Dt'^3 - Bt + Ct^2 - Dt^3$$

$$+ Ett' - Ftt'^2 + Ft^2t' \ ,$$

where

(2.4.16)
$$\begin{cases} A = \lambda t + 6\lambda^2\tau^2 + 4\lambda^3\tau^3 \ , \\ B = \lambda + 12\lambda^2\tau + 12\lambda^3\tau^2 \ , \\ C = 6\lambda^2 + 12\lambda^3\tau \ , \\ D = 4\lambda^3 \ , \\ E = -\,(12\lambda^2 + 24\lambda^3\tau) \ , \end{cases}$$

and $$\lfloor F = 12\lambda^3 .$$

Upon integrating $\varphi(t,t')$ with respect to $t$ and denoting the result by $\Phi(t,t')$, we obtain

$$\Phi(t,t') = [A + Bt' + Ct'^2 + Dt'^3]t - \frac{Bt^2}{2} + \frac{Ct^3}{3} - \frac{Dt^4}{4}$$
$$+ \frac{E}{2} t't^2 - \frac{F}{2} t'^2t^2 + \frac{F}{3} t't^3 .$$

Therefore,

$$\Phi(t,t') \Big]_{t=t'}^{t=T-2\tau}$$
$$= \left( A\tau - \frac{B\tau^2}{2} + \frac{C\tau^3}{3} - \frac{D\tau^4}{4} \right)$$
$$+ \left( C\tau^2 - D\tau^3 + \frac{E\tau^2}{2} + \frac{F\tau^3}{3} \right) t'$$
$$+ \left( 2C\tau - \frac{3D\tau^2}{2} + E\tau + \frac{F\tau^2}{2} \right) t'^2$$
$$= \frac{\lambda\tau^2}{2} + 2\lambda^2\tau^3 + \lambda^3\tau^4 = C,$$

say, after substituting for A, B, C, D, E and F from (2.4.16). Hence

$$(2.4.17) \quad 2 \int_{t'=0}^{t'=T-2\tau} \int_{t=t'}^{t=t'+\tau} \text{Var } (N^2_{t'-t+\tau}) dt\, dt'$$
$$= 2 \int_{t'=0}^{t'=T-2\tau} C\, dt' = 2C(T - 2\tau) =$$

$$= (T - 2\tau)(\lambda\tau^2 + 4\lambda^2\tau^3 + 2\lambda^3\tau^4) \quad .$$

Now

$$\Phi(t,t')\Big]_{t=t'}^{t=T-\tau}$$

$$= [A + Bt' + Ct'^2 + Dt'^3](T - \tau) - \frac{B}{2}(T - \tau)^2$$

$$+ \frac{C}{3}(T-\tau)^3 - \frac{D}{4}(T-\tau)^4 + \frac{E}{2}t'(T-\tau)^2 - \frac{F}{2}t'^2(T-\tau)^2$$

$$+ \frac{F}{3}t'(T-\tau)^3 - At' - Bt'^2 - Ct'^3 - Dt'^4 + \frac{Bt'^2}{2} - \frac{Ct'^3}{3}$$

$$+ \frac{D}{4}t'^4 - \frac{E}{2}t'^3 + \frac{F}{2}t'^4 - \frac{F}{3}t'^4$$

$$= [A(T-\tau) - \frac{B}{2}(T-\tau)^2 + \frac{C}{3}(T-\tau)^3 - \frac{D}{4}(T-\tau)^4]$$

$$+ t'[B(T-\tau) + \frac{E}{2}(T-\tau)^2 + \frac{F}{3}(T-\tau)^3 - A]$$

$$+ t'^2[C(T-\tau) - \frac{F}{2}(T-\tau)^2 - \frac{B}{2}] + t'^3[D(T-\tau) - \frac{4C}{3} - \frac{E}{2}]$$

$$+ t'^4[\frac{F}{6} - \frac{3D}{4}] \quad .$$

Hence

(2.4.18)

$$\int_{t'=T-2\tau}^{t'=T-\tau}\int_{t=t'}^{t=T-\tau} \mathrm{Var}\,(N^2_{t'-t+\tau})dt\,dt'$$

$$= [A(T-\tau) - \frac{B}{2}(T-\tau)^2 + \frac{C}{3}(T-\tau)^3 - \frac{D}{4}(T-\tau)^4]\tau$$

$$+ \frac{1}{2}[B(T-\tau) + \frac{E}{2}(T-\tau)^2 + \frac{F}{3}(T-\tau)^3 - A]$$

$$\cdot [(T-\tau)^2 - (T - 2\tau)^2] \; +$$

$$+ \frac{1}{3} [C(T-\tau) - \frac{F}{2}(T-\tau)^2 - \frac{B}{2}][(T-\tau)^3 - (T-2\tau)^3]$$

$$+ \frac{1}{4} [D(T-\tau) - \frac{4C}{3} - \frac{E}{2}][(T-\tau)^4 - (T-2\tau)^4]$$

$$+ \frac{1}{5} [\frac{F}{6} - \frac{3D}{4}][(T-\tau)^5 - (T-2\tau)^5] .$$

After a straightforward and laborious simplification, the right-hand side of (2.4.18) reduces to

$$\frac{\lambda\tau^3}{3} + 3\frac{\lambda^2\tau^4}{2} + 4\frac{\lambda^3\tau^5}{5} .$$

Hence

$$(2.4.19) \qquad 2\int_{T-2\tau}^{T-\tau}\int_{t'}^{T-\tau} \mathrm{Var}\,(N^2_{t'-t+\tau})dt\,dt'$$

$$= \frac{2\lambda\tau^3}{3} + 3\lambda^2\tau^4 + \frac{8\lambda^3\tau^5}{5} ,$$

and, on substituting (2.4.19) and (2.4.17) in (2.4.15), we obtain

(2.4.20)

$$E(I_1) = \frac{1}{(T-\tau)^2}\int_0^{T-\tau}\int_0^{T-\tau} \mathrm{Cov}\,(N^2(t+\tau,t),N^2(t'+\tau,t'))dt\,dt'$$

$$= \frac{(T-2\tau)}{(T-\tau)^2}\left(\lambda\tau^2 + 4\lambda^2\tau^3 + 2\lambda^3\tau^4\right)$$

$$+ \frac{1}{(T-\tau)^2}\left(\frac{2\lambda\tau^3}{3} + 3\lambda^2\tau^4 + \frac{8\lambda^3\tau^5}{5}\right) =$$

$$= \frac{\lambda\tau^2 + 4\lambda^2\tau^3 + 2\lambda^3\tau^4}{T - \tau} - \frac{\lambda\tau^3 + \lambda^2\tau^4 + 2\lambda^3\tau^5}{(T - \tau)^2}$$

$$= \frac{\lambda\tau^2 + 4\lambda^2\tau^3 + 2\lambda^3\tau^4}{T} + o\left(\frac{1}{T}\right) .$$

Upon combining (2.4.9), (2.4.10), (2.4.13) and (2.4.20), we obtain

(2.4.21) $\mathrm{Var}(\hat{V}(\tau))$

$$= \frac{\lambda\tau^2 + 4\lambda^2\tau^3 + 2\lambda^3\tau^4}{T} + \frac{4\lambda^3\tau^4}{T} + o\left(\frac{1}{T}\right)$$

$$= \frac{\lambda\tau^2 + 4\lambda^2\tau^3 + 6\lambda^3\tau^4}{T} + o\left(\frac{1}{T}\right) ,$$

as $T \to +\infty$. From (2.4.21) it is evident that $\mathrm{Var}(\hat{V}(\tau))$ tends to zero as $T$ tends to $\infty$, and combining this result with the asymptotic unbiasedness of $\hat{V}(\tau)$ we have the following:

THEOREM 5: <u>When the underlying point process is Poisson,</u> $V(\tau)$ <u>is a consistent estimator of</u> $V(\tau)$.

We shall now obtain the correlogram of the process $\hat{V}(\tau)$, namely, $\mathrm{Cov}(\hat{V}(\tau), \hat{V}(t + h))$. Our main problem hinges upon evaluating

(2.4.22) $$E(I_1) = \frac{1}{(T - \tau)(T - \tau - h)} \int_{t=0}^{t=T-\tau} \int_{t'=0}^{t'=T-\tau-h} \times$$

$$\times \ \text{Cov}\ (N^2(t+\tau,t), N^2(t'+\tau+h,t'))dt\,dt' \quad .$$

To calculate $\text{Cov}\ (N^2(t+\tau,t), N^2(t'+\tau+h,t'))$, we consider the following cases:

<u>CASE I</u>: $t' > t$.

a) $t' > t + \tau$:

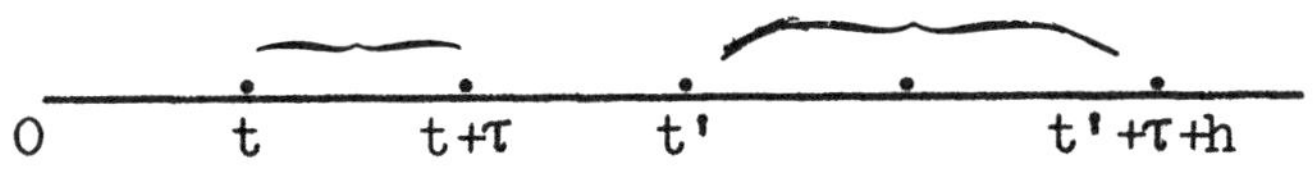


In this case, the covariance is zero for an underlying Poisson Process.

b) $t < t' < t + \tau$:

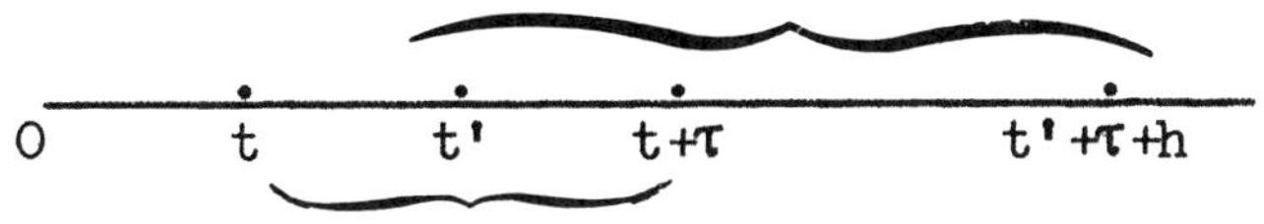


In this case, for an underlying Poisson Process,

$$\text{Cov}\ (N^2(t+\tau,t), N^2(t'+\tau+h,t'))$$
$$= \text{Var}\ (N^2_{t-t'+\tau}) \quad .$$

<u>CASE II</u>: $t > t'$.

a) $t > t' + \tau + h$:

In this case, the covariance vanishes.

b) $t' + h < t < t' + \tau + h$:

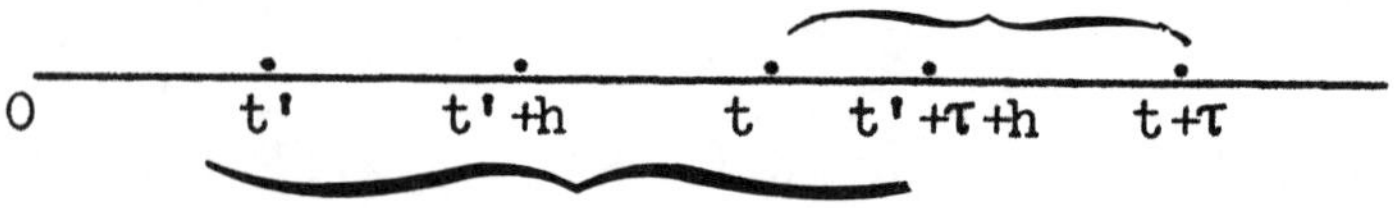


In this case

$$\mathrm{Cov}\,(N^2(t + \tau, t), N^2(t' + \tau + h, t'))$$
$$= \mathrm{Var}\,(N^2_{t'-t+\tau+h}) \quad .$$

c) $t' < t < t' + h$:

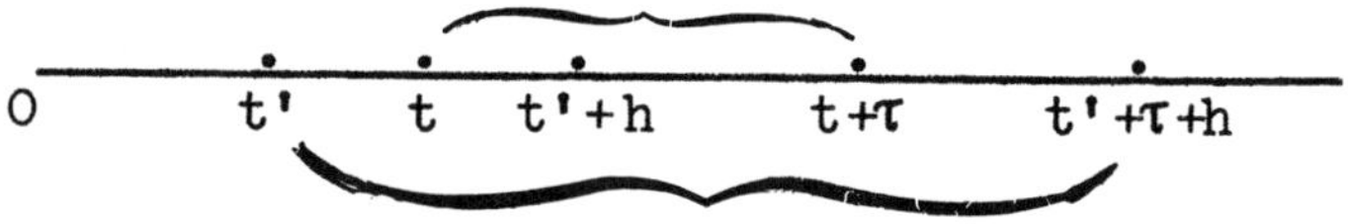


In this case

$$\mathrm{Cov}\,(N^2(t + \tau, t), N^2(t' + \tau + h, t')) = \mathrm{Var}\,(N^2_{\tau}) \quad .$$

Hence

(2.4.22)

$$\frac{1}{(T - \tau)(T - \tau - h)} \int_0^{T-\tau} \int_0^{T-\tau-h}$$
$$\times\ \mathrm{Cov}\,(N^2(t + \tau, t), N^2(t' + \tau + h, t'))dt\, dt'$$
$$= \frac{1}{(T - \tau)(T - \tau - h)} \int_{\mathcal{D}_1} \mathrm{Var}\,(N^2_{t-t'+\tau})dt\, dt' +$$

$$+ \frac{1}{(T-\tau)(T-\tau-h)} \int_{\mathcal{D}_2} \text{Var}\,(N_\tau^2)\,dt_1\,dt_2$$

$$+ \frac{1}{(T-\tau)(T-\tau-h)} \int_{\mathcal{D}_3} \text{Var}\,(N_{t'-t+\tau+h}^2)\,dt\,dt' \quad ,$$

where the domains of integration, $\mathcal{D}_1$, $\mathcal{D}_2$ and $\mathcal{D}_3$, are as given in the diagram below.

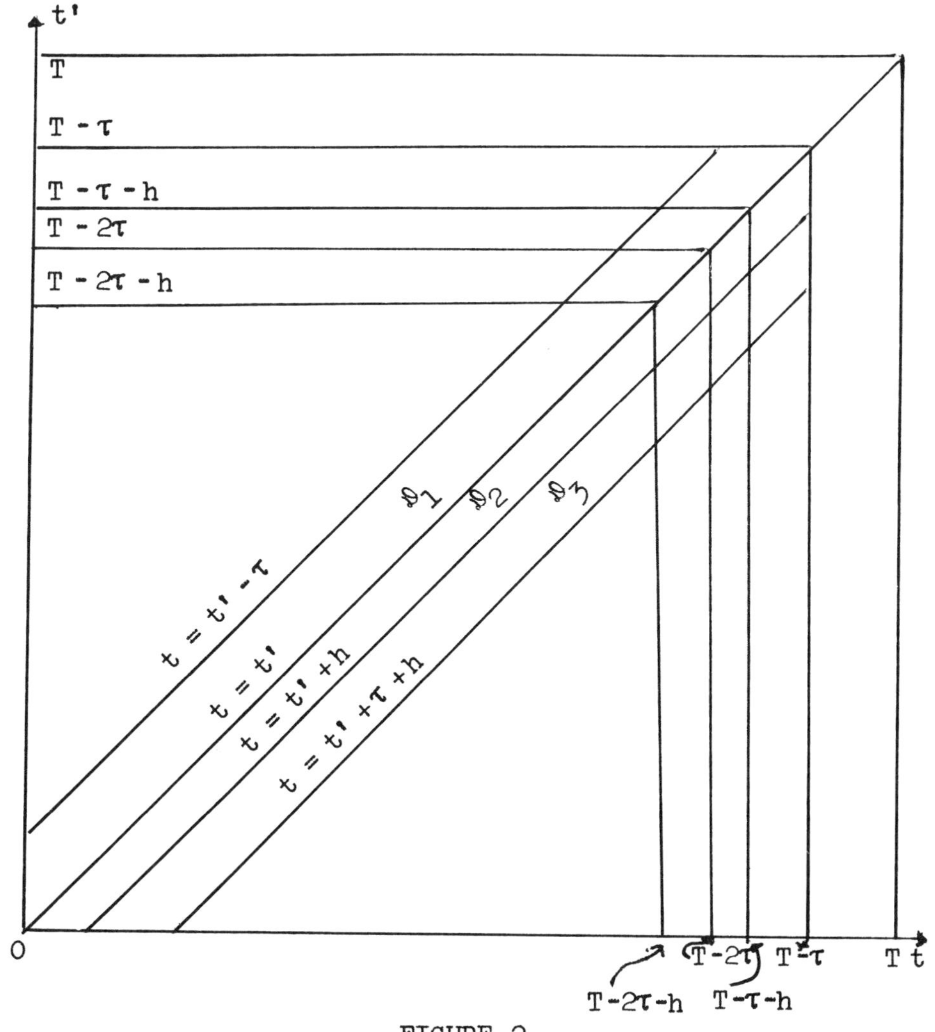


FIGURE 2
THE DOMAIN OF INTEGRATION, $\mathcal{D}_1$, $\mathcal{D}_2$, $\mathcal{D}_3$

(2.4.23)

$$\frac{1}{(T-\tau)(T-\tau-h)} \int_{\mathcal{D}_1} \text{Var}\,(N^2_{t-t'+\tau})dt\,dt'$$

$$= \frac{1}{(T-\tau)(T-\tau-h)} \int_{t=0}^{t=T-2\tau} \int_{t'=t}^{t'=t+\tau} \text{Var}\,(N^2_{t-t'+\tau})dt\,dt'$$

$$+ \frac{1}{(T-\tau)(T-\tau-h)} \int_{t=T-2\tau}^{t=T-\tau} \int_{t'=t}^{t'=T-\tau} \text{Var}\,(N^2_{t-t'+\tau})dt\,dt'$$

$$= \frac{\frac{\lambda\tau^2}{2} + 2\lambda^2\tau^3 + \lambda^3\tau^4}{T} + o\left(\frac{1}{T}\right) ,$$

in view of (2.4.20).

Also,

$$\int_{\mathcal{D}_2} \text{Var}\,(N^2_\tau)dt_1\,dt_2$$

$$= [\text{Area of } \mathcal{D}_2]\ \text{Var}\,(N^2_\tau)$$

$$= \left[\frac{h^2}{2} + (T-\tau-h)h\right][\text{Var}\,(N^2_\tau)] \quad .$$

Hence

(2.4.24)
$$\frac{1}{(T-\tau)(T-\tau-h)} \int_{\mathcal{D}_2} \text{Var}\,(N^2_\tau)dt_1\,dt_2$$

$$= \frac{h\ \text{Var}\,(N^2_\tau)}{T} + o\left(\frac{1}{T}\right) .$$

Now

(2.4.25)

$$\int_{\mathcal{D}_3} \operatorname{Var}(N^2_{t'-\tau+\tau+h})dt\,dt'$$

$$= \int_{t'=0}^{t'=T-2\tau-h} \int_{t=t'+h}^{t=t'+\tau+h} \operatorname{Var}(N^2_{t'-t+\tau+h})dt\,dt'$$

$$+ \int_{t'=T-2\tau-h}^{t'=t-\tau-h} \int_{t=t'+h}^{t=T-\tau} \operatorname{Var}(N^2_{t'-t+\tau+h})dt\,dt' \quad .$$

If we put $t'' = t' + h$, then (2.4.25) becomes

$$(2.4.26) \quad \int_{t''=h}^{t''=T-2\tau} \int_{t=t''}^{t=t''+\tau} \operatorname{Var}(N^2_{t''-t+\tau})dt\,dt''$$

$$+ \int_{t''=T-2\tau}^{t''=T-\tau} \int_{t=t''}^{t=T-\tau} \operatorname{Var}(N^2_{t''-t+\tau})dt\,dt'' \quad .$$

But, from the calculations immediately preceding (2.4.17), we obtain

$$\int_{t=t''}^{t=t''+\tau} \operatorname{Var}(N^2_{t''-\tau+\tau})dt\,dt''$$

$$= \frac{\lambda\tau^2}{2} + 2\lambda^2\tau^3 + \lambda^3\tau^4 \quad ,$$

and the second part of (2.4.26) is, in view of (2.4.19), given by

$$(2.4.28) \quad \int_{t''=T-2\tau}^{t''=T-\tau} \int_{t=t''}^{t=T-\tau} \operatorname{Var}(N^2_{t''-t+\tau})dt\,dt''$$

$$= \frac{\lambda\tau^3}{3} + 3\,\frac{\lambda^2\tau^4}{2} + 4\,\frac{\lambda^3\tau^5}{5} \quad .$$

Thus

(2.4.29) $$\frac{1}{(T-\tau)(T-\tau-h)} \int_{\mathcal{D}_3} \text{Var}\,(N^2_{t'-t+\tau+h})dt\,dt'$$

$$= \frac{\frac{\lambda\tau^2}{2} + 2\lambda^2\tau^3 + \lambda^3\tau^4}{T} + o\left(\frac{1}{T}\right) .$$

Upon combining (2.4.29), (2.4.24), (2.4.23) and (2.4.22), we obtain

(2.4.30)

$$\frac{1}{(T-\tau)(T-\tau-h)} \int_0^{T-\tau} \int_0^{T-\tau-h}$$

$$\times \text{ Cov }(N^2(t+\tau,t), N^2(t'+\tau+h,t'))dt\,dt'$$

$$= \frac{\lambda\tau^2 + 4\lambda^2\tau^3 + 2\lambda^3\tau^4 + h \text{ Var } N^2_\tau}{T} + o\left(\frac{1}{T}\right) .$$

Upon combining (2.4.30), (2.4.9), (2.4.10) and (2.4.13), we obtain

(2.4.31)

$$\text{Cov}\,(\hat{V}(\tau), \hat{V}(\tau+h))$$

$$= \frac{\lambda\tau^2 + 4\lambda^2\tau^3 + 2\lambda^3\tau^4 + 4\lambda^3\tau^2(\tau+h)^2 + h \text{ Var }(N^2_\tau)}{T} + o\left(\frac{1}{T}\right)$$

Note that, when $h = 0$, (2.4.31) reduces to the formula for $\text{Var}\,(\hat{V}(\tau))$ obtained in (2.4.21).

We have seen that

$$(2.4.32) \qquad \hat{V}(\tau) = \hat{V}_1(\tau) - \hat{V}_2(2) \ ,$$

where

$$(2.4.33) \qquad \hat{V}_1(\tau) = \frac{1}{T - \tau} \int_0^{T-\tau} (N(t + \tau, t))^2 \, dt \ ,$$

and

$$(2.4.34) \qquad \hat{V}_2(\tau) = \frac{\tau^2}{T^2} (N(0,T))^2 \ .$$

When the underlying Point Process is Poisson, we have proved that

$$(2.4.35) \qquad \begin{cases} E\,(\hat{V}_1(\tau)) = \lambda\tau + \lambda^2\tau^2 \\ \\ \operatorname{Var}\,(\hat{V}_1(\tau)) = \dfrac{\lambda\tau^2 + 4\lambda^2\tau^3 + 2\lambda^3\tau^4}{T} + O(\frac{1}{T}) \end{cases} ;$$

and

$$(2.4.36) \qquad \begin{cases} E\,(\hat{V}_2(\tau)) = \lambda^2\tau^2 + \dfrac{\lambda\tau^2}{T} \\ \\ \operatorname{Var}\,(\hat{V}_2(\tau)) = \dfrac{4\lambda^3\tau^4}{T} + O(\frac{1}{T}) \end{cases} ;$$

and finally,

$$(2.4.37) \qquad \mathrm{Cov}\,(\hat{V}_1(\tau),\hat{V}_2(\tau)) = O(\tfrac{1}{T}) .$$

We will establish the asymptotic normality of $\hat{V}(\tau)$ in several steps.

STEP 1: $V_1(\tau)$ is asymptotically normal.

Let

$$(2.4.38) \qquad W_t = \int_0^{t-\tau} (N(t+\tau,t))^2\,dt .$$

Consider the development of the underlying Poisson process on the nonnegative time axis. Let us say that the event "E" happens at $t = t_0$ if there are no Poisson events in the interval $(t_0, t_0 - \tau)$. Assume "E" happened at the origin 0. It is clear that the intervals separating the occurrences of the events "E" are independent and identically distributed, and the points on the time axis corresponding to the occurrences of "E" mark the development of a point process, say $\{t_i\}$. Let

$$T_n = t_1 + t_2 + \cdots + t_n$$

when the underlying point process is Poisson, we will show that $W_t$, as defined by (2.4.38) is a cumulative process in the sense of Smith [ 195 ] with respect to the regeneration points $\{T_n\}$. Let us write

$$(2.4.39) \qquad Y_n = \Delta_n W_t = W_{T_n} - W_{T_{n-1}}$$
$$= \int_{T_{n-1}-\tau}^{T_n-\tau} (N(t+\tau,t))^2\, dt \quad .$$

Since the number of Poisson events occurring in disjoint intervals are mutually, independently distributed, and since the $Y_n$'s are made up of Poisson events in disjoint intervals, the lengths of which are independently, identically distributed, the $Y_n$'s are therefore, independently distributed. Also, since the number of Poisson events in any finite $t$ interval, is finite with probability one, then $W_t$ of (2.4.38) is with probability one of bounded variation in every finite t-interval. Since $W_t$ is non-negative, Condition $(C_3)$ of Smith [195] is also satisfied. We have thus proved that $W_t$ is a cumulative process with respect to the regeneration $T_n$.

When $\mu_2 < \infty$, Smith [ 195 ] has proven that

$$(2.4.40) \qquad \sqrt{t}\left(\frac{W_t}{t} - \frac{\kappa_1}{\mu_1}\right) \xrightarrow[t\to\infty]{D} N[0,\theta^2]$$

where $\kappa_1$ is the mean of a $Y_n$.

Upon combining (2.4.40) with (2.4.35), we find that

$$(2.4.41) \quad \sqrt{T}\,(\hat{V}_1(\tau) - \lambda\tau - \lambda^2\tau^2) \underset{T\to\infty}{\overset{D}{\longrightarrow}} N[0,\theta^2] \quad ,$$

where

$$(2.4.42) \qquad \theta^2 = \lambda\tau^2 + 4\lambda^2\tau^3 + 2\lambda^3\tau^4 \quad .$$

<u>STEP II</u>: $W'_t = N(0,t)$ <u>is a cumulative process with respect to the same sequence of regeneration points</u> $T_n$.

For $Y'_n = \Delta_n W'_t = N(T_{n-1},T_n)$, are evidently independently, identically distributed random variables for an underlying Poisson process.

Therefore, according to the theorem of Smith [195] on the joint asymptotic normality of cumulative processes, referring to the same sequence of regeneration points, we have that

$$(2.4.43) \qquad \left\{ \begin{array}{l} \sqrt{T}\,(\hat{V}_1(\tau) - \lambda\tau - \lambda^2\tau^2) \\ \\ \sqrt{T}\,[(\hat{V}_2(\tau))^{1/2} - \lambda\tau] \end{array} \right. \quad ,$$

are asymptotically distributed according to a bivariate normal law.

<u>STEP III</u>: $\sqrt{T}\,[(\hat{V}_2(\tau))^{1/2} - \lambda\tau]$ <u>is asymptotically, normally distributed.</u>

For

$$(\hat{V}_2(\tau))^{1/2} = \frac{\tau}{T} N(0,T) \quad ,$$

where under the present hypothesis, $N(0,T)$ is distributed in Poisson form with parameter $\mu_T = \lambda T$. However,

$$(2.4.44) \qquad \frac{N(0,T) - \mu_T}{\sqrt{\mu_T}} \underset{T \to \infty}{\overset{D}{\longrightarrow}} N(0,1) \quad ,$$

from which the desired result is evident.

<u>STEP IV</u>: <u>As a consequence of the above three steps, we have that</u>

$$(2.4.45) \quad \sqrt{T}\,[\hat{V}_1(\tau) - E(\hat{V}_1(\tau))] - \sqrt{T}\,[(\hat{V}_2(\tau))^{1/2} - E(\hat{V}_2(\tau))^{1/2}]$$

is asymptotically, normally distributed.

<u>STEP V</u>:

$$(2.4.46) \quad \sqrt{T}\,[\hat{V}_2(\tau) - E(\hat{V}_2(\tau))] = \sqrt{T}\,[(\hat{V}_2(\tau))^{1/2} - E(\hat{V}_2(\tau))^{1/2}] + o_p(1) \quad ,$$

where $0_p(1)$ is a quantity which converges to zero in probability. To see this, we refer to Corollary 3, page 225, of Mann and Wald [134] putting $R = 1$, $j = 1$, $Y_n = 1$ and $X_n = X'_n/\lambda_n$, where $X'_n$ is Poisson with parameter $\lambda_n$.

Let

$$f(n) = \frac{1}{\sqrt{\lambda_n}} \quad \text{and} \quad g(x) = x^p ,$$

with $p$ real and not equal to 0. Then their $T_1(x,a) = g'(a)(x - a)$ and this implies that

$$x_n - 1 = 0_p\left(\frac{1}{\lambda_n}\right) ,$$

i.e.,

$$\frac{X'_n - \lambda_n}{\sqrt{\lambda_n}} = 0_p(1) ,$$

which follows from the fact that

$$\frac{X'_n - \lambda_n}{\sqrt{\lambda_n}} \underset{\lambda_n \to \infty}{\overset{D}{\longrightarrow}} N(0,1) .$$

The corollary then states that

$$\frac{X'^p_n - \lambda^p_n}{p\lambda_n^{p-(1/2)}} = \frac{X'_n - \lambda_n}{p\lambda_n^{p-(1/2)}} + 0_p(1) . \tag{2.4.47}$$

Upon putting $p = 2$ in the above, (2.4.46) is evident.

STEP VI:

(2.4.48) $$\sqrt{T}\,[\hat{V}_1(\tau) - E(\hat{V}_1(\tau)] - \sqrt{T}\,[\hat{V}_2(\tau) - E(\hat{V}_2(\tau))]$$

is asymptotically normal.

For, the difference between (2.4.45) which is asymptotically normal, and (2.4.48) above, converges to zero in probability, as is proven in Step V.

We have therefore proved:

THEOREM 6: When the underlying renewal process is Poisson, then

(2.4.49) $$\sqrt{T}\,\frac{(\hat{V}(\tau) - \lambda\tau)}{(\lambda\tau^2 + 4\lambda^2\tau^3 + 6\lambda^3\tau^4)^{1/2}}$$

is asymptotically $N(0,1)$.

Theorem 6, incidentally, provides a test of significance for the randomness of an underlying point process.

## 2.5. "Non-Estimability" and Some Difficulties in Obtaining Certain Non-Null Distributions of the Statistic

Cox and Smith [42] considered the following problem.

Suppose we observe a stochastic process which is assumed to be the superposition of $N$ independent point processes, each having the same underlying distribution function $F(x)$. How do we estimate the number of underlying point processes? Assuming equilibrium, and writing $C^2$ for the coefficient variation of the underlying point process, then as $t$ goes to $\infty$,

$$V_p(t) \sim C^2 t\lambda \ , \tag{2.5.1}$$

where $\lambda^{-1} = \mu/N$, the mean interval between events in the pooled output, and $V_p(t)$ is the variance of $N_t$ for the pooled output. Cox and Smith further assumed $F(x)$ to be of the $\chi^2$-type, in which case

$$V_p(t) \sim C^2 t\lambda + \frac{N}{6}(1 - C^4) \ , \tag{2.5.2}$$

and then equated the empirical (observed) slope of the asymptote and the intercept of the asymptote to the corresponding theoretical ones given in (2.5.1) and (2.5.2) in order to obtain estimates of $C^2$ and of $N$. In order to obtain confidence limits for $C$ and $N$, one needs to know the distribution of $\hat{V}(\tau)$, say, when the underlying process is of the $\chi^2$-type. Even in this simple case, we do not know how to evaluate terms like

$$E\,[N^2(t+\tau,t), N^2(t'+\tau,t')] \quad ,$$

for arbitrary $t$ and $t'$. Furthermore, little is known about the joint distribution of events in different intervals, not necessarily consecutive. With this in mind, let us define "estimability" of functions of events in different intervals on the time axis as follows:

Definition: Let $I_1, I_2, \ldots, I_k$ be a set of consecutive intervals on the time axis and let $N_{I_j}$, $j = 1,2,\ldots,k$ denote the number of events in the interval $I_j$, of a certain point process. Equilibrium may be assumed. Let $C$ be the class of intervals which consists of $I_1, I_2, \ldots, I_k$ and the intervals which are unions of any $r$ consecutive ones of them. A function

$$N_{I_{\ell_1}}^{m_1} \cdots N_{I_{\ell_r}}^{m_r} \quad \text{of} \quad N_{I_{\ell_1}}, N_{I_{\ell_2}} \cdots N_{I_{\ell_r}}$$

where $m_1, m_2, \ldots, m_r$ are nonnegative integers and

$$I_{\ell_1}, I_{\ell_2}, \ldots, I_{\ell_r}$$

are any $r$ of $I_j$, $j = 1,2,\ldots,k$, is said to be "estimable" if it can be identically represented as a linear combination with constant coefficients (being functionally independent of $N_I$'s) of the $(m_1 + m_2 + \cdots + m_r)^{th}$ powers of $N_I$ where $I \in C$.

Thus, if a function

$$N_{I_{\ell_1}}^{m_1}, N_{I_{\ell_2}}^{m_2} \cdots N_{I_{\ell_r}}^{m_r}$$

of the $N_I$'s is estimable, its expected value can be represented as a finite linear combination with constant coefficients of the expected values of the $(m_1 + m_2 + \cdots + m_r)^{th}$ powers of $N_I$ where $I \in C$. These expected values of the powers of $N_I$ where $I \in C$ are explicitly known in terms of the moments of the underlying point process.

These functions are, therefore, aptly termed "estimable" in that their expected values for any arbitrary underlying point process can be explicitly written down without the complication of running into intractable distribution problems.

2.5.1. <u>Examples of Estimable Functions</u>:

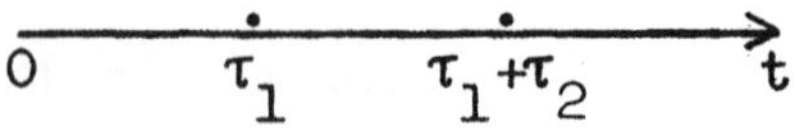


Consider the two intervals

$$I_1 = (0, \tau_1] \quad \text{and} \quad I_2 = (\tau_1, \tau_1 + \tau_2] \ .$$

In this case, the class $C$ consists of the three intervals $I_1$, $I_2$ and $I = I_1 + I_2 = (0, \tau_1 + \tau_2]$.

Squaring both sides of $N_I = N_{I_1} + N_{I_2}$ and rearranging, we get

$$N_{I_1} N_{I_2} = \frac{1}{2} (N_I^2 - N_{I_1}^2 - N_{I_2}^2) \ .$$

Hence $N_{I_1} N_{I_2}$ is estimable and

$$E(N_{I_1} N_{I_2}) = \frac{1}{2} [E(N_1^2) - E(N_{I_1}^2) - E(N_{I_2}^2)] \ .$$

Similarly,

$$N_{I_1}^2 N_{I_2} + N_{I_1} N_{I_2}^2 = \frac{1}{3} (N_1^3 - N_{I_1}^3 - N_{I_2}^3) \ .$$

Hence, the symmetric function of $N_{I_1}$ and $N_{I_2}$ on the left-hand side of the above is estimable and

$$E(N_{I_1}^2 N_{I_2} + N_{I_1} N_{I_2}^2)$$

$$= \frac{1}{3} [E(N_1^3) - E(N_{I_1}^3) - E(N_{I_2}^3)] \ .$$

### 2.5.2. Examples of Non-Estimable Functions:

The function $N_{I_1}^2 N_{I_2}$ is not estimable. For, if it is estimable, then $\ell_1$, $\ell_2$ and $\ell_3$, not functionally dependent on $N_i$, where $I \in C$, should exist such that

$$N_{I_1}^2 N_{I_2} \equiv \ell_1 N_{I_1}^3 + \ell_2 N_{I_2}^3 + \ell_3 N_{I_3}^3 .$$

This is only possible when $\ell_1 = \ell_2 = c$, $\ell_3 = -c$, where

$$c = -\frac{1}{3} \frac{N_{I_1}^2 N_{I_2}}{N_{I_1}^2 N_{I_2} + N_{I_1} N_{I_2}^2} ,$$

which contradicts the requirement that the $\ell$'s should be functionally independent of the $N_I$'s. Similarly, $N_{I_1}^2 N_{I_2}^2$ is not estimable.

However, in the particular case when the underlying process is Poisson, since events in disjoint intervals are independently distributed, all the above functions are estimable. For example, in Formula (2.4.7) we come across several non-estimable functions on the right-hand side for the case of arbitrary underlying point processes.

# CHAPTER 3. THE CUMULATIVE POINT PROCESS

This chapter is more or less expository in nature, the main object being to demonstrate a certain generalization of Renewal Processes proposed by Hammersley in [195], though unnecessarily complicated in the form considered by him, are an easy extension of Smith's theory of cumulative processes. By slightly changing the definition of Hammersley's proposed generalization, we will show that Smith's formulae for the asymptotic mean and variance of a cumulative process, extended by the author to a further degree of accuracy, can be directly applied to yield the asymptotic mean and variance of the random variable considered in the generalization. Also, to examine Hammersley's generalization in the light of Smith's theory of cumulative processes, we need to slightly modify the random variable considered by Smith [195]. Furthermore, we will demonstrate the necessity of the "global" assumption, namely, that the basic distribution function $F(x)$, is such that for some $k$, its $k^{th}$ convolution has an absolutely continuous component. Both Smith and the author have found this assumption necessary in order to obtain the asymptotic representation theorems for the cumulants of the point process and the general point process, respectively.

## 3.1. Introduction and Notation

Let $\{t_i\}$, $i = 1,2,\ldots,$ be a renewal process. Let $T_n = t_1 + t_2 + \cdots + t_n$, $n = 1,2,\ldots,$ where $T_n$ is the time instant corresponding to the occurrence of an event E. Let $W_t$ be a cumulative process defined with respect to the sequence of regeneration points $\{T_n\}$. Then

$$(3.1.1) \qquad y_n = \Delta_n W_t = W_{T_n} - W_{T_{n-1}}, \qquad n = 1,2,\ldots,$$

are independently, identically distributed random variables.

Let

$$(3.1.2) \qquad \kappa_r = E\, y_n^r \quad \text{and} \quad \mu_r = E\, t_n^r, \quad \mu_{ij} = E\,(t_n^i\, y_n^j)\ .$$

Smith [195] has considered the random variable $Y_t^S$, where

$$(3.1.3) \qquad Y_t^S = \sum_{i=1}^{N_t+1} y_i \ ,$$

where $N_t$ is the number of events up to time $t$ of the Point Process $\{t_i\}$. For the random variable $Y_t^S$, Smith [195] has shown that

(A) If $\kappa_1 < \infty$, $\mu_1 < \infty$

$$E\ (Y_t^S) = \frac{\kappa_1}{\mu_1} t + O(t)$$

as $t \to \infty$.

(B) If $\mu_2 < \infty$, $\kappa_2 < \infty$ and $\mu_{11} = E\ (t_i\ y_i) < \infty$

$$\text{Var}\ (Y_t^S) = \frac{t}{\mu_1} \left( \kappa_2 + \frac{\mu_2}{\mu_1^2} \kappa_1^2 - \frac{2\kappa_1\ \mu_{11}}{\mu_1} \right) + O(t)$$

as $t \to \infty$.

Before we consider Hammersley's random variable $Y_t^H$, we need to extend formulae (A) and (B) to a further degree of accuracy.

Let $G(t,y)$ denote the joint distribution of $t_i$ and $y_i$, and let

(3.1.4) $$\Psi_t^S(y) = \Pr\ (Y_t^S \leq y) \quad ,$$

where $\Psi_t^S(y)$ denotes the distribution function of $Y_t^S$. Then, it may be seen that

(3.1.5) $$\Psi_t^S(y) = [G(\infty,y) - G(t,y)] + \int_{-\infty}^{\infty} \int_0^t \Psi_{t-t'}^S(y - y')dt'\ dy'\ G(t',y') \quad .$$

Let

$$(3.1.6) \quad G_s^*(\omega) = \int_{t=0}^{\infty} \int_{y=-\infty}^{\infty} - e^{st+i\omega y} \, dt \, dy \, G(t,y) \, .$$

and write

$$(3.1.7) \quad \Psi_s^{S*}(y) = s \int_0^{\infty} e^{-st} \, \Psi_t(y) dt \quad ,$$

for the Laplace-Stieltjes transform of $\Psi_t(y)$. It is easily seen that, for fixed $x$, $\Psi_s^{S*}(y)$ is a distribution function in $y$. It is also seen that

$$(3.1.8) \quad \Psi_s^{S*}(\omega) = \int_{-\infty}^{\infty} e^{i\omega y} \, dy \, \Psi_s^{S*}(y)$$

is a characteristic function.

From (3.1.6) we see that $G_0^*(\omega)$ is the characteristic function of the random variable $y_n$, and if we write $F(t) = G(t,\infty)$ for the distribution function of $t_n$, then we have $G_s^*(0) = F^*(s)$, the Laplace-Stieltjes transform of $F(t)$.

## 3.2. The Asymptotic Mean and Variance of the Process $Y_t^S$

We now proceed to obtain the asymptotic mean and variance of the process $Y_t^S$.

Applying the transform (3.1.6) on both sides of

(3.1.5), we discover that

$$(3.2.1) \qquad Y_s^{S*}(\omega) = G_0^*(\omega) - G_s^*(\omega) + \Psi_s^{S*}(\omega) G_s^*(\omega) \quad ,$$

and, hence

$$(3.2.2) \qquad \Psi_s^{S*}(\omega) = \frac{G_0^*(\omega) - G_s^*(\omega)}{1 - G_s^*(\omega)} \quad .$$

Noticing that the left-hand side of (3.2.2) is the characteristic function of the distribution function $\Psi_s^{S*}(\omega)$ and also that for $\Re e\ (s) > 0$, if $\kappa_1 < \infty$, the right-hand side is differentiable with respect to $\omega$, and we obtain

$$(3.2.3) \qquad i \int_{-\infty}^{\infty} y\, dy\, \Psi_s^{S*}(y) = \frac{G_0'^*(\omega)}{1 - G_s^*(\omega)}\Bigg]_{\omega=0} = \frac{i\kappa_1}{1 - F^*(s)} \quad .$$

and we have

$$(3.2.4) \qquad \int_{-\infty}^{\infty} y\, dy\, \Psi_s^{S*}(y) = \frac{\kappa_1}{1 - F^*(s)} \quad .$$

If $\mu_2 < \infty$, we know from a basic lemma of Smith that there exists another distribution function $F_{(2)}(t)$ such that

$$F^*(s) = 1 - \mu_1 s + \frac{\mu_2}{2} s\, F_{(2)}^*(s) \quad .$$

Hence

$$(3.2.5) \qquad \frac{\kappa_1}{1 - F^*(s)} = \frac{\kappa_1}{\mu_1 s}\left( 1 + \frac{\mu_2 s}{2\mu_1} F_{(2)}^*(s) + O(s) \right) =$$

$$= \frac{\kappa_1}{\mu_1 s} + \frac{\kappa_1 \mu_2}{2\mu_1^2} F^*_{(2)}(s) + o(1)$$

$$= \frac{\kappa_1}{\mu_1 s} + \frac{\kappa_1 \mu_2}{2\mu_1^2} + \frac{\kappa_1 \mu_2}{2\mu_1^2} (F^*_{(2)}(s) - 1) + o(1)$$

$$= \frac{\kappa_1}{\mu_1 s} + \frac{\kappa_1 \mu_2}{2\mu_1^2} + o(1) \quad \text{as} \quad s \longrightarrow +0 .$$

But, the left-hand side of (3.2.4) is the Laplace-Stieltjes transform of

(3.2.6) $$E\,(Y_t^S) = \int_{-\infty}^{\infty} y \, dy \, \Psi_s^S(y) .$$

Hence, if $\kappa_1 < \infty$, $\mu_2 < \infty$, then

(A') $$E\,(Y_t^S) = \frac{\kappa_1 t}{\mu_1} + \frac{\kappa_1 \mu_2}{2\mu_1^2} + o(1) \quad \text{as} \quad t \longrightarrow \infty .$$

Now, for $\Re e\,(s) > 0$, if $\kappa_2 < \infty$, the right-hand side of (3.2.2) is twice differentiable with respect to $\omega$ and we find, as shown earlier by Smith [195],

(3.2.7) $$\int_{-\infty}^{\infty} y^2 \, dy \, \Psi_s^{S*}(y)$$

$$= \frac{\kappa_2}{1 - F^*(s)} + \frac{2\kappa_1}{(1 - F^*)^2} R^*(s)$$

where $R^*(s)$ is the Laplace-Stieltjes transform of a function of bounded variation and

(3.2.8) $$R^*(s) = \frac{1}{i} \frac{d}{d\omega} (G_s^*(\omega)) \Big]_{\omega=0} .$$

Now, if $\mu_{21} < \infty$, then the Laplace-Stieltjes

transform $R^*(s)$ of $R(t)$ can be written as

$$(3.2.9) \qquad R^*(s) = \kappa_1 - s\mu_{11} + \frac{\mu_{21}\, s^2}{2!} + O(s^2)$$

as $s \to +0$. Also, if $\mu_3 < \infty$, then

$$(3.2.10) \qquad \frac{2}{(1 - F^*)^2} = \frac{2}{\mu_1^2 s^2} + \frac{2\mu_2}{\mu_1^3 s} + \frac{3\mu_2^2}{2\mu_1^4} - \frac{2\mu_3}{3\mu_1^3} + O(1)$$

as $s \to +0$, and

$$(3.2.11) \qquad \frac{\kappa_2}{1 - F^*(s)} = \frac{1}{\mu_1 s} + \frac{\mu_2}{2\mu_1^2} + O(1)$$

as $s \to +0$.

Combining (3.2.7), (3.2.9), (2.3.10) and (3.2.11) we find that if $\mu_3 < \infty$, $\mu_{21} < \infty$, then

$$(3.2.12) \qquad \int_{-\infty}^{\infty} y^2 \, dy \, \Psi_s^{S*}(y)$$

$$= \frac{2}{s^2}\left(\frac{\kappa_1^2}{\mu_1^2}\right) + \frac{1}{s}\left(\frac{2\kappa_1^2\mu_2}{\mu_1^3} - \frac{2\kappa_1\mu_{11}}{\mu_1^2} + \frac{\kappa_2}{\mu_1}\right)$$

$$+ \frac{3\kappa_1^2\mu_2^2}{2\mu_1^4} - \frac{2\kappa_1^2\mu_3}{3\mu_1^3} - \frac{2\kappa_1\mu_2\mu_{11}}{\mu_1^3} + \frac{\kappa_1\mu_{21}}{\mu_1^2}$$

$$+ \frac{\kappa_2\mu_2}{2\mu_1^2} + O(1)$$

as $s \to +0$. Noticing that the left-hand side of (3.2.12)

of the Laplace-Stieltjes transform of $E\,(Y_t^S)^2$, we discover that

$$(3.2.13)\quad E\,(Y_t^S)^2 = \frac{t^2}{\mu_1^2}\kappa_1^2 + \frac{t}{\mu_1}\left(\kappa_2 + \frac{2\kappa_1^2\mu_2}{\mu_1^2} - \frac{2\kappa_1\mu_{11}}{\mu_1}\right) + \frac{3\kappa_1^2\mu_2^2}{2\mu_1^4} - \frac{2\kappa_1^2\mu_3}{3\mu_1^3} - \frac{2\kappa_1\mu_2\mu_{11}}{\mu_1^2} + \frac{\kappa_2\mu_2}{2\mu_1^2} + O(1)$$

as $t \to +\infty$.

Now, when $\kappa_1 < \infty$, $\mu_2 < \infty$, we have proved that

$$(3.2.14)\quad E\,(Y_t^S) = \frac{\kappa_1}{\mu_1}t + \frac{\kappa_1\mu_2}{2\mu_1^2} + O(1) \quad \text{as} \quad t \to \infty .$$

If we square both sides of (3.2.14), we obtain a term such as $t \times O(1)$, whose behavior as $t \to +\infty$ is not known to us so far.

We now appeal to the cumulant representation theorem of Smith [195] for the Renewal Process, proved under the global assumption that, if $\mu_{n+p+1} < \infty$, $p > 0$, then

$$\psi_n(t) = \gamma_n t + \gamma_{n+1} + \frac{\lambda(t)}{(1+t)^p} ,$$

where $\lambda(t) \in R$. Since

$$\frac{1}{1 - F^*} = \varphi_1^* = \psi_1^* ,$$

and since $\mu_3 < \infty$, the remainder in (3.2.14) is actually $O(1/t)$ and, hence, under the global assumption, if $\mu_3 < \infty$, the term $t \times O(1)$ above, tends to zero as $t \to +\infty$. Thus, if $F(x)$ satisfies the global assumption, and if $\mu_3 < \infty$, $\kappa_1 < \infty$, then

$$(3.2.15)\quad E(Y_t^S)^2 = \frac{\kappa_1^2}{\mu_1^2} t^2 + \frac{\kappa_1^2 \mu_2^2}{4\mu_1^4} + \frac{\kappa_1^2 \mu_2}{\mu_1^3} t + O(1) \quad .$$

as $t \to \infty$.

Subtracting (3.2.15) from (3.2.13), we find that, if $F(x)$ satisfied the global assumption [we omit this statement, hereafter, to avoid tedious repetition], and if $\kappa_2 < \infty$, $\mu_3 < \infty$ and $\mu_{21} < \infty$, then

$$(B')\quad \text{Var } Y_t^S = \frac{t}{\mu_1} \kappa_2 + \frac{\kappa_1^2 \mu_2}{\mu_1^2} - \frac{2\kappa_1 \mu_{11}}{\mu_1} + \frac{5\kappa_1^2 \mu_2^2}{4\mu_1^4} - \frac{2\kappa_1^2 \mu_3}{3\mu_1^3}$$

$$- \frac{2\kappa_1 \mu_2 \mu_{11}}{\mu_1^3} + \frac{\kappa_1 \mu_{21}}{\mu_1^2} + \frac{\kappa_2 \mu_2}{2\mu_1^2} + O(1)$$

as $t \to \infty$.

Thus, (A') and (B') are extensions of Smith's (A) and (B), to an additional degree of accuracy. If we put $y_n \equiv 1$, (A') and (B') reduce to Smith's original formulae for the expectation and variance of $N_t$, which, incidentally, provided us with a check on our formulae (A') and (B').

## 3.3. The Asymptotic Mean and Variance of the Process $Y_t^H$

Let $\{t_n, \underline{y}_n(p\times 1)\}$, $n = 1,2,\ldots,$ be a sequence of independently, identically distributed random variables with the same distribution function $G(t, \underline{y}_n(p\times 1))$, where $t_n$ is a one-dimensional nonnegative random variable, while $\underline{y}_n(p\times 1)$ is a p-dimensional random vector.

Then, Hammersley [195] considers the random variable

$$\eta_1(t) = \sum_{n=1}^{N_t} \underline{y}_n(p\times 1) \tag{3.3.1}$$

where $N_t$, as before, is the number of events up to a specified time instant $t$, with respect to the Point Process $\{t_n\}$.

In this section we will only consider the one-dimensional version of Hammersley's generalization (3.3.1), and in the next chapter we will show that, by a certain "linearization" technique we can at once obtain the results corresponding to the asymptotic covariances of the components of $\underline{y}_n(p\times 1)$ from the one-dimensional results of this section. We will denote the one-dimensional version of $\eta_1(t)$ of (3.3.1) by $Y_t^H$ where

$$(3.3.2) \qquad Y_t^H = \sum_{n=1}^{N_t} y_n \ ,$$

$\{y_n\}$ being independently and identically distributed random variables. Notice that the only difference between $Y_t^S$ of Smith and $Y_t^H$ of Hammersley is that, while Smith takes the summation from 1 to $N_t + 1$, Hammersley takes it from 1 to $N_t$. This simple difference introduces a lot of complication in the calculations, as will be shown below. This complication was forseen by the former author, but evidently not by the latter. We will adhere to the notation of the previous section. As before, $G(t,y)$ denotes the joint distribution of $t_i$ and $y_i$.

Let

$$\Psi_t^H(y) = \Pr\,(Y_t^H \leq y) \ .$$

Then

$$(3.3.3) \qquad \Psi_t^H(y) = 1 - G(t,\infty) + \int_{-\infty}^{\infty}\int_0^t \Psi_{t-t'}^H(y - y')dt'\,dy'\,G(t',y') \ .$$

Applying the transform (3.1.6) on both sides of (3.3.3), we find

$$\Psi_s^{H*}(\omega) = 1 - G_s^*(0) + \Psi_s^{H*}(\omega)\, G_s^*(\omega) .$$

Hence

$$(3.3.4) \qquad \Psi_s^{H*}(\omega) = \frac{1 - G_s^*(0)}{1 - G_s^*(\omega)} .$$

Bearing in mind that the left-hand side of the above is the characteristic function of the distribution function $\Psi_s^{H*}(y)$ and that for $\Re e\,(s) > 0$, the right-hand side is differentiable with respect to $\omega$, we find that the first absolute moment of $\Psi_s^{H*}(y)$ is finite and that

$$i \int_{-\infty}^{\infty} y\, dy\, \Psi_s^{H*}(y) = \left. \frac{(1 - G_s^*(0))\, G_s^*(\omega)}{(1 - G_s^*(\omega))^2} \right]_{\omega=0}$$

$$= \frac{i\, R^*(s)}{1 - F^*(s)} .$$

Thus

$$(3.3.5) \quad \int_{-\infty}^{\infty} y\, dy\, \Psi_s^{H*}(y)$$

$$= \frac{R^*(s)}{1 - F^*(s)} = \frac{\kappa_1}{\mu_1 s} + \frac{\kappa_1 \mu_2}{2\mu_1^2} - \frac{\mu_{11}}{\mu_1} + O(1) ,$$

as $t \to \infty$. Since the left-hand side is the L-S.T. of $E(Y_t^H)$ and assuming $\kappa_1 < \infty$, $\mu_2 < \infty$ and $\mu_{11} < \infty$, then

$$(3.3.6) \quad E(Y_t^H) = t\, \frac{\kappa_1}{\mu_1} + \frac{\kappa_1 \mu_2}{2\mu_1^2} - \frac{\mu_{11}}{\mu_1} + O(1) \quad \text{as} \quad t \longrightarrow \infty .$$

Similarly

$$-\int_{-\infty}^{\infty} y^2\, dy\, \Psi_s^{H*}(y) = \frac{G_s^{*''}(\omega)]_{\omega=0}}{1 - F^*(s)} + 2\frac{\left[G_s^{*'}(\omega)]_{\omega=0}\right]^2}{(1 - F^*(s))^2}$$

$$= -\frac{Q^*(s)}{1 - F^*(s)} + 2\frac{(i\, R^*(s))^2}{(1 - F^*(s))^2}$$

where

$$Q^*(s) = -G_s^{*''}(\omega)]_{\omega=0}$$

is the Laplace-Stieltjes transform of

$$Q(t) = \int_{-\infty}^{\infty} y^2\, dy\, G(t,y) \quad ,$$

a function of bounded variation. Hence

$$(3.3.7) \qquad \int_{-\infty}^{\infty} y^2\, dy\, \Psi_s^{H*}(y)$$

$$= \frac{Q^*(s)}{1 - F^*(s)} + 2\frac{(R^*(s))^2}{(1 - F^*(s))^2} \quad .$$

After a straightforward calculation, we find

$$(3.3.8) \qquad E(Y_t^H)^2 = \frac{\kappa_1^2 t^2}{\mu_1^2} + \left(\frac{\kappa_1^2 2\mu_2}{\mu_1^3} - \frac{4\kappa_1\mu_{11}}{\mu_1^2} + \frac{\kappa_2}{\mu_1}\right) t$$

$$+ \frac{3\kappa_1^2\mu_2^2}{2\mu_1^4} - \frac{2\kappa_1^2\mu_3}{\mu_1^3} + \frac{2\kappa_{11}^2}{\mu_1^2} + \frac{2\kappa_1\mu_{21}}{\mu_1^2}$$

$$- \frac{4\kappa_1\mu_{11}\mu_2}{\mu_1^3} + \frac{\kappa_2\mu_2}{2\mu_1^2} - \frac{\mu_{12}}{\mu_1} + o(1),$$

as $t \to \infty$, if $\kappa_2 < \infty$, $\mu_3 < \infty$, $\mu_{21} < \infty$ and $\mu_{12} < \infty$.

We finally discover, upon combining (3.3.8) and (3.3.6), that if $\kappa_2 < \infty$, $\mu_3 < \infty$, $\mu_{21} < \infty$ and $\mu_{12} < \infty$ then

$$(3.3.9)\ \mathrm{Var}\ (Y_t^H) = t\left(\frac{\kappa_2}{\mu_1} + \frac{\kappa_1^2\mu_2}{\mu_1^3} - \frac{2\kappa_1\mu_{11}}{\mu_1^2}\right)$$

$$+ \frac{5\kappa_1^2\mu_2^2}{4\mu_1^4} - \frac{2\kappa_1^2\mu_3}{3\mu_1^3} - \frac{3\kappa_1\mu_{11}\mu_2}{\mu_1^3} + \frac{\mu_{11}^2}{\mu_1^2}$$

$$+ \frac{2\kappa_1\mu_{21}}{\mu_1^2} + \frac{\kappa_2\mu_2}{2\mu_1^2} - \frac{\mu_{12}}{\mu_1} + o(1)$$

as $t \to \infty$.

In the special case $y_n \equiv 1$, both $E\ (Y_t^H)$ and $\mathrm{Var}\ (Y_t^H)$ reduce to Smith's formulae for the asymptotic mean and variance of $N_t$. By taking the summation from 1 to $N_t$, we become involved in the complication of dealing with $Q^*(s)$, which could be easily avoided by taking the summation from 1 to $N_t+1$, as in $Y_t^S$.

# CHAPTER 4. THE MULTIDIMENSIONAL POINT PROCESS

The multidimensional case is a vector-valued point process of which each component is a General Point Process. In this chapter, we will consider the case of the two-dimensional point processes in both versions of Smith [195] and Hammersley [195] and will show that by using a simple trick, the representation theorems for the individual variances of the component process as well as their covariance, can be obtained to order $O(1)$ as the time $t$ gets longer. Some of these results were obtained earlier by Hammersley and Smith [195] to orders up to $O(t)$ only. Thus, our results are the most general ones that one can obtain and, therefore, can apply in situations where the theory of processes apply.

## 4.1. Moments of the Multidimensional Cumulative Point Process, Using the One-Dimensional Component Process

We will now consider the multidimensional version of $Y_t^H$, namely $\eta_1(t)$, given by (3.3.1). Suppose we want to obtain the asymptotic covariance of $\eta_{1j}(t)$ and $\eta_{1k}(t)$,

$j \neq k$, for any two components $\eta_{1j}$ and $\eta_{1k}$ of the p-dimensional vector $\eta_1$.

Let

$$(4.1.1) \qquad \eta_{1j}(t) = \sum_{n=1}^{N_t} y_n^{(j)}$$

and

$$(4.1.2) \qquad \eta_{1k}(t) = \sum_{n=1}^{N_t} y_n^{(k)}$$

where $y_n^{(j)}$ and $y_n^{(k)}$ are the $j^{th}$ and $k^{th}$ components of the vector $\underline{y}_n(p \times 1)$. Consider

$$(4.1.3) \qquad \eta(t) = \eta_{1j}(t) + \eta_{1k}(t) = \sum_{n=1}^{N_t} y_n$$

where

$$(4.1.4) \qquad y_n = y_n^{(j)} + y_n^{(k)} .$$

Clearly, $\{y_n\}$ are independently, identically distributed random variables, since $\{\underline{y}_n(p \times 1)\}$ are independently, identically distributed; and furthermore, the summation in (4.1.1), (4.1.2) and (4.1.3) is over the number of events with respect to the same point process $\{t_i\}$. Hence, taking the variance of both sides of (4.1.3), we obtain

$$\text{Var}\ (\eta(t)) = \text{Var}\ (\eta_{1j}(t)) + \text{Var}\ (\eta_{1k}(t)) + 2\ \text{Cov}\ (\eta_{1j}(t), \eta_{1k}(t)) \quad ,$$

and so

$$(4.1.5) \quad \text{Cov}\ (\eta_{1j}(t), \eta_{1k}(t)) = \frac{1}{2}\ [\text{Var}\ (\eta(t)) - \text{Var}\ (\eta_{1h}(t)) - \text{Var}\ (\eta_{1k}(t))] \quad .$$

In the notation of Hammersley, let us write

$$\mu_{\alpha\beta\gamma} = E\ [y_n^{(j)}]^{\alpha}\ [y_n^{(k)}]^{\beta}\ t_n^{\gamma}$$

and

$$\rho = \frac{1}{\mu_1} = \frac{1}{\mu_{001}} \quad .$$

Then, our Formula (3.3.9) for $\text{Var}\ (\eta(t))$ in the above notation becomes

(4.1.6)

$$\begin{aligned}\text{Var}\ (\eta(t)) = {} & t[\rho(\mu_{200} + \mu_{020} + 2\mu_{110}) - 2\rho^2(\mu_{100} + \mu_{010}) \\ & \times (\mu_{101} + \mu_{011}) + \rho^3(\mu_{100} + \mu_{010})^2\ \mu_{002}] \\ & + \frac{5\rho^4}{4}\ (\mu_{100} + \mu_{010})^2\ \mu_{002}^2 - \frac{2\rho^3}{3}\ (\mu_{100} + \mu_{010})^2 \\ & \times \mu_{003} - 3\rho^3(\mu_{100} + \mu_{010})(\mu_{101} + \mu_{011})\ \mu_{002} \\ & + \rho^2(\mu_{101} + \mu_{011})^2 + 2\rho^2(\mu_{100} + \mu_{010})(\mu_{102} + \mu_{012})\end{aligned}$$

$$+ \frac{2\rho^2}{2} \mu_{002}(\mu_{200} + \mu_{020} + 2\mu_{110})$$

$$- \rho(\mu_{201} + \mu_{021} + 2\mu_{111}) + o(1)$$

as $t \to \infty$. Var $(\eta_{1j}(t))$ becomes

(4.1.7)

$$\text{Var } \eta_{1j}(t) = t(\rho\, \mu_{200} + \rho^3\, \mu_{100}^2\mu_{002} - 2\rho^2\, \mu_{100}\mu_{101})$$

$$+ \frac{5\rho^2}{4} \mu_{100}^2\mu_{002}^2 - \frac{2\rho^3}{3} \mu_{100}^2\mu_{003} - 3\rho^3\, \mu_{100}\mu_{101}\mu_{002} + \rho^2\mu_{101}^2$$

$$+ 2\rho^2\, \mu_{100}\mu_{102} + \frac{2\rho^2}{2} \mu_{002}\mu_{200} - \rho\, \mu_{201} + o(1)$$

as $t \to \infty$, and

(4.1.8)

$$\text{Var } (\eta_{2j}(t)) = t(\rho\, \mu_{020} + \rho^3\, \mu_{010}^2\mu_{002} - 2\rho^2\, \mu_{010}\mu_{011})$$

$$+ \frac{5\rho^2}{4} \mu_{010}^2\mu_{002}^2 - \frac{2\rho^3}{3} \mu_{010}^2\mu_{003} - 3\rho^3\, \mu_{010}\mu_{011}\mu_{002}$$

$$+ \rho^2\, \mu_{011}^2 + 2\rho^2\, \mu_{010}\mu_{012} + \frac{2\rho^2}{2} \mu_{002}\mu_{020}$$

$$- \rho\, \mu_{021} + o(1)$$

as $t \to \infty$. Combining (4.1.5), (4.1.6), (4.1.7) and (4.1.8), we find

(4.1.9)

$$\text{Cov } (\eta_{1j}, \eta_{1k})$$

$$= \rho t(\mu_{110} - \rho\, \mu_{101}\mu_{010} - \rho\, \mu_{011}\mu_{100} + \rho^2\, \mu_{100}\mu_{010}\mu_{002})$$

$$+ \frac{5\rho^4}{4} \mu_{100}\mu_{010}\mu_{002}^2 - \frac{2\rho^3}{3} \mu_{100}\mu_{010}\mu_{003}$$

$$- \frac{3\rho^3}{2} \mu_{100}\mu_{011}\mu_{002} - \frac{3\rho^3}{2} \mu_{010}\mu_{101}\mu_{002} + \rho^2 \mu_{101}\mu_{011}$$

$$+ \rho^2 \mu_{100}\mu_{012} + \rho^2 \mu_{010}\mu_{102} + \frac{\rho^2}{2} \mu_{002}\mu_{110}$$

$$- \rho \mu_{111} + O(1)$$

as $t \to \infty$.

Using our formula for $\mathrm{Var}\ (Y_t^S)$, we find, after simplification, that

(4.1.10)

$$\mathrm{Cov}\ (\eta_{1j}^S, \eta_{1k}^S)$$

$$= \rho t(\mu_{100} - \rho \mu_{101}\mu_{010} - \rho \mu_{011}\mu_{100} + \rho^2 \mu_{100}\mu_{010}\mu_{002})$$

$$+ \frac{5\rho^4}{4} \mu_{100}\mu_{010}\mu_{002}^2 - \frac{2\rho^3}{3} \mu_{100}\mu_{010}\mu_{003}$$

$$- \rho^3(\mu_{100}\mu_{011}\mu_{002} + \mu_{010}\mu_{101}\mu_{002})$$

$$+ \frac{\rho^2}{2} (\mu_{100}\mu_{012} + \mu_{010}\mu_{102} + \mu_{002}\mu_{110}) + O(1)$$

as $t \to \infty$.

Both (4.1.9) and (4.1.10) reduce to Smith's original limit for $\mathrm{Var}\ N_t$ when $\underline{y}_n(p \times 1) \equiv 1$, and this has also, incidentally, provided a check on the formulae.

Actually, there is nothing special about Formula (4.1.9) which is not in (4.1.10), and what we have essentially demonstrated is that our extended formulae, (which are extensions of Smith's formulae A and B) can be exploited to meet completely, the requirements of Hammersley's proposed generalization, which is, as Smith very aptly terms in his symposium [195] a complication rather than a generalization, in any real sense.

# CHAPTER 5. ESTIMATION OF THE VARIANCE OF THE COUNTS RESULTING FROM A TWO-DIMENSIONAL PROCESS

## 5.1 The Proposed Estimator

Throughout this chapter we shall use $\underline{x}$ to denote a point in two-dimensional Euclidean space with Cartesian coordinates $(x_1,x_2)$ and polar coordinates $(r,\Theta)$; thus, $d\underline{x}$ will denote the differential element $dx_1\, dx_2$ in Cartesians, or $rd\, rd\Theta$ in polars.

For a point process, let $N(t,t+\tau)$ denote the number of events observed in the interval $(t,t+\tau)$ and $N(0,T)$ the number of events observed in the interval $(0,T)$. Further, let $V(N_\tau)$ denote the variance of the number of events observed in an interval of length $\tau$. It was suggested in Chapter 2 as an estimate of $V(\tau)$

$$\hat{V}(\tau) = \left( \frac{1}{T-\tau} \right) \int_0^{T-\tau} N^2(t,t+\tau)dt - \left( \frac{\tau}{T} \right)^2 N^2(0,T)$$

as an estimator of $V(N_\tau)$ and investigated its properties.

Here, we consider the analogous estimator for a two-dimensional point process. Since we shall be interested primarily in the Poisson process and, more generally, in the center-satellite process, it will be convenient to refer to the members of a realization of the process as satellites. Thus, let $N(r,\theta\,;\rho)$ denote the number of satellites observed in a circle with center $(r,\theta)$ and radius $\rho$, and let $N(0,R)$ denote the number of satellites in a circle with center at the origin and with radius $R$. Further, let $V(N_\rho)$, or simply $V(\rho)$, denote the variance of the number of satellites observed in a circle of radius $\rho$. We shall take

(5.1.2)

$$\begin{aligned}\hat{V}(\rho) &= \left(\frac{1}{\pi(R-\rho)^2}\right)\int_0^{2\pi}\int_0^{R-\rho} N^2(r,\theta\,;\rho)rd\,rd\theta \\ &\qquad - \left(\frac{\rho}{R}\right)^4 N^2(0,R) \\ &= \hat{V}_1(\rho) - \hat{V}_2(\rho) \ ,\end{aligned}$$

say, as an estimator of $V(\rho)$.

In what follows we shall write $C(0,R)$ for the circle with center at $0$ and with radius $R$. Consider

$$\hat{V}_1(\rho) = \left(\frac{1}{\pi(R-\rho)^2}\right)\int_0^{2\pi}\int_0^{R-\rho} N^2(r,\theta\,;\rho)rd\,rd\theta \ .$$

Interpreting the integral in the usual manner we see that, with each point in $C(0,R-\rho)$ we associate a nonnegative integer equal to the number of satellites within a distance $\rho$ of the point considered. The square of the number constitutes a function defined for every point, $(r,\theta)$, in $C(0,R-\rho)$ and this function is integrated in the usual sense. However, we may look at this from another direction. Suppose that, on every satellite in $C(0,R)$ as center, we construct a circle of radius $\rho$. If there are $N$ satellites in $C(0,R)$ we then obtain $N$ circles which we shall denote by $C_1, C_2, \ldots, C_N$. These may or may not overlap. The circle $C(0,R-\rho)$ is then divided into the following sets with $\underline{x}$ always required to be in $C(0,R-\rho)$;

$$S_0 = \left\{\underline{x} \mid \underline{x} \notin \bigcup_{i=1}^{N} C_i\right\} = \left\{\underline{x} \mid \underline{x} \text{ is in none of the } C_1, C_2, \ldots, C_N\right\}$$

$$S_1 = \left\{\underline{x} \mid \underline{x} \text{ is in one and only one of the } C_1, C_2, \ldots, C_N\right\}$$

$$S_2 = \left\{\underline{x} \mid \underline{x} \text{ is in two and only two of the } C_1, C_2, \ldots, C_n\right\}$$

. . . . . . . . . . . . . . . . . . . . . . . . . . . . . . .

$$S_N = \left\{\underline{x} \mid \underline{x} \in \bigcap_{i=1}^{N} C_i\right\} = \left\{\underline{x} \mid \underline{x} \text{ is in all of the } C_1, C_2, \ldots, C_n\right\}$$

Some of these sets may, of course, be empty; they are disjoint and their union is the Circle $C(0,R-\rho)$.

If $\underline{x} = (r,\theta)$ is in the set $S_n$, then $N(r,\theta\,;\rho) = n$.

If we write $A_{S_n}$ for the area of the set $S_n$ it follows that

$$(5.1.3) \quad \int_0^{2\pi} \int_0^{R-\rho} N^2(r,\theta\,;\rho) r d\,r d\theta \;=\; \sum_{n=1}^{N} n^2 A_{S_n} \;.$$

5.2 Methods of Evaluation

We now consider methods for evaluating $\Sigma_{n=1}^{N} n^2 A_{S_n}$ .

Clearly, the value could be obtained by constructing a map of $C(0,R)$ and the $N$ satellites contained therein, demarcating the sets $S_0, S_1, \ldots, S_N$ and measuring their areas. One could, perhaps, draw the map on a uniformly dense material, of constant thickness, cut out the sections and weigh them, their weights being proportional to their areas.

A basically different approach is as follows. Place $m$ sampling points, independently and randomly, in $C(0,R-\rho)$. Denote these by $\alpha_1, \alpha_2, \ldots, \alpha_m$. Denote the number of satellites within $\rho$ of $\alpha_i$ by $n_i$. Then, the possible values of the $n_i$ are $0,1,2,\ldots,N$. Let $f_j$ denote the number of

$n_i = j$, $j = 0,1,2,\ldots,N$. Write

$$(5.2.1) \qquad f = \sum_{j=0}^{N} f_j = m .$$

It is logical to take $f_i/f$ as an estimator of $A_{S_i}/(\pi(R - \rho)^2)$ and, thus, estimate $\Sigma_{n=1}^{N} n^2 A_{S_n}$ by

$$(5.2.2) \qquad \pi(R - \rho)^2 \sum_{n=1}^{N} n^2 \frac{f_n}{f} = \left(\frac{A}{m}\right) \sum_{n=1}^{N} n^2 f_n ,$$

say, where

$$A = \pi(R - \rho)^2 = \sum_{n=0}^{N} A_{S_n} .$$

We now show that this estimator is unbiased and obtain its variance. First

$$(5.2.3) \qquad \mathcal{E}\left\{\left(\frac{A}{m}\right) \sum_{n=1}^{N} n^2 F_n\right\} = \left(\frac{A}{m}\right) \sum_{n=1}^{N} n^2 \mathcal{E} f_n .$$

Now, the probability that $f_n$ will be equal to $h$ is the probability that exactly $h$ of the $m$ sampling points will fall in the set $S_n$; i.e.,

$$(5.2.4) \qquad P\left(f_n = h\right) = \binom{m}{h}\left(\frac{A_{S_n}}{A}\right)^h \left(1 - \frac{A_{S_n}}{A}\right)^{m-h}$$

and hence

$$(5.2.5) \qquad \mathcal{E} f_n = \frac{mA_{S_n}}{A} .$$

Therefore

$$(5.2.6) \quad \mathcal{E}\left\{ \left(\frac{A}{m}\right) \sum_{n=1}^{N} n^2 f_n \right\} = \left(\frac{A}{m}\right) \sum_{n=1}^{N} n^2 \frac{mA_{S_n}}{A}$$

$$= \sum_{n=1}^{N} n^2 A_{S_n} .$$

Next, we remark that

(5.2.7)

$$\mathrm{Var}\left( A \sum_{n=1}^{N} n^2 \frac{f_n}{n} \right) = \left(\frac{A}{m}\right)^2 \mathrm{Var}\left( \sum_{n=1}^{n} n^2 f_n \right)$$

$$= \left(\frac{A}{m}\right)^2 \sum_{n=1}^{N} n^4 \mathrm{Var}\,(f_n) + \left(\frac{A}{m}\right)^2 \sum_{n \neq r}^{N}\sum n^2 r^2 \mathrm{Cov}\,(f_n, f_r).$$

Now

$$(5.2.8) \qquad \mathrm{Var}\,(f_n) = m \left(\frac{A_{S_n}}{A}\right)\left(1 - \frac{A_{S_n}}{A}\right) ,$$

and since

$$(5.2.9)\quad P(f_n = h, f_r = k) = \frac{m!}{h!k!(m-h-k)!} \cdot \left(\frac{A_{S_n}}{A}\right)^h \left(\frac{A_{S_r}}{A}\right)^k \left(1 - \left(\frac{A_{S_n} + A_{S_r}}{A}\right)\right)^{m-h-k}$$

we have

$$(5.2.10)\qquad \mathrm{Cov}\,(f_n, f_r) = -\, mA_{S_n} \frac{A_{S_r}}{A^2} .$$

Thus

(5.2.11)

$$\mathrm{Var}\left(A \sum_{n=1}^{N} n^2 \frac{f_n}{f}\right) = \left(\frac{A}{m}\right)^2 \sum_{n=1}^{N} n^4\, m \left(\frac{A_{S_n}}{A}\right)\left(1 - \frac{A_{S_n}}{A}\right)$$

$$- \left(\frac{A}{m}\right)^2 \sum_{n \neq r}^{N}\sum n^2 r^2\, mA_{S_n} \frac{A_{S_r}}{A^2}$$

$$= \frac{\left\{ A\, \Sigma_{n=1}^{N}\, n^4 A_{S_n} - \left(\Sigma_{n=1}^{N}\, n^2 A_{S_n}\right)\right\}}{m} .$$

For example, a circle of radius $R$ was drawn and points located at random in the plane until the circle enclosed 20 points. These points represent the satellites. Takine $R/\rho = 5$, the following values were obtained for the $A_{S_i}$, standardized so that $A = \pi(R-\rho)^2 = 1$.

$$A_{S_0} = 0.4956; \quad A_{S_1} = 0.3292; \quad A_{S_2} = 0.1111;$$

$$A_{S_3} = 0.0588; \quad A_{S_4} = 0.0054; \quad A_{S_j} = 0, \quad j > 4.$$

Then

$$\sum_{n=1}^{N} n^2 A_{S_n} = 1.3892 \quad \text{and} \quad \sum_{n=1}^{N} n^4 A_{S_n} = 8.2520$$

and we have

$$\operatorname{Var}\left( A \sum_{n=1}^{N} n^2 \frac{f_n}{f} \right) = \frac{8.2520 - 1.3892^2}{m}$$

$$= \frac{6.3221}{m} \quad .$$

From such an analysis we can obtain an idea of how many sampling points, $m$, need to be used to reduce the standard error of our approximation to within prescribed limits.

Observe that in the above, we have located our sampling points independently and at random throughout the circle $C(0,R - \rho)$. It may be thought that it would be more efficient to use a lattice of sampling points, and this may often be the case. However, the efficiency depends on the type of process, and, in general, is extremely difficult to evaluate. The little work that has been done suggests that it is quite possible for the lattice scheme to have a lesser efficiency than the random point scheme for some simple and realistic processes.

It is also feasible to use the satellites themselves as sampling points, but again, the efficiency of such a procedure is, in general, most difficult to evaluate.

## 5.3 The Expectation of the Estimator

We now turn from the question of evaluating

$$\int_0^{2\pi} \int_0^{R-\rho} N^2(r,\theta\,;\rho)rd\ rd\theta$$

to study some of the properties of the estimator $\hat{V}(\rho)$.

We will first consider $\mathcal{E}\,\hat{V}(\rho)$ for the case of a Poisson process with intensity $\lambda$. Then

(5.3.1)

$$\mathcal{E}\left(\frac{1}{\pi(R-\rho)^2}\right)\int_0^{2\pi}\int_0^{R-\rho} N^2(r,\theta\,;\rho)rd\ rd\theta$$

$$=\left(\frac{1}{\pi(R-\rho)^2}\right)\int_0^{2\pi}\int_0^{R-\rho} \mathcal{E}\,N^2(r,\theta\,;\rho)rd\ rd\theta\ =$$

$$= \left( \frac{1}{\pi(R - \rho)^2} \right) \int_0^{2\pi} \int_0^{R-\rho} \left( \pi^2\lambda^2\rho^4 + \pi\lambda\rho^2 \right) rd\, rd\theta$$

$$= \pi^2\lambda^2\rho^4 + \pi\lambda\rho^2 \quad .$$

Also

$$(5.3.2) \quad \mathcal{E} \left( \frac{\rho}{R} \right)^4 N^2(0,R) = \left( \frac{\rho}{R} \right)^4 (\pi^2\lambda^2R^4 + \pi\lambda R^2)$$

$$= \pi^2\lambda^2\rho^4 + \frac{\pi\lambda\rho^4}{R^2} \quad .$$

Therefore, from (5.1.2), (5.3.1) and (5.3.2) we have

$$(5.3.3) \qquad \mathcal{E}\, \hat{V}(\rho) = \pi\lambda\rho^2 \left( 1 - \frac{\rho^2}{R^2} \right) .$$

Thus, for a Poisson process $(R^2\, \hat{V}(\rho))/(R^2 - \rho^2)$ is an exactly unbiased estimator of $V(\rho)$ and $\hat{V}(\rho)$ is an asymptotically unbiased restimator as $R \to \infty$.

For the case of a center-satellite process, with all the satellites located at their respective cluster centers, it has been shown that the first two factorial cumulants are

$$\lambda_{10} = \lambda G'(1)\, \mu(w) \quad \text{and} \quad \lambda_{20} = \lambda G''(1)\, \mu(w) \quad .$$

The second cumulant is then

$$\kappa_{20} = \lambda\mu(w)[G'(1) + g''(1)]$$

and the second noncentral moment

$$\alpha_{20} = \lambda\mu(w)[G'(1) + G''(1)] + \lambda^2\mu^2(w)[G'(1)]^2 .$$

Noting that $\mu(w) = \pi\rho^2$ or $\pi R^2$ appropriately, we see that

$$(5.3.4)\ \mathcal{E}\left(\frac{1}{\pi(R - \rho)^2}\right)\int_0^{2\pi}\int_0^{R-\rho} N^2(r,\theta\,;\rho)rd\ rd\theta$$

$$= \pi\lambda\rho^2[G'(1) + G''(1)] + \pi^2\lambda^2\rho^4[G'(1)]^2$$

and

$$(5.3.5)\ \mathcal{E}\ (\frac{\rho}{R})^4\ N^2(0,R)$$

$$= (\frac{\rho}{R})^4\{\pi\lambda R^2[G'(1) + G''(1)] + \pi^2\lambda^2 R^4[G'(1)]^2\} .$$

Therefore

$$(5.3.6)\qquad \mathcal{E}\ \hat{V}(\rho) = \pi\lambda\rho^2[G'(1) + G''(1)](1 - \rho^2 R^2)$$

$$= \kappa_{20}\left(1 - \frac{\rho^2}{R^2}\right) .$$

For such a process we again have that

$$\frac{R^2 \hat{V}(\rho)}{R^2 - \rho^2}$$

is an exactly unbiased estimator of $V(\rho)$, and $\hat{V}(\rho)$ is an asymptotically unbiased estimator as $R \to \infty$.

Finally, we consider the general center-satellite process. We have shown that

$$\lambda_{10} = \lambda G'(1) \int p(\underline{u})d\underline{u} \quad ,$$

$$\lambda_{20} = \lambda G''(1) \int p^2(\underline{u})d\underline{u} \quad ,$$

$$\kappa_{20} = \lambda G'(1) \int p(\underline{u})d\underline{u} + \lambda G''(1) \int p^2(\underline{u})d\underline{u} \quad ,$$

$$\alpha_{20} = \lambda G'(1) \int p(\underline{u})d\underline{u} + \lambda G''(1) \int p^2(\underline{u})d\underline{u} + \lambda^2 G'(1)^2 \int p(\underline{u})d\underline{u}^2 \ .$$

Recalling that

$$\int p(\underline{u})d\underline{u} = \mu(w)$$

we see that

(5.3.7)

$$\mathcal{E}\left(\frac{1}{\pi(R-\rho)^2}\right)\int_0^{2\pi}\int_0^{R-\rho} N^2(r,\theta\,;\rho)rd\ rd\theta$$

$$= \lambda G'(1)\pi\rho^2 + \lambda G''(1)\int p_\rho^2(\underline{u})d\underline{u}$$

$$+ \lambda^2[G'(1)]^2\,\pi^2\rho^4$$

and

(5.3.8)

$$\mathcal{E}\left(\frac{\rho}{R}\right)^4 N^2(0,R) = \left(\frac{\rho}{R}\right)^4 [\lambda G'(1)\pi R^2 + \lambda G''(1)\int p_R^2(\underline{u})d\underline{u}$$

$$+ \lambda^2[G'(1)]^2\,\pi^2 R^4] \quad ,$$

where $p_\rho(\underline{u})$ denotes the probability that a satellite of a cluster with center at $\underline{u}$ lies in a circle of radius $\rho$ and, similarly for $p_R(\underline{u})$. Therefore

(5.3.10) $$\mathcal{E}\,\hat{V}(\rho) = \lambda G'(1)\,\rho^2\left(1-\frac{\rho^2}{R^2}\right)$$

$$+ \lambda G''(1)\int p_\rho^2(\underline{u})d\underline{u} - \left(\frac{\rho}{R}\right)^4\int p_R^2(\underline{u})d\underline{u} \quad .$$

Provided that

$$\int p_R^2(\underline{u})d\underline{u} \le O(R^3)$$

we see that $\hat{V}(\rho)$ is an asymptotically unbiased estimator of $V(\rho)$, but in general $(R^2\,\hat{V}(\rho))/(R^2 - \rho^2)$ is not exactly unbaised.

## 5.4 An Interesting Property

Observe that, for a Poisson process

$$(5.4.1)\quad \mathcal{E}\int_0^{2\pi}\int_0^{R-\rho} N(r,\theta\,;\rho)rd\, rd\theta$$

$$= \mathcal{E}\sum_{h=1}^{N} nA_{S_n}$$

$$= \mathcal{E}\left\{A_{S_1} + 2A_{S_2} + 3A_{S_3} + \cdots + NA_{S_N}\right\} .$$

Consider the total area obtained by adding the areas within $C(0,R - \rho)$ of all circles of radius $\rho$ about the $N$ satellites in $C(0,R)$; see the figure on the following page. Overlapping areas are counted according to their multiplicity. This total area is also

$$A_{S_1} + 2A_{S_2} + 3A_{S_3} + \cdots + NA_{S_N} .$$

Thus, from this viewpoint we see that

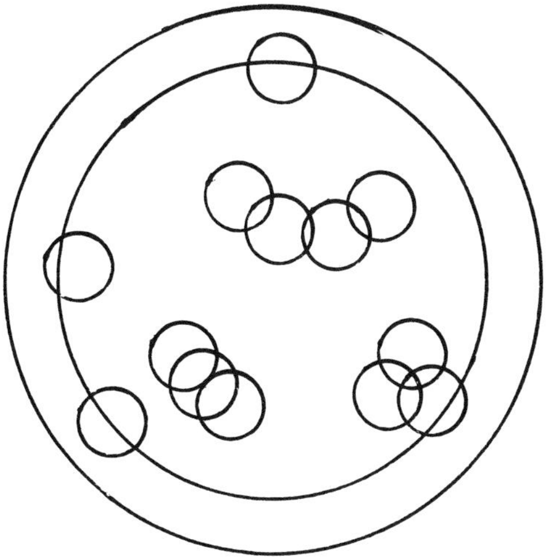

FIGURE 3a

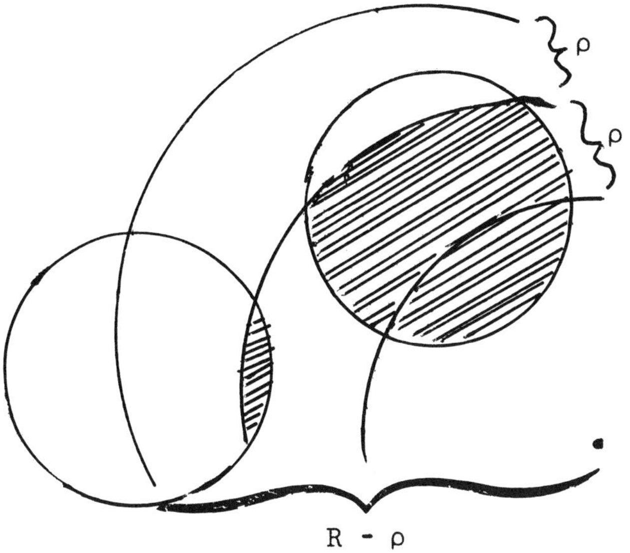


FIGURE 3b

$$(5.4.2)\quad \pi\rho^2\,\mathcal{E}\,N(0,R-\rho) = \mathcal{E}\left\{A_{S_1} + 2A_{S_2} + 3A_{S_3} + \quad + NA_{S_N}\right\}.$$

In (5.4.2) we have the expectation of the areas <u>within</u> $C(0,R-\rho)$ of circles of radius $\rho$, about <u>all</u> satellites in $C(0,R)$, and in (5.4.1) we have the expectation of the <u>total</u> area of circles of radius $\rho$, about <u>only</u> those satellites in $C(0,R-\rho)$. These expectations are equal; that is, the omitting of satellites outside $C(0,R-\rho)$ is exactly compensated for by the including of areas outside $C(0,R-\rho)$; see Figure 3b. It will be seen that this must mean that

$$(5.4.3)\quad \int_0^\rho [\pi\rho^2 - V_2(R,\rho\,;R-x)]\,\lambda\pi(R-x)dx = \int_0^\rho V_2(R,\rho\,;R+x)\,\lambda\pi(R+X)dx\ .$$

This result is quite difficult to establish directly. However, (5.4.3) is verified in the Appendix of Warren [210].

## 5.5 <u>The Variance of the Estimator</u>

We now wish to obtain the variance of the estimator

$\hat{V}(\rho)$ and study its behavior as $R \to \infty$. Unfortunately, this has proven to be extremely complicated, even for the case of a Poisson process. We can here provide only the basic steps of our argument; a certain amount of additional detail is given in Appendix VI of Warren [210] but the limitations of space prohibit the presentation of every step in full.

Our approach parallels that of Chapter 2 in that we shall firstly examine the covariance of $\hat{V}(\rho)$ and $\hat{V}(\rho + \eta)$.

By definition

$$(5.5.1)\quad \mathrm{Cov}\,\{\hat{V}(\rho),\hat{V}(\rho + \eta)\} = \mathcal{E}\,(\hat{V}(\rho) - \mathcal{E}\,\hat{V}(\rho))(\hat{V}(\rho+\eta) - \mathcal{E}\,\hat{V}(\rho+\eta)) \quad .$$

Now

(5.5.2)

$$\hat{V}(\rho) - \mathcal{E}\,\hat{V}(\rho) = \left(\frac{1}{\pi(R-\rho)^2}\right)\int_0^{2\pi}\int_0^{R-\rho}[N^2(r,\Theta\,;\rho) - \mathcal{E}\,N^2(r,\Theta\,;\rho)rd\,rd\Theta$$

$$- \left(\frac{\rho}{R}\right)^4 [N^2(0,R) - \mathcal{E}\,N^2(0,R)]$$

or, on writing $N_\rho$ for $N(r,\Theta\,;\rho)$ and $N_R$ for $N(0,R)$,

(5.5.3) $\hat{V}(\rho) - \mathcal{E}\,\hat{V}(\rho)$

$$= \left(\frac{1}{\pi(R - \rho)^2}\right)\int_0^{2\pi}\int_0^{R-\rho} [N_\rho^2 - \mathcal{E}\,N_\rho^2]rd\ rd\theta$$

$$- \left(\frac{\rho}{R}\right)^5 [N_R^2 - \mathcal{E}\,N_R^2] \quad .$$

Let

$$\Delta N_0^2 = N_0^2 - \mathcal{E}\,N_0^2 \quad \text{and} \quad \Delta N_R^2 = N_R^2 - \mathcal{E}\,N_R^2 \quad .$$

Then

(5.5.4)

$(\hat{V}(\rho) - \mathcal{E}\,\hat{V}(\rho))(\hat{V}(\rho + \eta) - \mathcal{E}\,\hat{V}(\rho + \eta))$

$$= \left[\left(\frac{1}{\pi(R - \rho)^2}\right)\int_0^{2\pi}\int_0^{R-\rho} \Delta N_\rho^2\ rd\ rd\theta - \left(\frac{\rho}{R}\right)^4 \Delta N_R^2\right]$$

$$\cdot \left[\left(\frac{1}{\pi(R - \rho - \eta)^2}\right)\int_0^{2\pi}\int_0^{R-\rho-\eta} \Delta N_{\rho+\eta}^2\ rd\ rd\theta - \left(\frac{\rho + \eta}{R}\right)^4 \Delta N_R^2\right]$$

$$= \left(\frac{1}{\pi^2(R - \rho)^2(R - \rho - \eta)^2}\right)\int_0^{2\pi}\int_0^{R-\rho} \Delta N_\rho^2\ rd\ rd\theta$$

$$\cdot \int_0^{2\pi}\int_0^{R-\rho-\eta} \Delta N_{\rho+\eta}^2\ rd\ rd\theta$$

$$- \left(\frac{\rho}{R}\right)^4 \Delta N_R^2 \left(\frac{1}{\pi(R - \rho - \eta)^2}\right)\int_0^{2\pi}\int_0^{R-\rho-\eta} \Delta N_{\rho+\eta}^2\ rd\ dr\theta$$

$$- \left(\frac{\rho + \eta}{R}\right)^4 \Delta N_R^2 \left(\frac{1}{\pi(R - \rho)^2}\right)\int_0^{2\pi}\int_0^{R-\rho} \Delta N_\rho^2\ rd\ rd\theta \quad +$$

$$+ \left(\frac{\rho}{R}\right)^4 \left(\frac{\rho + \eta}{R}\right)^4 \left[\Delta N_R^2\right]^2$$

$$= I_1 - I_2 - I_3 + I_4, \text{ say.}$$

Thus, in brief

(5.5.5) $\text{Cov}\,\{\hat{V}(\rho),\hat{V}(\rho + \eta)\} = \mathcal{E}\,\{I_1 - I_2 - I_3 + I_4\}$ .

We now obtain these expectations for the case of a two-dimensional Poisson process. It will be convenient to take them in the reverse order.

(5.5.6) $$\mathcal{E}\, I_4 = \left(\frac{\rho}{R}\right)^4 \left(\frac{\rho/\eta}{R}\right)^4 \mathcal{E}\left[\Delta N_R^2\right]^2 .$$

Now

(5.5.7)

$$\mathcal{E}\left[\Delta N_R^2\right]^2 = \mathcal{E}\left[N_R^2 - \mathcal{E}\, N_R^2\right]^2 = \text{Var}\, N_R^2 = \mathcal{E}\, N_R^4 - \mathcal{E}^2\, N_R^2$$

$$= (\lambda\pi R^2)^4 + 6(\lambda\pi R^2)^3 + 7(\lambda\pi R^2)^2 + (\lambda\pi R^2)$$

$$- [(\lambda\pi R^2)^2 + (\lambda\pi R^2)]$$

$$= 4\lambda^3\pi^3R^6 + 6\lambda^2\pi^2R^4 + \lambda\pi R^2 .$$

Thus

$$(5.5.8) \qquad \mathcal{E}\, I_4 = \left(\frac{\rho}{R}\right)^4 \left(\frac{\rho+\eta}{R}\right)^4 \cdot (4\lambda^3\pi^3R^6 + 6\lambda^2\pi^2R^4 + \lambda\pi R^2) \ .$$

Taking $\eta = 0$

$$(5.5.9) \qquad \mathcal{E}\, I_4 = \left(\frac{\rho}{R}\right)^8 (4\lambda^3\pi^3R^6 + 6\lambda^2\pi^2R^4 + \lambda\pi R^2) = O(R^{-2}) \ .$$

Next

$$(3.5.10) \qquad \mathcal{E}\, I_3 = \left(\frac{\rho+\eta}{R}\right)^4 \left(\frac{1}{\pi(R-\rho)^2}\right) \cdot \int_0^{2\pi}\int_0^{R-\rho} \mathcal{E}\, \Delta N_R^2\, \Delta N_\rho^2 \, r d\, r d\Theta \ .$$

Now

$$(5.5.11) \qquad \mathcal{E}\, \Delta N_R^2\, \Delta N_\rho^2 = \mathcal{E}\,(N_R^2 - \mathcal{E}\, N_R^2)(N_\rho^2 - \mathcal{E}\, N_\rho^2) = \mathcal{E}\, N_R^2\, N_\rho^2 - \mathcal{E}\, N_R^2\, \mathcal{E}\, N_\rho^2 = \mathcal{E}_1 - \mathcal{E}_2, \text{ say.}$$

Let $N_{R\bar{\rho}}$ denote the number of satellites in $C(O,R)$ but not in $C(r,\Theta\,;\rho)$. Then

$$N_R = N_{R\bar{\rho}} + N_\rho \ .$$

Noting that for a Poisson process $N_{R\bar{\rho}}$ and $N_\rho$ are independent random variables, we have

(5.5.12)

$$\mathcal{E}_1 = \mathcal{E}\,(N_{R\bar{\rho}} + N_\rho)^2 N_\rho^2$$

$$= \mathcal{E}\,(N_{R\bar{\rho}}^2 N_\rho^2 + 2N_{R\bar{\rho}} N_\rho^3 + N_\rho^4)$$

$$= [\lambda^2\pi^2(R^2 - \rho^2)^2 + \lambda\pi(R^2 - \rho^2)][\lambda^2\pi^2\rho^4 + \lambda\pi\rho^2]$$

$$+ 2[\lambda\pi(R^2 - \rho^2)][\lambda^3\pi^3\rho^6 + 3\lambda^2\pi^2\rho^4 + \lambda\pi\rho^2]$$

$$+ [\lambda^4\pi^4\rho^8 + 6\lambda^3\pi^3\rho^6 + 7\lambda^2\pi^2\rho^4 + \lambda\pi\rho^2] \quad ,$$

and

$$(5.5.13) \quad \mathcal{E}_2 = [\lambda^2\pi^2R^4 + \lambda\pi R^2][\lambda^2\pi^2\rho^4 + \lambda\pi\rho^2] \quad .$$

Bringing together (5.5.11), (5.5.12) and (5.5.13), we have

$$(5.5.14)\ \mathcal{E}\, I_3 = \left( \frac{\rho + \eta}{R} \right)$$

$$\cdot\ [4\lambda^2\pi^2\rho^4(1 + \lambda\pi R^2) + \lambda\pi\rho^2(1 + 2\lambda\pi R^2)] \quad .$$

Taking $\eta = 0$

$$(5.5.15)\ \mathcal{E}\, I_3 = \left( \frac{\rho}{R} \right)^4 [4\lambda^2\pi^2\rho^4(1 + \lambda\pi R^2) + \lambda\pi\rho^2(1 + 2\lambda\pi R^2)]$$

$$= O(R^{-2}) \quad .$$

In a like manner

(5.5.16)

$$\mathcal{E}\, I_2 = \left( \frac{\rho}{R} \right)^4 \left[4\lambda^2\pi^2(\rho+\eta)^4 (1+\lambda\pi R^2) + \lambda\pi(\rho+\eta)^2 (1+2\lambda\pi R^2)\right] ,$$

and taking $\eta = 0$

(5.5.17)

$$\mathcal{E}\, I_2 = \left( \frac{\rho}{R} \right)^4 \left[4\lambda^2\pi^2\rho^4(1+\lambda\pi R^2) + \lambda\pi\rho^2(1+2\lambda\pi R^2)\right]$$

$$= O(R^{-2}) \quad .$$

Observe that, for $\eta = 0$, we have $\mathcal{E}\, I_2 = \mathcal{E}\, I_3$.

Finally, we require

(5.5.18)

$$\mathcal{E}\, I_1 = \mathcal{E}\left( \frac{1}{\pi^2(R-\rho)^2\,(R-\rho-\eta)^2} \right.$$

$$\left. \cdot \int_0^{2\pi}\int_0^{R-\rho} \Delta N_\rho^2 \; rd\; rd\theta \int_0^{2\pi}\int_0^{R-\rho-\eta} \Delta N_{\rho+\eta}^2 \; rd\; rd\theta \right) .$$

It will be convenient to modify the notation slightly. We shall write

$$N_\rho = N(r,\theta\,;\rho) \quad \text{and} \quad N_{\rho'} = N(r',\theta'\,;\rho) \quad .$$

Then

(5.5.19)

$$\mathcal{E}\, I_1 = \mathcal{E}\left( \frac{1}{\pi^2 (R - \rho)^2\ (R - \rho - \eta)^2} \right)$$

$$\cdot \int_0^{2\pi} \int_0^{2\pi} \int_0^{R-\rho-\eta} \int_0^{R-\rho} \Delta N_\rho^2 \, \Delta N_{(\rho+\eta)'}^2 \, rr' \, dr \, dr' \, d\theta \, d\theta'$$

$$= \left( \frac{1}{\pi^2 (R - \rho)^2\ (R - \rho - \eta)^2} \right) \int_0^{2\pi} \int_0^{2\pi} \int_0^{R-\rho-\eta} \int_0^{R-\rho}$$

$$\cdot\ \mathcal{E}\, \Delta N_\rho^2 \, \Delta N_{(\rho+\eta)'}^2 \; rr' \; dr \; dr' \; d\theta \; d\theta' \quad .$$

Consider

(5.5.20) $$\mathcal{E}\, \Delta N_\rho^2 \, \Delta N_{(\rho+\eta)'}^2$$

$$= \mathcal{E}\ (N_\rho^2 - \mathcal{E}\, N_\rho^2)(N_{(\rho+\eta)'}^2 - \mathcal{E}\, N_{(\rho+\eta)'}^2)$$

$$= \mathcal{E}\, N_\rho^2\, N_{(\rho+\eta)'}^2 - \mathcal{E}\, N_\rho^2\, \mathcal{E}\, N_{(\rho+\eta)'}^2 \quad .$$

Now, the circles $C(r,\theta\,;\rho)$ and $C(r',\theta';\rho+\eta)$ may or may not overlap. If they do not overlap, the random variables $N_\rho$ and $N_{(\rho+\eta)'}$ are independent and

$$\mathcal{E}\, \Delta N_\rho^2 \, \Delta N_{(\rho+\eta)'}^2 = 0 \quad .$$

In this case, $|\underline{x} - \underline{x}'| > 2\rho + \eta$, where, in our usual notation $\underline{x} = (x_1,x_2) = (r,\theta)$ and $|\underline{x} - \underline{x}'|$ denotes the distance between the two points $\underline{x}$ and $\underline{x}'$. For $|\underline{x} - \underline{x}'| < 2\rho + \eta$, $N_\rho$ and $N_{(\rho+\eta)'}$ are not independent.

We introduce the following notation:

Let

$N_{\rho,(\rho+\eta)'}$ denote the number of satellites in the intersection of $C(r,\theta\,;\rho)$ and $C(r',\theta'\,;\rho+\eta)$, and

$N_{\rho,\overline{(\rho+\eta)'}}$ denote the number of satellites in $C(r,\theta\,;\rho)$, but not in $C(r',\theta'\,;\rho+\eta)$, etc.

Then

$$N_\rho = N_{\rho,\overline{(\rho+\eta)'}} + N_{\rho(\rho+\eta)'} \;,$$

and

$$N_{(\rho+\eta)'} = N_{\bar\rho,(\rho+\eta)'} + N_{\rho,(\rho+\eta)'} \;.$$

Thus

(5.5.21)

$$N_\rho^2\, N_{(\rho+\eta)'}^2 = (N_{\rho,\overline{(\rho+\eta)'}} + N_{\rho,(\rho+\eta)'})(N_{\bar\rho,(\rho+\eta)'} + N_{\rho,(\rho+\eta)'})$$

$$= N^2_{\rho,\overline{(\rho+\eta)'}}\, N^2_{\bar\rho,(\rho+\eta)'} + 2N^2_{\rho,\overline{(\rho+\eta)'}}\, N_{\bar\rho,(\rho+\eta)'}\, N_{\rho,(\rho+\eta)'}$$

$$+ N^2_{\rho,\overline{(\rho+\eta)'}}\, N_{\rho,(\rho+\eta)'} + 2N_{\rho,\overline{(\rho+\eta)'}}\, N_{\rho,(\rho+\eta)'}\, N^2_{\bar\rho,(\rho+\eta)'}$$

$$+ 4N_{\rho,\overline{(\rho+\eta)'}}\, N_{\bar\rho,(\rho+\eta)'}\, N^2_{\rho,(\rho+\eta)'} + 2N_{\rho,\overline{(\rho+\eta)'}}\, N^3_{\rho,(\rho+\eta)'} +$$

$$+ N^2_{\bar{\rho},(\rho+\eta)'} N^2_{\rho,(\rho+\eta)'} + 2N_{\bar{\rho},(\rho+\eta)'} N^3_{\rho,(\rho+\eta)'} + N^4_{\rho,(\rho+\eta)'} .$$

In this way, we have expressed $N^2_\rho N^2_{(\rho+\eta)'}$ as a sum of products of random variables which are independent in the case of a Poisson process.

Further evaluation for $\eta > 0$ is extremely difficult. Since we are primarily interested in $\mathrm{Var}\,\hat{V}(\rho)$, we now set $\eta = 0$ and obtain

$$(5.5.22)\quad N^2_\rho N^2_{\rho'} = N^2_{\rho,\bar{\rho}'} N^2_{\bar{\rho},\rho'} + 2N^2_{\rho,\bar{\rho}'} N_{\rho,\rho'} + N^2_{\rho,\bar{\rho}'} N^2_{\rho,\rho'}$$

$$+ 2N_{\rho,\bar{\rho}'} N_{\rho,\rho'} N^2_{\bar{\rho},\rho'} + 4N_{\rho,\bar{\rho}'} N^2_{\rho,\rho'}$$

$$+ 2N_{\rho,\bar{\rho}'} N^3_{\rho,\rho'} + N^2_{\bar{\rho},\rho'} N^2_{\rho,\rho'} + 2N_{\bar{\rho},\rho'} N^3_{\rho,\rho'}$$

$$+ N^4_{\rho,\rho'} .$$

Write $c = \pi\rho^2$ and $v = V_2(\rho,\rho' ; |\underline{x} - \underline{x}'|)$. Then

$$(5.5.23)\quad \mathcal{E}\, N^2_{\rho,\bar{\rho}'} N^2_{\bar{\rho},\rho'}$$

$$= \mathcal{E}\, N^2_{\rho,\bar{\rho}'}\ \mathcal{E}\, N^2_{\bar{\rho},\rho'}$$

$$= [\lambda^2(c - v)^2 + \lambda(c - v)][\lambda^2(c - v)^2 + \lambda(c - v)]$$

and

$$(5.5.24)\qquad \mathcal{E}\, N^2_{\rho,\bar{\rho}'}\, N_{\bar{\rho},\rho'}\, N_{\rho,\rho'}$$

$$= \mathcal{E}\, N^2_{\rho,\bar{\rho}'}\ \mathcal{E}\, N_{\bar{\rho},\rho'}\ \mathcal{E}\, N_{\rho,\rho'}$$

$$= [\lambda^2(c-v)^2 + \lambda(c-v)]\ \lambda(c-v)\ \lambda v\ ,$$

etc. That is, in a like manner, we obtain the expectations of all the terms of (5.5.22) and after some lengthy, but straightforward algebra, we derive

$$(5.5.25)\ \mathcal{E} N^2_{\rho} N^2_{\rho'} = c^2\lambda^2(1+c\lambda)^2 + \lambda v(1+2c\lambda)^2 + 2\lambda^2 v^2\ .$$

Also

$$(5.5.26)\qquad \mathcal{E}\, N^2_{\rho}\ \mathcal{E}\, N^2_{\rho'} = (\lambda^2c^2+\lambda c)(\lambda^2c^2+\lambda c)$$

$$= \lambda^2c^2(1+\lambda c)^2\ .$$

Therefore, by (5.5.20), (5.5.25) and (5.5.26)

$$(5.5.27)\qquad \mathcal{E}\ \Delta N^2_{\rho}\ \Delta N^2_{\rho'} = \lambda v(1+2\lambda c)^2 + 2\lambda^2 v^2\ .$$

Thus, with $\eta = 0$

(5.5.28)

$$\mathcal{E}\, I_1 = \left( \frac{1}{\pi^2 (R - \rho)^4} \right) \int_0^{2\pi} \int_0^{2\pi} \int_0^{R-\rho} \int_0^{R-\rho}$$

$$\cdot \; [\lambda v(1 + 2\lambda c)^2 + 2\lambda^2 v^2] r r' \, dr\, dr' \, d\theta\, d\theta' \quad .$$

It follows that we can obtain $\mathcal{E}\, I_1$ if we can evaluate

$$\iint_{C(0,R-\rho)} V_2(\rho,\rho\, ;\, |\underline{x} - \underline{x}'|) d\underline{x}\; d\underline{x}'$$

and

$$\iint_{C(0,R-\rho)} V_2^2(\rho,\rho\, ;\, |\underline{x} - \underline{x}'|) d\underline{x}\; d\underline{x}' \quad .$$

The techniques of obtaining these integrals are found in Appendix VI of Warren [210]. It turns out that

(5.5.29) $$\mathcal{E}\, I_1 = O(R^{-2}) \quad .$$

Combining (5.5.9), (5.5.15), (5.5.17) and (5.5.29), we have

(5.5.30) $$\mathrm{Var}\; \hat{V}(\rho) = O(R^{-2}) \quad .$$

Alternatively, we may write

(5.5.31) $$\mathrm{Var}\; \hat{V}(\rho) = KR^{-2} + O(R^{-3})$$

where K is a constant, the value of which can be obtained explicitly from the expressions, as derived in Appendix VI of Warren [210].

The above has treated the case of the Poisson process. It is clear that (5.5.30) also holds for a center-satellite process in which all satellites are located at their cluster centers. The problem for a general center-satellite process is much more complicated and is not attempted herein, although it is conjectured that (5.5.30) is still valid.

## 5.6 Conclusions

To conclude this chapter, we summarize the results of the above sections.

For the case of a center-satellite process, provided that

$$\int p_R^2(\underline{u})d\underline{u} = \int \left( \int_{C(0,R)} f(\underline{x} - \underline{u})d\underline{x} \right)^2 du$$

$$\leq O(R^3) ,$$

$\hat{V}(\rho)$ defined by (5.1.2) is, as $R \to \infty$, an asymptotically unbiased estimator of $V(\rho)$, the variance of the number of satellites in a circle of radius $\rho$. For a Poisson process, or a center-satellite process in which all satellites are located at their cluster centers, $(R^2 \hat{V}(\rho))/(R^2 - \rho^2)$ is an exactly unbiased estimator of $V(\rho)$.

For a Poisson process, or a center-satellite process in which all satellites are located at their cluster centers, $\mathrm{Var}\ \hat{V}(\rho) = O(R^{-2})$.

We, therefore, have the following theorem:

THEOREM 7. _For a Poisson process, or a center-satellite process in which all satellites are located at their cluster centers,_ $\hat{V}(\rho)$ _is a consistent estimator of_ $V(\rho)$.

# CHAPTER 6. APPLICATIONS TO THE THEORY OF CUMULATIVE FATIGUE DAMAGE OF STRUCTURES

## 6.1 Introduction

In what follows, the word "device" is used to denote the given piece of equipment or hardware under consideration. At time $t = 0$, say, the device is put to use. As time passes by, the device steadily wears out until it fails or no longer performs the functions it should. Let $T$ denote the time to failure. Let $X(t)$ denote the accumulated wear-out or damage the device has suffered by time $t$. $X(t)$ is a random function of the argument $t$, while $T$ is a random variable. Let $C$ denote the "critical" damage the device can stand. $C$ is considered to be a constant without loss of generality. The inequality

$$(6.1.1) \qquad X(t) > C$$

is now the event that, by time $t$, the accumulated damage the device has suffered is greater than the critical damage; in other words, the device has failed by time $t$. Thus, (6.1.1) is the same event as $T \leq t$.

Let

$$(6.1.2) \qquad P[X(t) \leq x] = G(t,x)$$

and

$$(6.1.3) \qquad P[T \leq t] = F(t) \quad .$$

Then

$$(6.1.4) \qquad F(t) = 1 - G(t,C) \quad .$$

Equation (6.1.4) expresses the fundamental relationship between the accumulated damage $X(t)$ and the time to failure $T$. Figure 4 below illustrates these concepts.

## 6.2 The Point Process Model for Damage and the Corresponding Law of Failure

Let $E$ stand for the event of the device undergoing damage. Let $\{t_i\}$, $i = 1,2,\ldots,$ denote the sequence of intervals of time between successive occurrence of $E$. Let

$$(6.2.1) \qquad T_n = t_1 + t_2 + \cdots + t_n, \qquad n = 1,2,\ldots,$$

be the actual time instants corresponding to the occurrence of $E$. In other words, $T_1, T_2, T_3, \ldots,$ are the successive instants of time when the device suffers damage. Let $y_n$

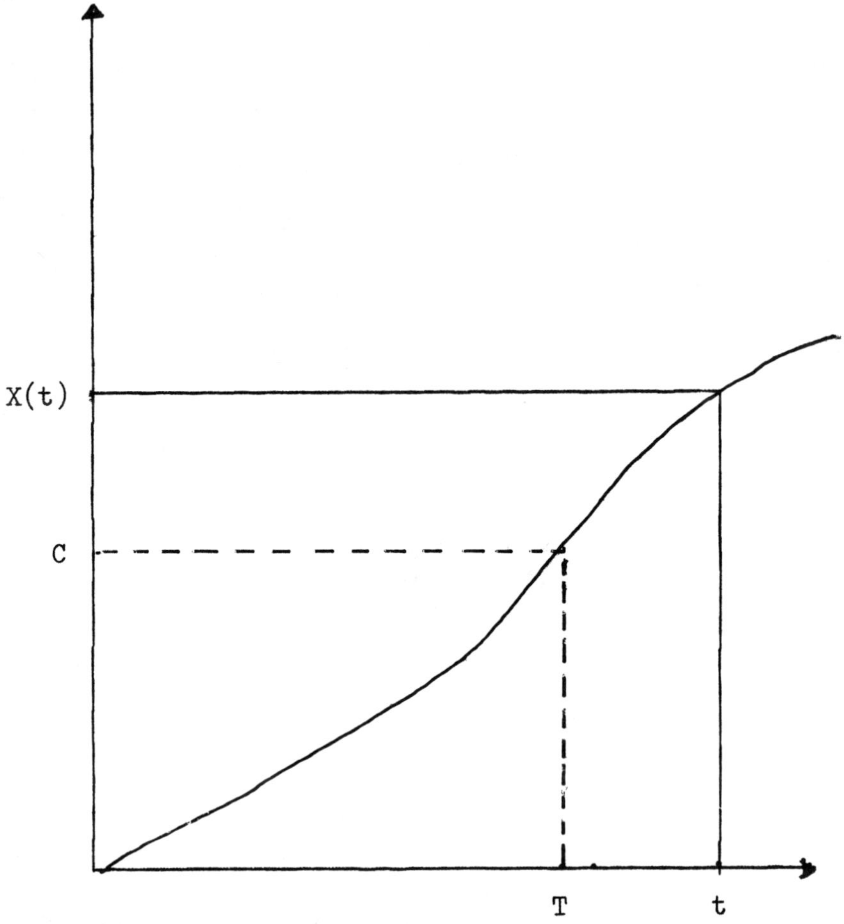


FIGURE 4

RELATIONSHIP BETWEEN X(t) AND T

denote the amount of damage the device experiences at time $T_n$, $n = 1,2,\ldots,$ . We will now assume that $\{t_n, y_n\}$, $n = 1,2,\ldots,$ is a sequence of independently, identically distributed random variables with the same distribution function $H(t,y)$. Clearly now $\{t_n\}$, $n = 1,2,\ldots,$ and $\{y_n\}$, $n = 1,2,\ldots,$ are both ordinary point processes. Under this set-up the cumulative damage $X(t)$, suffered by the device by time $t$, is given by

$$X(t) = \sum_{n=1}^{N_t} y_n \tag{6.2.2}$$

where $N_t$ is the number of events up to the specified time $t$ with respect to the point process $\{t_n\}$. For the cumulative damage process $X(t)$ given by (6.2.2), the corresponding distribution is given by

(6.2.3)

$$G(t,x) = P[X(t) \leq x] = P\left[\sum_{n=1}^{N_t} y_n < x\right]$$

$$= 1 - H(t,\infty) + \int_{-\infty}^{\infty}\int_{0}^{t} G(t - t_1, x - x_1)dH_{t_1,x_1}(t_1,x_1)$$

because $1 - H(t,\infty)$ denotes the probability that there is no event in the specified interval; that $X(t) = 0 < x$. In the remaining mutually exclusive cases, there is some first event in the interval and the last term on the right-hand side of (6.2.3) gives this probability.

If we use the fundamental relationship (6.2.4), the underlying law of failures associated with the cumulative damage process (6.3.2) is given by

$$(6.3.4) \quad F(t) = H(t,\infty) - \int_{-\infty}^{\infty}\int_{0}^{t} G(t-t_1, C-x_1)\, dH_{t_1,x_1}(t_1,x_1) \ .$$

## 6.3 The Closed Form Expression for the Law of Failure for a Poisson Point Process

We will now specialize (6.2.3) and (6.2.4) for the case of a Poisson process for the events E and discover some basic properties of the exponential law of failures. In this case

(6.3.1)

$$G(t,x) = P\left[\sum_{n=1}^{N_t} y_n \leq x\right]$$

$$= \sum_{n=0}^{\infty} P[N_t = n]\ P[y_1 + y_2 + \cdots + y_n < x \mid N_t = n] \ .$$

Since $H(\infty,x)$ denote the distribution of a $y_i$, we let $H^{(n)}(\infty,x)$ denote the n-fold convolution of $H(\infty,x)$ with itself. Also, since $N_t$ is the number of events in the interval $(0,t)$ according to a Poisson process, say, with parameter $\lambda$

$$P[N_t = n] = \frac{e^{-\lambda t}(\lambda t)^n}{n!} \quad . \tag{6.3.2}$$

Hence

$$G(t,x) = \sum_{n=0}^{\infty} \frac{e^{-\lambda t}(\lambda t)^n}{n!} H^{(n)}(\infty,x) \tag{6.3.3}$$

where

$$\begin{cases} H^{(0)}(\infty,x) = \begin{cases} 0 & \text{for } x < 0 \\ 1 & \text{for } x \geq 0 \end{cases} , \\ H^{(1)}(\infty,x) = H(\infty,x) , \end{cases} \tag{6.3.4}$$

and for $n > 1$

$$H^{(n)}(\infty,x) = \int_{-\infty}^{\infty} H^{(n-1)}(\infty,x - z)\, dH(\infty,z) \quad .$$

Combining (6.3.3) and (6.3.4) we can write

$$(6.3.5)\quad G(t,x) = e^{-\lambda t} + \sum_{n=1}^{\infty} \frac{e^{-\lambda t}(\lambda t)^n}{n!} H^{(n)}(\infty,x) \quad .$$

From (6.1.4) and (6.3.5) we discover that in this case

$$(6.3.6)\quad G(t) = (1 - e^{-\lambda t}) - \sum_{n=1}^{\infty} \frac{e^{-\lambda t}(\lambda t)^n}{n!} H^{(n)}(\infty,C) \quad .$$

Equation (6.3.6) is a special case of Equation (6.2.4), when the events $E$ form a Poisson process. We will not interpret the fundamental implications of Equations (6.2.4) and (6.3.6).

Let $D$ stand for the event that by time $t$ the device has experienced damage. Now

$$(6.3.7)\qquad P(D) = P(t_1 \leq t) = H(t,\infty) \quad .$$

Let $A$ stand for the event that the device failed by time $t$ and $\bar{A}$ its complement. Clearly

$$D = (DA) \cup (D\bar{A}) = A \cup (D\bar{A}) \quad ,$$

since $A \subset D$. Hence,

$$(6.3.8)\qquad P(D) = P(A) + P(D\bar{A})$$

but

$$(6.3.9) \qquad P(A) = F(t)$$

and

$$(6.3.10) \quad P(D\bar{A}) = \int_{-\infty}^{\infty} \int_{0}^{t} G(t - t_1, C - x_1) dH_{t_1,x_1}(t_1, x_1) \quad .$$

Thus, Equation (6.2.4) is clearly identical with Equation (6.3.8).

We discover from (6.2.4), in the general case, that

$$(6.3.11) \qquad F(t) \leq H(t, \infty) \quad ,$$

the equality sign holding, if and only if

$$(6.3.12) \qquad C = 0 \quad .$$

The condition (6.3.12) that the critical damage $C$ is zero is equivalent to saying that the cumulative damage process $X(t)$ is a constant, independent of $t$, i.e., the device does not deteriorate due to damage or wear-out. In this case, the event $E$ of the device undergoing damage, between $t$ and $t + dt$, is synonymous with the event of the device failing between $t$ and $t + dt$.

There has been a popular misconception that the exponential law of failures is characterized by the situation that the cumulative damage is independent of time. Equations (6.3.6), (6.3.11) and (6.3.12) now establish that, when the cumulative damage process is constant in time, the underlying law of failures is identical with the distribution of the intervals between consecutive occurrences of E and is exponential only when the events E are Poisson.

## 6.4 Asymptotic Properties of Cumulative Damage

We have, from (6.2.3), for the distribution function of cumulative damage $X(t) = \Sigma_{n=1}^{N_t} Y_n$, the following

(6.4.1)

$$G(t,x) = P[X(t) \leq x] = P\left[\sum_{n=1}^{N_t} Y_n \leq x\right] = 1 - H(t,\infty)$$

$$+ \int_{-\infty}^{\infty} \int_0^t G(t-t_1, x-x_1) d_{t_1,x_1} H(t_1,x) \quad .$$

For the point process $\{t_n, y_n\}$, $n = 1,2,\ldots,$ with common distribution $H(t,y)$, let

$$\mu_r = E(t_n^r) \quad ; \quad \nu_r = E(y_n^r)$$

and

$$\mu_{ij} = E(t_n^i \, y_n^j) \quad .$$

Define the transform

$$(6.4.2) \quad H^*(s,\theta) = \int_0^\infty \int_{-\infty}^\infty e^{-st+i\theta y}\, d_{t,y}\, H(t,y) \quad .$$

Applying the transform (6.1.2) to both sides of Equation (6.1.1) we obtain

$$(6.4.3) \quad G^*(s,\theta) = 1 - H^*(s,0) + G^*(s,\theta)\, H^*(s,\theta) \quad .$$

Hence

$$(6.4.4) \qquad G^*(s,\theta) = \frac{1 - H^*(s,0)}{1 - H^*(s,\theta)} \quad .$$

Noting that the left-hand side of Equation (6.1.4) is the characteristic function of the distribution function $G^*(s,y)$, and that for the real part of $s$ greater than zero, the right-hand side is differentiable with respect to $\theta$, we obtain that the first absolute moment of $G^*(s,y)$ is finite and

$$(6.4.5) \quad i \int_{-\infty}^\infty y d_y\, G^*(s,y) = \left. \frac{(i - H^*(s,0))\, H^{*\prime}(s,\theta)}{[1 - H^*(s,\theta)]^2} \right|_{\theta=0}$$

$$= \frac{i\, R^*(s)}{1 - H^*(s,0)} \quad ,$$

where the symbol 'prime' denotes differentiation with respect to $\theta$ and

$$(6.4.6) \qquad R^*(s) = \frac{1}{i} H^{*\prime}(s,\theta)|_{\theta=0} \; .$$

If $\nu_1, \mu_2$ and $\mu_{11}$ are finite, we obtain from Chapter 1 that

$$(6.4.7) \quad \int_{-\infty}^{\infty} y \, d_y G^*(s,y) = \frac{R^*(s)}{1 - H^*(s,0)}$$

$$= \frac{\nu_1}{\mu_1 s} + \frac{\nu_1 \mu_2}{2\mu_1^2} \frac{\mu_{11}}{\mu_1} + o(1) \; ,$$

as $s \to +0$. Since the left-hand side of Equation (6.4.7) is the Laplace-Stieltjes transform (L-S.T) of $E(X(t))$, we obtain that

$$(6.4.8) \quad E\,(X(t)) = t\,\frac{\nu_1}{\mu_1} + \frac{\nu_1 \mu_2}{2\mu_1^2} - \frac{\mu_{11}}{\mu_1} + o(1) \; ,$$

as $t \to \infty$. Similarly,

$$(6.4.9) \quad -\int_{-\infty}^{\infty} y^2 \, d_y \, G^*(s,y)$$

$$= \frac{H^{*\prime\prime}(s,\theta)|_{\theta=0}}{1 - H^*(s,0)} + 2 \, \frac{[H^{*\prime}(s,\theta)|_{\theta=0}]^2}{[1 - H^*(s,0)]^2}$$

$$= - \frac{Q^*(s)}{1 - H^*(s,0)} + 2 \, \frac{[i\, R^*(s)]^2}{[1 - H^*(s,0)]^2} \; ,$$

where

$$Q^*(s) = -H^{*''}(s,\theta)\big|_{\theta=0}$$

is the Laplace-Stieltjes transform of

$$Q(t) = \int_{-\infty}^{\infty} y^2 \, d_y \, H(t,y) \quad .$$

Hence

$$(6.4.10) \quad \int_{-\infty}^{\infty} y^2 \, d_y \, G^*(s,y)$$

$$= \frac{Q^*(s)}{1 - H^*(s,0)} + \frac{2[R^*(s)]^2}{[1 - H^*(s,0)]^2} \quad .$$

If $\nu_2, \mu_3, \mu_{21}$ and $\mu_{12}$ are finite, we obtain, after a straightforward calculation that

(6.4.11)

$$E\,(X^2(t)) = \frac{\nu_1^2}{\mu_1^2} t^2 + t \left( \frac{2\mu_2 \, \nu_1^2}{\mu_1^3} - \frac{4\nu_1 \, \mu_{11}}{\mu_1^2} + \frac{\nu_2}{\mu_1} \right)$$

$$+ \frac{3\nu_1 \, 2\mu_2^2}{2\mu_1^4} - \frac{2\nu_1^2 \, \mu_3}{3\mu_1^3} + \frac{2\mu_{11}^2}{\mu_1^2} + \frac{2\nu_1 \, \mu_{21}}{\mu_1^2}$$

$$- \frac{4\nu_1 \, \mu_{11} \, \mu_2}{\mu_1^3} + \frac{\mu_2 \, \nu_2}{2\mu_1^2} - \frac{\mu_{12}}{\mu_1} + o(1) \quad ,$$

as $t \to \infty$.

Combining (6.4.8) and (6.4.11), we finally discover that

(6.4.12)

$$\mathrm{Var}\ (X(t)) = t\left(\frac{\nu_2}{\mu_1} + \frac{\nu_1^2\,\mu_2}{\mu_1^3} - \frac{2\nu_1\,\mu_{11}}{\mu_1^2}\right)$$

$$+ \frac{5\nu_1^2\,\mu_2^2}{4\mu_1^4} - \frac{2\nu_1^2\,\mu_3}{3\mu_1^3} - \frac{3\nu_1\,\mu_{11}\,\mu_2}{\mu_1^3} + \frac{\mu_{11}^2}{\mu_1^2}$$

$$+ \frac{2\nu_1\,\mu_{21}}{\mu_1^2} + \frac{\mu_2\,\nu_2}{2\mu_1^2} - \frac{\mu_{12}}{\mu_1} + o(1)\ ,$$

as $t \to \infty$.

## 6.5 Extensions to Multicomponent Structures

In the previous section, the damage $y_n$ was considered a scalar. In the case of a general structure, consisting of $m$ components, at each occurrence of $E$, say, at time $T_n = t_1 + t_2 + \cdots + t_n$, the damage the structure suffers can be denoted by an m-dimensional random vector

$$y_n = \begin{pmatrix} y_{1n} \\ y_{2n} \\ \vdots \\ y_{mn} \end{pmatrix} .$$

The assumption in this case is that the sequence $\{t_n, y_n\}$, $n = 1,2,\ldots,$ is a point process with a common $(m+1)$-dimensional distribution given by

$$(6.5.1) \qquad P\{t_n < t, y_n < y\} = H(t, y_1, y_2, \ldots, y_m) \ .$$

The corresponding m-dimensional damage proces is then

$$\begin{pmatrix} X_1(t) \\ X_2(t) \\ \vdots \\ X_m(t) \end{pmatrix} = \begin{pmatrix} \Sigma_{n=1}^{N_t} y_{1n} \\ \Sigma_{n=1}^{N_t} y_{2n} \\ \vdots \\ \Sigma_{n=1}^{N_t} y_{mm} \end{pmatrix} .$$

Now, the m-dimensional joint distribution of life lengths of the $m$ components is given by

$$(6.5.3) \quad F(t_1, t_2, \ldots, t_m)$$
$$= P[X_1(t_1) > C_1, \ldots, X_m(t_m) > C_m] \ ,$$

where $C_i$, $i = 1,2,\ldots,m$ is the critical threshold for the $i^{th}$ component of the structure.

Using procedures similar to the single component situation, we can obtain, explicitly, $F(t_1, t_2, \ldots, t_m)$ in terms of $H(t, y_1, y_2, \ldots, y_m)$ and its convolutions evaluated at the critical threshold. Also, the mean vector and the variance-covariance matrix of the m-dimensional cumulative damage process $X(t_m)$ can be easily evaluated.

## 6.6 Empirical Estimation of F

Let $H_k(\cdot,\cdot)$ denote the two-dimensional empirical distribution function for $H(\cdot,\cdot)$. That is, $H_k(t,x) = 1/n$, (number of observations $(T_i,X_i)$ with $T_i < t$ and $X_i < x$).

This will then produce an $F_k$ where

$$F_k(t) = H_k(t,\infty) - \int_{-\infty}^{+\infty} \int_0^t G_k(t - t_1, C - x_1) dH_k(t_1,x_1) .$$

THEOREM 8. <u>Let</u> G <u>be a continuous function with respect to the usual product topology on</u> $E^2$. <u>Then,</u>

$$F_k(t) \to F(t)$$

<u>completely, or, in the sense of Feller, properly.</u>

<u>Proof</u>: One has

$$(6.6.1) \quad |F_k(t) - F(t)| \leq |H_k(t,\infty) - H(t,\infty)| +$$

$$+ \left| \int_{-\infty}^{+\infty} \int_{0}^{t} G_k(t - t_1, C - x_1) dH_k\ (t_1, x_1) \right.$$

$$\left. - \int_{-\infty}^{+\infty} \int_{0}^{t} G(t - t_1, C - x_1) dH\ (t_1, x_1) \right| .$$

The first term in (6.6.1) tends to 0 since $H_k$ is the empirical distribution function for H. For the second term, one has

(6.6.2)

$$\left| \int_{\infty}^{+\infty} \int_{0}^{t} G_k(t - t_1, C - x_1) dH_k\ (t_1, x_1) \right.$$

$$\left. - \int_{-\infty}^{+\infty} \int_{0}^{t} G(t - t_1, C - x_1) dH\ (t_1, x_1) \right|$$

$$\leq \left| \int_{\infty}^{+\infty} \int_{0}^{t} G(t - t_1, C - x_1) dH_k\ (t_1, x_1) \right.$$

$$\left. - \int_{-\infty}^{+\infty} \int_{0}^{t} G(t - t_1, C - x_1) dH\ (t_1, x_1) \right|$$

$$+ \left| \int_{-\infty}^{+\infty} \int_{0}^{t} G_k(t - t_1, C - x_1) - G(t - t_1, C - x_1) dH_k(t_1, x_1) \right|$$

The first summand in (6.6.2) tends to 0 as $k \to \infty$ by the two-dimensional version of the Helly-Bray theorem. The second term in (6.6.2) is bounded by

(6.6.3)

$$\int_{-\infty}^{+\infty}\int_{0}^{t} |G_k(t-t_1,C-x_1)-G(t-t_1,C-x_1)|\,dH_k\,(t_1,x_1) \quad .$$

To show this tends to 0 as $k$ tends to $\infty$, we first consider

$$\psi_k(a,t) = \int_{-a}^{a}\int_{0}^{t} g_k(t-t_1,C-x_1)\,dH_k\,(t_1,x_1)$$

where

$$g_k(t-t_1,C-x_1)$$
$$= |G_k(t-t_1,C-x_1) - G(t-t_1,C-x_1)| \; .$$

Expressing the finite multiple integral as the limit of the Riemann-Stieltjes sums, and interchanging limits, one obtains

$$\psi_k(a,t) \to 0 \quad \text{as} \quad k \to \infty \; .$$

Hence,

$$\lim_{a\to\infty}\ \lim_{k\to\infty}\ \psi_k(a,t) = 0$$

and, since $g_k$ is bounded and $H_k(\cdot,\cdot)$ is a distribution function, we obtain

$$\lim_{k\to\infty} \lim_{a\to\infty} \psi_k(a,t) = \lim_{k\to\infty} \psi_k(\infty,t) = 0 .$$

In the particular case for the Poisson process one defines $G_k(t,x)$ by

$$(6.6.4) \qquad G_k(t,x) = \sum_{n=0}^{\infty} e^{-\lambda t} \frac{(\lambda t)^n}{n!} H_k^{(n)}(\infty,x)$$

where $H_k(\cdot,\cdot)$ is the two-dimensional empirical distribution function.

THEOREM 9. <u>With</u> $G_k$ <u>as in</u> (6.6.4) <u>and</u> $G$ <u>as in</u> (6.2.3), $G_k(\cdot,\cdot)$ <u>converges completely to</u> $G(\cdot,\cdot)$.

<u>Proof</u>: One first observes the following inequality

$$(6.6.5) \left|G_k(t,x) - g(t,x)\right| \le \sum_{n=0}^{\infty} e^{-\lambda t} \frac{(\lambda t)^n}{n!} \left|H_k^{(n)}(\infty,x) - H^{(n)}(\infty,x)\right| .$$

For the right-hand side we employ Lemma 2, p. 252 of Feller [70] which states that, for $\mathcal{H}_k$ and $\mathcal{H}$ as the respective operators of $H_k$ and $H$, and $u$ a continuous function on $E^1$, the inequality

$$\|\mathcal{H}_k^{(n)}(u) - \mathcal{H}^{(n)}(u)\| < n\|\mathcal{H}_k(u) - \mathcal{H}(u)\|$$

holds. If we let $k \to \infty$ it follows that $H_k^{(n)} \to H^{(n)}$ by Theorem 1, p. 249 of Feller [70]. Now, by letting $k \to \infty$ in (6.6.5), since the limit can be brought inside the summation sign, it can be seen that the right-hand side tends to 0.

## 6.7 Conditions for DMR and IHR

In this section, we assume $\{t_i\}$ forms a Poisson process and derive sufficient conditions for $F$, defined in (6.3.6) to be DMR (decreasing mean residual life) and IHR (increasing hazard rate). The section is concluded with an example whose derived $F$ is IHR.

Set $p_n = H^{(n)}(\infty, C)$. Then, one has the following theorem.

THEOREM 10. *A sufficient condition for* $F$ *to be* DMR *is for the following inequalities to be satisfied for all* $N > M$ *for some positive integer* $M$.

$$(6.7.1) \qquad \sum_{j=0}^{k} \binom{k}{j} p_j \left( \sum_{i=k-j+2}^{N} p_i \right)$$

$$\leq \sum_{j=k-N+1}^{k} \binom{k}{j} p_{j+1} \left( \sum_{i=k-j+1}^{N} p_i \right)$$

for $0 \leq k \leq N-1$ .

$$(6.7.2)\qquad \sum_{j=k-N+2}^{N} \binom{k}{j} p_j \left( \sum_{i=k-j+2}^{N} p_i \right) \leq \sum_{j=k-N+1}^{N-1} \binom{k}{j} p_{j+1} \left( \sum_{i=k-j+1}^{N} p_i \right)$$

for $N \leq k \leq 2N-2$.

Proof: The quantity we wish to consider is

$$(6.7.3)\qquad \psi(t) = \frac{\int_t^\infty (1 - F(x))dx}{1 - F(t)}$$

for $t > 0$.

To show this is nonincreasing in $t$, we evaluate

$$\psi(t) = \frac{\Sigma_{n=0}^{\infty} \frac{p_n}{\lambda} e^{-\lambda t} \Sigma_{j=0}^{n} \frac{(\lambda t)^j}{j!}}{e^{-\lambda t} \Sigma_{n=0}^{\infty} \frac{(\lambda t)^n}{n!} p_n} .$$

Without loss of generality we can assume $\lambda = 1$. Differentiating $\psi$ with respect to $t$, one has $\psi'(t) < 0$ if and only if

$$(6.7.5)\quad \Big(\sum_{n=0}^{\infty} \frac{p_n t^n}{n!}\Big)\Big(\sum_{n=2}^{\infty} p_n \sum_{j=0}^{n-2} \frac{t^j}{j!}\Big)$$

$$\leq \Big(\sum_{n=1}^{\infty} p_n \sum_{j=0}^{n-1} \frac{t^j}{j!}\Big)\Big(\sum_{n=0}^{\infty} p_{n+1} \frac{t^n}{n!}\Big) .$$

Now, restrict the summations to finite summations for $N > 2$. One has

$$(6.7.6)\quad \Big(\sum_{n=0}^{N} \frac{p_n t^n}{n!}\Big)\Big(\sum_{n=2}^{N} p_n \sum_{j=0}^{n-2} \frac{t^j}{j!}\Big)$$

$$\leq \Big(\sum_{n=1}^{N} p_n \sum_{j=0}^{n-1} \frac{t^j}{j!}\Big) \sum_{n=0}^{N-1} p_{n+1} \frac{t^n}{n!} .$$

Considering the coefficients of the polynomials, one has for the left-hand side of (6.7.6)

$$(6.7.7)\quad \sum_{k=0}^{N-1} \sum_{j=0}^{k} \frac{p_j}{j!}\Big(\sum_{i=k-j+2}^{N} \frac{p_i}{(k-j)!}\Big) t^k$$

$$+ \sum_{k=N}^{2N-2} \sum_{j=k-N+2}^{N} \frac{p_j}{j!}\Big(\sum_{j=k-j+2}^{N} \frac{p_i}{(k-j)!}\Big) t^k .$$

For the right-hand side one has

$$(6.7.8)\quad \sum_{k=0}^{N-1} \sum_{j=0}^{k} \frac{p_{j+1}}{j!}\Big(\sum_{j=k-j+1}^{N} \frac{p_i}{(k-j)!}\Big) t^k$$

$$+ \sum_{k=N}^{2N-2} \sum_{j=k-N+1}^{N} \frac{p_{j+1}}{j!}\Big(\sum_{j=k-j+1}^{N} \frac{p_i}{(k-j)!}\Big) t^k .$$

Substituting the expressions in (6.7.7) and (6.7.8) into (6.7.6), and comparing coefficients, one obtains (6.7.1) and (6.7.2).

THEOREM 11: <u>A sufficient condition for</u> $F$ <u>to be</u> IHR <u>is for the following to hold for</u> $N \geq M$ <u>for some</u> $M \geq 1$

$$(6.7.9) \quad \sum_{j=0}^{k} \binom{k}{j} p_{j+1}\, p_{k-j+1} \geq \sum_{j=0}^{k} \binom{k}{j} p_j\, p_{k-j+2}$$

<u>for</u> $0 \leq k \leq N - 1$, and

$$(6.7.10) \quad \sum_{j=k-N+1}^{N-1} \binom{k}{j} p_{j+1}\, p_{k-j+1} \geq \sum_{j=k-N+2}^{N} \binom{k}{j} p_j\, p_{k-j+2}$$

<u>for</u> $N < k < 2N - 2$.

<u>Proof</u>: We wish to show that

$$\frac{F(t + x) - F(t)}{1 - F(t)}$$

is nondecreasing in $t$ for $x > 0$. Substituting for $F$ one has

$$(6.7.11) \quad \psi_x(t) = 1 - \frac{e^{-\lambda x} \;\Sigma_{n=0}^{\infty} \frac{(\lambda(t + x))^n}{n!} \; p_n}{\Sigma_{n=0}^{\infty} \frac{(\lambda t)^n}{n!} \; p_n} \quad .$$

As in the preceding section on Theorem 10, we first can set $\lambda = 1$ and then simplify by finding $e^x(1 - \psi_x(t))$, which is

$$(6.7.11) \qquad \varphi_x(t) = e^x(1 - \psi_x(t)) = \frac{\Sigma_{n=0}^{\infty} \frac{(t+x)^n}{n!} p_n}{\Sigma_{n=0}^{\infty} \frac{t^n}{n!} p_n} .$$

We wish to derive conditions on $\{p_n\}$ so that the expression in (6.7.11) will be nonincreasing. Differentiating $\varphi_x(t)$ with respect to $t$, one has $\varphi_x(t) \leq 0$ if and only if

$$\sum_{n=0}^{\infty} \frac{t^n}{n!} p_n \left( \sum_{n=0}^{\infty} \frac{(t+x)^n}{n!} p_{n+1} \right)$$
$$\leq \sum_{n=0}^{\infty} \frac{(t+x)^n}{n!} p_n \left( \sum_{n=0}^{\infty} \frac{t^n}{n!} p_{n+1} \right)$$

or, equivalently,

$$(6.7.12) \qquad \frac{\Sigma_{n=0}^{\infty} \frac{t^n}{n!} p_n}{\Sigma_{n=0}^{\infty} \frac{t^n}{n!} p_{n+1}} \leq \frac{\Sigma_{n=0}^{\infty} \frac{(t+x)^n}{n!} p_n}{\Sigma_{n=0}^{\infty} \frac{(t+x)^n}{n!} p_{n+1}} .$$

Since we are considering this expression for any $x > 0$, (6.7.12) will hold, if and only if

$$\mu(t) = \frac{\Sigma_{n=0}^{\infty} \frac{t^n}{n!} p_n}{\Sigma_{n=0}^{\infty} \frac{t^n}{n!} p_{n+1}}$$

is nondecreasing in $t$. Differentiating $\mu(t)$ one has $\mu'(t) \geq 0$, if and only if

$$\left(\sum_{n=0}^{\infty} \frac{t^n}{n!} p_{n+1}\right)^2$$

$$\geq \left(\sum_{n=0}^{\infty} \frac{t^n}{n!} p_n\right)\left(\sum_{n=0}^{\infty} \frac{t^n}{n!} p_{n+2}\right).$$

Restricting to finite summations, say $N$, one has

$$(6.7.13)\quad \left(\sum_{n=0}^{N-1} \frac{t^n}{n!} p_{n+1}\right)^2$$

$$\leq \left(\sum_{n=0}^{N} \frac{t^n}{n!} p_n\right)\left(\sum_{n=0}^{N-2} \frac{t^n}{n!} p_{n+2}\right).$$

The polynomial on the left-hand side of (6.7.13) is

$$(6.7.14)\quad \sum_{k=0}^{N-1} \sum_{j=0}^{k} \frac{1}{j!(k-j)!} p_{j+1} p_{k-j+1} t^k$$

$$+ \sum_{k=N}^{2N-2} \sum_{j=k-N+1}^{N-1} \frac{1}{j!(k-j)!} p_{j+1} p_{k-j+1} t^k$$

and the polynomial on the right-hand side of (6.7.13) is

$$(6.7.15)\quad \sum_{k=0}^{N-1} \left[\sum_{j=0}^{k} \frac{1}{j!(k-j)!} p_j p_{k-j+2}\right] t^k \; +$$

$$+ \sum_{k=N}^{2N-2} \left[ \sum_{j=k-N+2}^{N} \frac{1}{j!(k-j)!} p_j \, p_{k-j+2} \right] t^k .$$

Comparing the respective coefficients in (6.7.14) and (6.7.15), one obtains the statement of the theorem.

Example

An example of a distribution function $F$ satisfying (6.7.1), (6.7.2), (6.7.9) and (6.7.10) is given herein.

Assume $\{y_j\}$ are independent, identically distributed random variables with common distribution function exponential with, say, parameter 1. Then $p_n$ is given by

$$(6.7.16) \qquad p_n(x) = P\left[ \sum_{j=1}^{n} y_j \le x \right]$$

$$= 1 - e^{-x} \left[ \sum_{j=0}^{n-1} \frac{x^j}{j!} \right] .$$

That the expressions in the statements of Theorems 10 and 11 are satisfied, can be seen by direct substitution.

## 6.8 A Very General Model for Fatigue Damage

We shall consider structures which can only be in one of two states: they either function or fail. Failure will be assumed to be caused by accumulated damage, and we shall denote by $X(t)$ the accumulated damage at time $t$ and by $C$, the critical damage the structure can withstand, so that the "time-to-failure" of "life-length" of the structure is

$$T = \sup \{t : X(t) \leq C\} \quad . \tag{6.8.1}$$

Several formal assumptions will be made in the following about $X(t)$ and $C$. These assumpsions are, we believe, realistic in certain practical situations and hence, should lead to realistic conclusions.

Assumption A. $\{X(t), t \geq 0\}$ is a stochastic process and $C$ is a random variable, independent of that process.

The assumption of the independence of $C$ and $X(t)$ allows us to account for variations between individual specimens of a metal, and the differences between the specimens which lead to different values of $C$ may be due to impurities, variations in molecular composition, etc.

We first consider situations in which time is measured in discrete units of some length $\Delta$, so that the state of the structure as well as the amount of damage are noted at times, $0, \Delta, 2\Delta, \ldots, n\Delta, \ldots$ . The increment of damage in the $j^{th}$ time is

$$(6.8.2) \quad y(j\Delta) = X(j\Delta) - X(j-1)\Delta), \qquad j = 1,2,\ldots, \ .$$

For these increments of the stochastic process

$$\{X(j\Delta) \ ; \ j = 0,1,2,\ldots\}$$

we shall assume dependence of a kind suggested by the following intuitive considerations.

In practical situations, damage is caused by environmental influences which are referred to as "loading." In our model we shall decompose the damage increment, $y(j\Delta)$, into a component, $y^*(j\Delta)$, which is due exclusively to the loading in the $j^{th}$ time interval, and the remainder, $y(j\Delta) - y^*(j\Delta)$, which is a delayed effect of all the preceding damage increments and hence, will be written

$$(6.8.3) \quad y(j\Delta) - y^*(j\Delta) = f_{j-1}[y^*(0), y^*(\Delta), \ldots, y^*(j-1)\Delta)] \ .$$

Setting, by definition, $x(0) = y(0) = y^*(0)$, and combining (6.8.2) and (6.8.3), one has

(6.8.4)

$$
\begin{aligned}
X(0) &= y(0) = y^*(0) \\
X(\Delta) &= y(0) + y(\Delta) = y^*(\Delta) + f_0[y^*(0)] \\
X(2\Delta) &= y(0) + y(\Delta) + y(2\Delta) = y^*(2\Delta) + f_1[y^*(0), y^*(\Delta)] \\
&\vdots \\
X(n\Delta) &= y(0) + y(\Delta) + \cdots + y(n\Delta) \\
&= y^*(n\Delta) + f_{n-1}[y^*(0), y^*(\Delta), \ldots, y^*(n-1)\Delta)] \quad .
\end{aligned}
$$

It should be noted that the function, $f_{n-1}$, summarizes all contributions of the past damages to the total damage at time $n\Delta$ in such a manner that, intuitively speaking, it accounts for all the damage increments due to the loads at the time when they occurred, i.e.,

$$y^*(0), y^*(\Delta), y^*(2\Delta), \ldots, y^*((n-1)\Delta),$$

and, in addition for their "after-effects" at the time $n\Delta$. It will, therefore, be reasonable to assume that

$$
\text{(6.8.5)} \quad f_{n-1}[y^*(0), y^*(\Delta), \ldots, y^*((n-1)\Delta)] \geq y^*(0) + y^*(\Delta) + \cdots + y^*((n-1)\Delta) \quad .
$$

We shall now make the following specific assumptions about the damage increments $y^*$ and the structure of the functions $f_n$.

<u>Assumption B</u>. $y^*(0), y^*(\Delta) y^*(2\Delta), \ldots,$ are totally independent random variables.

<u>Assumption C</u>. The functions $f_0, f_1, \ldots,$ are of the form

(6.8.6)

$$f_{n-1}[y^*(0), y^*(\Delta), y^*(2\Delta), \ldots, y^*((n-1)\Delta)]$$
$$= y^*(0)\,\theta(n\Delta) + y^*(\Delta)\,\theta((n-1)\Delta) + \ldots + y^*((n-1)\Delta)\,\theta(\Delta)$$

where $\theta(t)$ is a function satisfying the conditions

(6.8.7) $$\theta(0) = 1$$

and

(6.8.8) $$\theta(t) \geq 1 \quad \text{for} \quad t > 0 .$$

Clearly, under this assumpgion, $f_{n-1}$ satisfies (6.8.5).

Using (6.8.6) and (6.8.7), we can now write the expression (6.8.4) for the total accumulated damage in the form

$$
\begin{aligned}
(6.8.9)\qquad X(0) &= y^*(0)\,\theta(0) \\
X(\Delta) &= y^*(\Delta)\,\theta(0) + y^*(0)\,\theta(\Delta) \\
X(2\Delta) &= y^*(2\Delta)\,\theta(0) + y^*(\Delta)\,\theta(\Delta) + y^*(0)\,\theta(2\Delta) \\
&\vdots \qquad\qquad\qquad \vdots \\
X(n\Delta) &= \Sigma_{j=0}^{n}\, y^*((n-j)\Delta)\,\theta(j\Delta) \quad .
\end{aligned}
$$

The assumptions (6.8.7) and (6.8.8) on the weight function $\theta(t)$ correspond to the intuitive property that the damages due to loading in the time unit, immediately preceding the time $n\Delta$, contribute to the total damage at time $n\Delta$ with the weight 1, while those corresponding to loadings which have occurred $j\Delta$ time units ago have already contributed at that time with the weight 1 and, in addition, contribute at time $n\Delta$ an "after-effect" with weight $\theta(j\Delta) - 1$. In most practical situations, it will be plausible to assume that at $t$ increases from 0 to $+\infty$, the function $\theta(t)$ first increases until it reaches a maximum value

$$M = \max_{0 \leq t < +\infty} \theta(t)$$

and then decreases to 1.

We shall now make the further assumption that the

random variables $y^*(j\Delta)$ have finite variances and that the expectation and the variance of each $y^*(j\Delta)$, $j = 0,1,2,\ldots,$ is approximately proportional to $\Delta$. More specifically, this assumption may be formulated as follows.

<u>Assumption D</u>. The variance of $y^*(j\Delta)$ exists for $j = 0,1,2,\ldots,$ and the expectations and variances of these random variables can be written in the form

$$(6.8.10)\qquad \begin{cases} E[y^*(j\Delta)] = \beta(j\Delta)\Delta + o^{(1)}_{j\Delta}(\Delta) \\ \mathrm{Var}\,[y^*(j\Delta)] = \tau^2(j\Delta) + o^{(2)}_{j\Delta}(\Delta) \end{cases}$$

where $\beta(t)$, $\tau(t)$ are real-valued functions such that

$$\int_0^T \beta(t)dt \quad \text{and} \quad \int_0^T \tau^2(t)dt$$

exist for every $T > 0$, and $o^{(1)}_{j\Delta}(\Delta)/\Delta$ and $o^{(2)}_{j\Delta}/\Delta$ tend to $0$ uniformly for all $j = 0,1,2,\ldots,$ as $\Delta$ decreases to $0$.

From this assumption and (6.8.10) one obtains

$$(6.8.11)\quad E[X(n\Delta)] = \Delta \sum_{j=0}^{n} \beta((n-j)\Delta)\,\Theta(j\Delta) + o(\Delta)$$

$$(6.8.12)\quad \mathrm{Var}\,[X(n\Delta)] = \Delta \sum_{j=0}^{n} \tau^2((n-j)\Delta)\, \theta^2(j\Delta) + o(\Delta) \quad .$$

In some practical situations, such as that of a cyclic loading with period $\Delta$, the random variables $y^*(j\Delta)$ are identically distributed for $j = 0,1,2,\dots,$. If this is the case, then in (6.8.10) we may write $\beta(j\Delta) = \beta$ and $\tau^2(j\Delta) = \tau^2$ for $j = 0,1,2,\dots,$. For future reference we note the following.

Remark: If $\beta(j\Delta) = \beta$ and $\tau^2(j\Delta) = \tau^2$ for $j = 0,1,2,\dots,$ then

$$(6.8.13)\qquad E\,[X(n\Delta)] = \beta\Delta \sum_{j=0}^{n} \theta(j\Delta) + o(\Delta) \quad ,$$

$$(6.8.14)\qquad \mathrm{Var}\,[X(n\Delta)] = \tau^2\Delta \sum_{j=0}^{n} \theta^2(j\Delta) + o(\Delta) \quad .$$

The expressions which have preceded assume a very simple form if one lets $\Delta$ decrease to zero, and thereby, make the transition to a mathematical model with continuous time.

Let us assume that $\theta(t)$ is bounded. Then, for $\Delta \to 0$, the expressions (6.8.11) and (6.8.12) immediately yield

$$(6.8.15) \qquad E[X(T)] = \int_0^T \beta(t)\, \theta(T-t)dt$$

$$(6.8.16) \qquad \mathrm{Var}[X(T)] = \int_0^T \tau^2(t)\, \theta^2(T-t)dt$$

for every $t > 0$.

Next, we shall make some specific assumptions on the probability distributions of the random variables $y^*(j\Delta)$, $j = 0,1,2,\ldots,$ and of $C$, and study the resulting distributions of the life-length $T$.

We now assume that $y^*(j\Delta)$, the part of the damage increment which is due exclusively to the loading in the $j^{th}$ time interval for $j = 0,1,2,\ldots,$ is a normal random variable, and that (6.8.10) holds with $\beta(j\Delta) = \beta$, $\tau^2(j\Delta) = \tau^2$ for all $j$, hence, in view of Assumption B, the normal random variables $y^*(j\Delta)$ are independently and identically distributed. We furthermore assume that the critical damage, $C$, is also normally distributed with mean $\mu$ and variance $\sigma^2$. It follows that the random variable

$$C - X(n\Delta) = C - \sum_{j=0}^{n} y^*((n-j)\Delta)\, \theta(j\Delta)$$

has normal distribution with mean

$$\mu - \Delta\beta \sum_{j=0}^{n} \theta(j\Delta)$$

and variance

$$\sigma^2 + \Delta\tau^2 \sum_{j=0}^{n} \theta^2(j\Delta) .$$

From (6.8.1) one obtains, therefore, for the life-length T, the probability

$$P[T \geq t] = P[X([t/\Delta]\Delta) \leq C] = \varphi(L)$$

where $[t/\Delta]$ is the largest integer contained in $[t/\Delta]$ and $\varphi(\cdot)$ is the standardized normal distribution function, and

$$L = \frac{\mu - \beta \, \Sigma_{j=0}^{[t/\Delta]} \theta(j\Delta)}{\sqrt{\sigma^2 \, \Delta\tau^2 \, \Sigma_{j=0}^{[t/\Delta]} \theta^2(j\Delta)}} .$$

Letting $\Delta \to 0$ and noting that

$$\lim_{\Delta \to 0} \Delta[t/\Delta] = t ,$$

one obtains for continuous time

$$(6.8.17) \qquad P\{T \geq t\} = \varphi\left(\frac{\mu - \beta \int_0^t \theta(s)ds}{\sqrt{\sigma^2 + \tau^2 \int_0^t \theta(s)ds}}\right).$$

In the model considered here, the normal random variables $y^*(j\Delta)$ are capable of negative values, which would mean that an actual repair of some of the damage can occur. In the earlier part of the second stage of fatigue, as indicated in the introduction to this section, this possibility cannot be completely dismissed. It is conceivable that negative damage increments with values close to zero may occur at that stage, according to the nature of the material and the kind and amount of the load. In the later stages of the damage process, this would appear to be impossible. By choosing $\beta$ sufficiently large with regard to $\tau$ we can make the probability of a negative damage increment as small as we wish. Similarly, by choosing $\mu$ large with regard to $\sigma$, one can make the probability of a negative value of $C$ arbitrarily small.

The continuous life lengths with probability distributions of the form (6.8.17) form a family which depends on the parameters $\beta$, $\tau^2$, $\mu$, $\sigma^2$, and on the weight function

$\theta(t)$ which accounts for the dependence of the total damage on past damages.

If $\theta(t) \equiv 1$, i.e., there is no delayed effect of past damages, and if $C$ is a constant $c$, then one obtains, as a special case of (6.8.17), the life distribution

$$(6.8.18) \qquad P\{T \geq t\} = \varphi\left( \frac{c - \beta t}{\tau \sqrt{t}} \right) .$$

This is the case considered in [20].

Now, if the assumption on the damage increments is the same as in the preceding section, but the critical damage $C$ is a constant $c$, then one obtains for the resulting life-length $T$, the probability

$$P[T \geq t\,; c] = \varphi\left( \frac{c - \beta \int_0^t \theta(s)ds}{\tau \sqrt{\int_0^t \theta^2(s)ds}} \right) .$$

If one now assumes that $C$ is a random variable with the distribution function $P[C \leq c] = F(c)$, then it follows that

$$(6.8.19) \quad P[T \geq t] = \int_{-\infty}^{+\infty} \varphi\left( \frac{c - \beta \int_0^t \theta(s)ds}{\tau \sqrt{\int_0^2 \theta^2(s)ds}} \right) dF(c) .$$

This is a family of life-distributions which depend on the parameters $\beta$, $\tau$, on the function $\theta(s)$ and on the distribution function $F(c)$. It clearly contains the family described by (6.8.14) and hence, as a special case, the family (6.8.15).

One sees immediately that the family (6.8.16) does not have the property IHRA (increasing hazard rate average), i.e., that there are life distributions of the form (6.8.16) which do not have that property. This follows from the fact shown in [20] that the family in (6.8.14) does not have that property.

One can also show that even if only Gamma distributions are allowed for $C$, the probability distributions (6.8.16) do not have the IHRA property.

It may be quite difficult to compute the expectation and the variance of the life-length $T$ when its probability distribution is of the form (6.8.16), and one may have to resort to numerical methods in specific cases. There are, however, simple bounds on $E(T)$ and $Var(T)$, which can be obtained from the following inequalities.

If

$$\sup_{0 \leq t < +\infty} \theta(t) = M < +\infty ,$$

and T satisfies (6.8.19), then

$$(6.8.20)\quad \frac{1}{\beta M}\,E(C) + \frac{1}{2}\left(\frac{\tau}{\beta}\right)^2 \le \frac{1}{\beta}\,E(C) + \frac{1}{2}\left(\frac{\tau}{\beta}\right)^2 ,$$

$$(6.8.21)\quad \frac{1}{\beta^2 M^2}\,E(C^2) + \frac{2\tau^2}{\beta^3 M}\,E(C) + \frac{3\tau^4}{2\beta^4}$$

$$\le E(T^2) \le \frac{1}{\beta^2}\,E(C^2) + \frac{2\tau^2}{\beta^3}\,E(C) + \frac{3\tau^4}{2\beta^4}$$

To prove these inequalities, one first observes that

$1 \le \Theta(t) \le M < +\infty$ implies

$$(6.8.22)\quad \frac{c - \beta M t}{\tau\, t^{1/2} M} \le \frac{c - \beta \int_0^t \Theta(s)ds}{\tau \sqrt{\int_0^t \Theta^2(s)ds}}$$

$$\le \frac{c - \beta t}{\tau\, t^{1/2}}$$

for every real c. Keeping in mind that

$$E(T) = \int_0^{+\infty} P[T \ge t]dt$$

and

$$E(T^2) = 2\int_0^{+\infty} t\,P[T \geq t)dt \quad ,$$

one obtains from (6.8.19) and (6.8.22) the inequalities

$$\int_0^{+\infty}\int_{-\infty}^{+\infty} \varphi\left(\frac{c - \beta M t}{\tau\, t^{1/2}{}_M}\right) dF(c)dt$$

$$\leq E(T^2) \leq \int_0^{+\infty}\int_{-\infty}^{+\infty} \varphi\left(\frac{c - \beta t}{\tau\, t^{1/2}}\right) dF(c)dt \, ,$$

$$2\int_0^{+\infty}\int_{-\infty}^{+\infty} t\varphi\left(\frac{c - \beta M t}{\tau\, t^{1/2}{}_M}\right) dF(c)dt$$

$$\leq E(T^2) \leq 2\int_0^{+\infty}\int_{-\infty}^{+\infty} t\varphi\left(\frac{c - \beta t}{\tau\, t^{1/2}{}_M}\right) dF(c)dt.$$

By interchanging the order of integrations by Fubini's theorem and using the expression found in [20] and the expression in the next line, one obtains (6.8.20) and (6.8.21).

## 6.9 Applied Cumulative Fatigue Damage

### 6.9.1 State of the Art of Applied Cumulative Fatigue Damage Models

A model for the cumulative fatigue damage of metal should, as stressed by Gnedenko [86] give the closest representation to the actual physical phenomena that is possible. The scatter in the results of fatigue tests is due to load history, properties of the material and the mechanism of fracture, and is not accounted for by current models, as pointed out by Bastenaire [16], Kowalewski [124], McMillan and Pelloux [137], Davis [47] and Ravishankar [174]. As a result of the failure of models to predict metal life under load and in the face of the great need for such prediction as summarized by Dougherty and Spicer [53], many empirical methods have been developed to extrapolate test data to program loads. At the base of any empirical method, however, lies some assumption about the behavior of metal under fatigue -- whether it be an assumption on the shape of the S-N curve or on a cumulative damage law. Some of the methods currently used for fatigue life prediction of full scale systems are described in the following papers: Albrecht [ 2 ], Barrois [12], Bastenaire [16], Christensen [29], Dmitrichenko [50], Dougherty and Spicer [53],

Eggwertz [58], Ford, et. al. [72], Freudenthal and Heller [78], Impellizzeri [110], Lundberg and Eggwertz [132], Mittenbergs [142], Raithby [170], Schijve [187] and Smith [195].

Other papers present methods for combining experimental results of cyclic load tests, to give performance under program loads. The papers by Kowalewski [124], Miner [141] and Serensen and Kogaev [182] are based on Miner's rule.

Miner's model has been somewhat successful and is widely used. Many authors have derived Miner's rule and have proposed modifications of the rule; among them are: Freudenthal and Heller [79], Sorenson [197], Cioclor [30], Hubbard [108], Madayag [133] and Ju, et. al. [115].

The model proposed by Miner is based on an abstract concept of damage and is a method of combining S-N measurements to predict cycles-to-failure under program loads. The model is not directly related to the physical theory of fatigue failure; it does not give a distribution for time-to-failure, it combines experimental data and it does not account for load dependence. Experimentally, Davis [47] reports that Miner's rule gives reasonable results when all possible load sequences are used.

It does not give good results when particular load sequences are applied, as experimentally determined by Ravishankar [172] and by many others. Modifications of Miner's rule, made by assuming various types of damage functions, as explained by Madayag [133], attempt to incorporate stress dependence. All such methods combine results of tests made with cyclic loads at a fixed level and do not model the known physical behavior of fatigue failure. Coleman [33], [34], [35] models fatigue failure in fibers by assuming, a priori, that damage is a function of load and time. Several functions lead to distributions of breaking strengths which have been derived by the weakest-link theory and which also give cycle dependence, which appears compatible with known experimental results. The model, however, does not closely follow the physical theories of metal fatigue. In addition, Yokobori [219] points out that the concept of damage applied to determine cumulative damage does not correspond to experimental fact.

The inconclusiveness of current quantitative models is due to the fact that any model with several parameters, selected to fit empirical data, can fairly well reproduce experimental results. The difficulty of obtaining extensive results in the tails of the distributions prevents clear cut rejection of the current models. The fitting of experimental results cannot be accepted as the criterion for a model. The realism, as stated by Freudenthal [78], of the model to the actual fatigue mechanism must be considered as the principal criterion.

Models of the strength of metals and of the fatigue strength of metals (for a definition of terms refer to ASTM Special Technical Publication No. 91-A) had their origin and need in the 100 to 1 discrepancy between the theoretical strength of metal and its actual strength, as discussed by Eaton [57]. Early models assumed a weakest-link theory based on flaws, randomly distributed through the metal. Epstein [64] surveys several such models. Weibull [213] found that the distribution now named after him fits observations better than other known distribution functions for the yield strength of steel and for the fatigue life of steel. He states that it is utterly hopeless to expect a theoretical basis for a distribution function of random variables, such as strength properties of materials, by saying: "In such cases, the only practical way of progressing is to choose a simple function, test it empirically, and stick to it as long as none better has been found." Chavez [28] proposed a model with random variable V, the log of the number of cycles-to-failure, with expected value pV where p is a probability of crack extension.

Even with this intuitive model, the resulting three-parameter distribution function closely fits empirical data. A model of the effect of inclusions on fatigue life by Johnson [114], based on assumed functions relating life and stress, produces interesting but untested formulas. Other models make the assumption that crack growth is a random variable times the size of the previous crack. According to Singpurwalla [186] and Aitchison and Brown [ 1 ], for a large number of cycles, this model gives crack length distributed as a log normal random variable. All such models provide theoretical support for the assumption that fatigue life is proportional to log N, rather than N, where N is the number of cycles-to-failure. This fact, along with experimental evidence that fatigue failure does not occur below a certain stress level, as stated by Thompson and Wadsworth [206] and by Freudenthal and Heller [79], leads to a survivorship function

$$\ell(N) = \exp\left( - \left( \frac{N - N_0}{V - N_0} \right)^{\alpha} \right)$$

for each stress level, where $N_0$, $V$ and $\alpha$ are constants and $N$ is the number of cycles-to-failure. Bastenaire [16], by using 3000 pooled observations, shows that

$$N = \frac{A}{S - E} \exp\left( - C(S - E) \right)$$

for a fixed probability of fracture, and that the scatter about this value is normally distributed. Ford, et. al [73], on the basis of pooled observations from many sources, were able to fit fatigue life to a log normal distribution with constant variance independent of stress level. Serensen and Kogaev [182] also fit experimental data to a log normal distribution. A model based on reality, that predicts the general shapes of S-N curves, is needed. To obtain a cumulative fatigue damage estimate, the S-N measurements at certain stress levels are combined to determine the number of cycles-to-failure under a mixture of stress levels.

Data on the number of cycles-to-failure at given stress level measurements are combined to determine the number of cycles-to-failure under random loading situations by means of a cumulative damage model. Miner [141] proposed a model which assumed that inception of a crack constituted failure. The concept of damage was introduced as the number of cycles applied at a given stress level, divided by the number of cycles required to produce crack inception at the given stress level. When total damage at all stress levels equals 1, a crack is started and failure occurs. Considerable effort has been made to substantiate this rule, as has been previously mentioned. But, as McMillan and Pelloux [137] show, Miner's rule does not give satisfactory results. Miner assumed that crack inception constituted failure. As has been shown in more recent research by Thompson and Wadsworth [206], for example, crack inception occurs at approximately 5 percent of the total fatigue life; most of the remaining time is required for crack propagation and, for crack propagation, load sequence is an important factor. The concept of damage may have application in modeling the crack initiation stage. The difficulty of obtaining experimental results in this stage has prevented comparison of predicted and measured times.

No model found in a survey of the literature on cumulative fatigue damage that closely fits the reality of fatigue has been fully developed. Saunders [178] has shown that a model of crack growth, under very general assumptions, gives expected failure time as a Miner type of rule.

The concept of damage has been used to develop models more sophisticated than Miner's. None has been extensively applied, perhaps because they lack reality. Modification of Miner's rule by interaction factors has been moderately successful, but, since the factors must be empirically determined by means of tests which are difficult to run, they have had only limited use.

An approach to fatigue life estimation of a structure could be based on a very general a priori assumption of the bath-tub hazard rate function, as is done is product reliability. This approach must be modified, since fatigue does not occur if load is not applied. The a priori shape must in some way account for load sequence. This could be done by assuming a hazard rate that is a function of a random parameter, as do Harris and Singpurwalla [98] and Singpurwalla [186].

### 6.9.2 Properties of Models

A model of fatigue failure should be realistic so that improvements can be incorporated as understanding of the fatigue process is developed. It is desirable to be able to predict the average life and to know the distribution of the life and of the average life for particular load sequences. A model that enables calculation of fatigue life, under a particular load sequence, may very well be quite complicated -- if it is even possible. More likely, it would be a model that predicts average fatigue life for a class of loads and which enables worst case predictions.

Essentially, three interrelated types of models are needed: a model of fatigue failure of a single element, a model of a structure of several elements under controlled conditions, and a model for a system of elements -- such as an aircraft -- under diverse loading and operating conditions. The articles by Garg [81], Heller and Donat [102], Mohan, et. al. [143], and Morrison and David [147] present methods for obtaining the overall reliability of complex systems.

As a result of the survey, it is apparent that no satisfactory mathematical model of cumulative fatigue damage has been fully developed.

### 6.9.3 Physical Properties of Fatigue Damage

We survey, with reference to [157] the main features of fatigue damage in metals.

Cracks are initiated during the first 5 to 10 percent of fatigue life. Little experimental evidence is available covering this stage. The time in this stage appears to be highly dependent on surface effects such as surface finish, surface area and surface exposure to atmosphere. Thompson and Wadsworth [206] report that metals stopped in this stage for frequent repolishing can last for double or triple the normal time to fatigue failure. The crack grows only during load increase, with the amount of growth dependent on the change in load, the maximum load level, and, apparently, on the shape of the crack tip and the state of the metal in the crack tip region. These last two factors, as reported by McMillan and Pelloux [137], account for the dependence of crack growth on the previous load. On compression, the surfaces on either side of the crack tip may be forced into contact, and, if the atmospheric conditions are such as to insure an exceptionally clean surface, the two sides may weld together, resulting in a decrease in crack growth. Crack growth depends on the previous load in the following way: If the load change is from high to low, crack growth increases due to the crack tip area's being shaped by the strain of the high load. A load change from low to high causes a decrease in crack growth, called in this case crack arrest, due to the crack front region's being worked by the low load level into a plastic region, which enables dissipation of the forces causing crack growth. Crack jump on the first cycle following a high load, after several low loads, is due to the crack tip's being sharpened by the low load cycles. The amount of crack growth is determined, apparently, by the toughness parameter, a material constant described by Davis [47], and by the load and change in load. An empirical function, given by McMillan and Pelloux [137], relating crack growth to load is

$$\alpha = C(\Delta S)^m (S_{max})$$

where $\alpha$ is crack growth in a cycle, $\Delta S$ is the change in stress, $S_{max}$ is the maximum stress, and $C$ and $m$ are material constants. The facts relating crack growth to load and previous load are under continuing investigation. However, any model of fatigue damage must be adaptable to new findings.

Fatigue failure can be defined by when the material fractures, or by when the crack reaches a certain fixed length that would be noticeable by inspection. Little is known about the actual progression to fracture, except that it occurs rapidly when the crack reaches a certain length. Fractures could be due to high stresses produced by the stress-riser effect of the crack, in which case the depth of the crack would be important, as well as the surrounding geometry of the material. A fracture may occur when crack growth reaches a critical point and progresses very rapidly.

It is reasonble to divide the progress of fatigue failure into three stages: 1) crack initiation, 2) crack propagation, and 3) final fracture. Different mechanisms are, apparently involved at each stage. Under normal circumstances, the second stage accounts for the major portion of the number of cycles-to-failure.

## 6.10 Mathematical Model of Fatigue Failure in a Single Element

A model of fatigue, in a single element where one crack dominates, will be developed here.

We propose that, due to the lack of experimental evidence on fatigue damage during stages 1 and 3, for the present, the times spent in stages 1 and 3 be considered random variables, $T_1$ and $T_3$, with small variance and a mean of 5 percent of the time spent in stage 2. Since most of the time is spent in stage 2, and some facts of crack growth are known for stage 2, a model of $T_2$, the time spent in this stage, that accounts for load dependence should be developed. We will deal, therefore, entirely with stage 2 and will refer to $T_2$ as $T$ and the number of cycles-to-failure as the number of cycles in stage 2. A mathematical model which appears to describe the events in stage 2 is provided by the theory of the general point process, as presented earlier.

Let the vector

$$\xi_i = \begin{vmatrix} t_i \\ X_i \end{vmatrix}$$

represent, for the $i^{th}$ load cycle, which is defined as the period during which the load is increasing, the duration of the load cycle $t_i$ and the growth of the dominant crack, hereafter referred to as the crack, $X_i$, in the cycle. We assume that failure occurs when the crack length reaches a constant value C. It may be convenient, at a later stage in the analysis, to let C be a random variable; however, at this stage in the development it is more important to concentrate on the actual crack growth and not on the mechanism of final failure. In modeling the crack length, it is necessary to consider the mathematical consequences of being realistic and expressing crack length as a continuous function of time, or a step function of time. By writing, for crack length

$$S(t) = S_{[nt]} + (nt - [nt])\, X_{[nt]+1}$$

where [nt] denotes the largest integer contained in nt,

we obtain crack length as a piecewise linear function of time, and failure will occur when $S(t) = C$ or, equivalently, $S(t) \geq C$ for the first time. This approach may well simplify the mathematics, but it involves further investigation into stochastic processes. By writing, for crack length, the equation

$$S_n = \sum_{i=1}^{n} X_i$$

we obtain a step function model of crack growth. The crack extends by an amount $X_i$ at the end of the $i^{th}$ cycle and remains that long until the end of the $(i+1)^{th}$ cycle. This is clearly not realistic, but has the mathematical advantage of being in the context of renewal theory, which is a well developed area of mathematics. In this model, failure occurs when $S_n \geq C$ for the first time, and this event may not be equivalent to $S_n = C$ as $S_n$ may jump over the value $C$ without actually equaling $C$. We will consider, initially, the potentially more fruitful area of renewal theory with fixed time and define the following

$$S_n = \sum_{i=1}^{n} X_i$$

$$N = \inf\{n : S_n \geq C\}$$

$$\underline{N} = \sup \{n : S_n < C\}$$

$$\psi = \sum_{i=1}^{N} X_i$$

and

$$T = \sum_{i=1}^{N} t_i$$

where each $X_i$ is nonnegative if we assume that the crack cannot weld, N is the number of the first cycle just after failure, $\underline{N}$ is the number of the last cycle just before failure, $\psi$ is the total crack length at failure and may be slightly above C, since failure occurs when $S_n \geq C$, and T is the total time to failure. We will obtain various models by making assumptions on the crack growths $X_i$. If models of S-N curves are desired for a particular stress or load to crack growth. Salt [176] has achieved successful fits of S-N curves, assuming an initial defect under deterministic loads, by using such methods. Several results of such assumptions will be presented below. If a model is desired that gives the number of cycles-to-failure based on individual S-N curves, such as a Miner's rule type of formula, then it is necessary only to assume independence of the $X_i$, as shown below. Models that account for load history, but that rely on individual S-N curves, can be developed by assuming a Markov-type dependence among the $X_i$. Models of complex structures that account for ground and maneuver forces, as well as failure due to multiple cracks with load dependence, can also be formulated.

### 6.10.1 Some General Renewal Theory Results Applicable to the Model

In this section we survey some facts from renewal theory that are of use in the proposed models. The time to failure $N$ (in cycles) is a stopping time, since it depends only on the events up to the $N^{th}$ step and not on any future events. This is shown by describing the event

$$(N = n) = (X_1 + X_2 + \cdots + X_{n-1} < C \text{ and } X_1 + \cdots + X_n \geq C).$$

We also know that $\underline{N}+1$ is a stopping time by writing out the event $(\underline{N}+1 = n) = (N = n)$ and we also identify $\underline{N}+1 \equiv N$. With a stopping time we can apply Wald's Theorem of Sequential Analysis if we have independently and identically distributed random variables $X_i$.

WALD'S THEOREM: *If* $X_i$ *are independently and identically distributed with finite mean and* $N$ *is a stopping time with finite mean, then*

$$E(S_N) = EN \cdot EX .$$

The generating function, $G(z)$, of $S_N$ is $H(P(z))$ when $P(z) = E(z^X)$ and $H(w) = =(w^N)$. $E\,S_N = G'(1) = H'(1) \cdot P'(1)$.

We expect that, since $S_N$ is very nearly $C$, that $E(S_N) \approx C$ and as a result $E\,N = C/E\,X$, which, as we will see below, is equivalent to Miner's rule. However, due to the step function nature of our definition of crack length, we cannot identically get equality. Before discussing how close we can get to equality, we need to state some other known results on the probability distribution of $N$ and its expected value and asymptotic distribution.

$$P(N = n) = F_{n+1}(C) - F_n(C)$$

where $F_n(C) = P(S_n < C)$ and is the $n^{th}$ convolution of $F$, the cumulative distribution function (c.d.f.) of $X$, with itself. We also have

$$E\,N = \sum_{n=1}^{\infty} P(N \geq n) = \sum_{n=1}^{\infty} F_n(C) .$$

THEOREM 12: <u>If</u> $X_1$ <u>has distribution</u>

$$F_1(t) = \frac{\int_0^t R(x)dx}{\mu}$$

and $X_2, X_3, \ldots,$ are independently and identically distributed with mean $\mu$, and reliability $R(x)$, then

$$E(N) = \frac{C}{\mu} .$$

Since $V(t) = E\,N_t$, when $N_t = \inf\{n : S_n \geq t\}$ satisfies the renewal equation $V = F_1 + F * V$ (with $*$ denoting convolution) for $V(t) = t/\mu$, we must have

$$F_1(t) = \frac{1}{\mu} \int_0^t R(x)dx .$$

## 6.11 Models Based on Assumed Forms of Load vs. Crack Growth

Let $F_i$ be the maximum load applied during cycle i. Assume, in the first model, that the crack growth is proportional to $F_i$,

$$X_i = \alpha_{F_i} F_i$$

where the proportionality constant $\alpha_F$ may depend on the load F. The function may be found by loading at F until failure. At failure $S_N = C$, and in this simple model

$$S_N = \sum_{i=1}^{N} \alpha_F F_i = C$$

or

$$\alpha_F = \frac{C}{N_F F}$$

where $N_F$ is the number of cycles-to-failure at load F.

If a load is composed of $n_1$ applications of $F_1$, $n_2$ applications of $F_2$, and $n_j$ applications of $F_j$ for $1 \leq j \leq J$, in any order, then failure occurs when $S_N = C$ or

$$\sum_{j=1}^{N} \left( \frac{n_i}{N_F} \right) = 1$$

where the $\alpha_F$ is determined by individual load tests. This, of course, is a nonstochastic derivation of Miner's rule.

### 6.11.1 Model Based on Binary Crack Growth

Assume that on each load application the crack grows a fixed amount $\delta_F$, with probability p, or it does not grow, with probability 1 - p. The growth $\delta_F$ may depend on the load F. Hence

$$X_i = \begin{cases} \delta_F & \text{with probability} \quad p \\ 0 & \text{with probability} \quad 1-p \end{cases} .$$

To correct a model proposed by Chavez, assume that $\delta_F = \delta$ for all loads.

Assume that the critical crack length is an integral multiple of $\delta$, so that $C = m\delta$ and

$$N = \inf \left\{ n : \sum_{i=1}^{n} X_i = c \right\}$$

giving the negative binomial distribution for $N$

$$P(N = n) = \binom{n-1}{m-1} p^m q^{n-m}$$

where $q = 1-p$. Also,

$$E\,N = \frac{m}{p} \quad \text{and} \quad \text{Var}\,N = \frac{mp}{q^2} .$$

By performing several tests under controlled conditions, the unknown parameters $m$ and $p$ can be estimated from the measured $\bar{N}_F$ at each load $F$. We assume that at each load level, $m_F$ and $p_F$ can be determined performing proper statistical tests. Also assume that load $F_i$ is applied $n_i$ times for $1 \leq i \leq J$. Further assume that the loads are grouped and that the groups are repeated. The number of times the group is applied is denoted by $M$ and we assume failure occurs only at the end of a group of loadings, so that failure occurs when

$$S_N = M(n_1\delta_1 + n_2\delta_2 + \cdots + n_J\delta_J) \quad .$$

Denote by $X_i^j$ the crack growth at cycle $i$ in group $j$. For any group

$$X_i^j = \begin{cases} \delta_i & \text{with probability} \quad p_i \\ 0 & \text{with probability} \quad q_i = 1 - p_i \end{cases} \quad .$$

In one group we have

$$n_1X_1^j + n_2X_2^j + \qquad + n_JX_J^j$$

and

$$M = n_1 + n_2 + \cdots + n_J \quad .$$

Let

$$\xi_j = n_1X_1^j + \qquad + n_JX_J^j$$

and assume that the $\xi_j$ are independent, identically distributed random variables. The number of groups to failure is K, where

$$K = \inf\left\{ K : \sum_{j=1}^{K} \xi_j \equiv C \right\}.$$

By Wald's identity

$$E\,K = \frac{C}{E\,\xi_1}$$

and

$$E\,\xi_1 = n_1\delta_1 p_1 + \cdots + n_J\delta_J p_J$$

$$= n_1 \frac{C}{\bar{N}_1} + \cdots + n_j \frac{C}{\bar{N}_J}$$

$$= C\left( \frac{n_1}{\bar{N}_1} + \cdots + \frac{n_j}{\bar{N}_J} \right).$$

Then the expected number of groups to failure is

$$E\,K = \frac{1}{\dfrac{n_1}{\bar{N}_1} + \cdots + \dfrac{n_j}{\bar{N}_J}},$$

or, stated as a Miner's Rule, failure occurs when

$$K\left( \frac{n_1}{\bar{N}_1} + \cdots + \frac{n_j}{\bar{N}_J} \right) = 1 .$$

In addition to obtaining Miner's rule in this model, one

can find the exact distribution of K.

## 6.12 A More General Model

Denote the cumulative distribution function of crack growth by $F(x)$. If the $X_i$ are independent and identically distributed, then the renewal equation gives

$$M(t) = F(t) + \int_0^t M(t-x)\, dF(x)$$

where $M(t) = E\,N_t$ and $t$ is used in place of $C$, as is typical in renewal theory. From the first section, for large $t$, we have

$$E\,N_t = \frac{t}{\mu} + \frac{\sigma^2 - \mu^2}{2\mu^2}$$

and

$$\operatorname{Var} N_t = \frac{\sigma^2 t}{\mu^3} + \left( \frac{1}{\sigma} + \frac{\sigma^4}{2\mu^4} - \frac{\mu_3}{3\mu^3} \right) .$$

If we assume that $C$ is large, relative to $E\,X_1 = \mu$, then

$$E\,N = \frac{C}{\mu} + \frac{2 - \mu^2}{2\mu^2}$$

$$= \frac{C}{\mu} + \frac{\sigma^2}{2\mu^2} - \frac{1}{2} .$$

Hence, if crack growth is a random function of load, but independent of past loads, where the average crack growth, $\mu$, does not depend on the load, then the mean growth is similar to the nondeterministic fixed load case. If we can consider the loads in groups of $J$ individual discrete loads with crack growth

$$\xi_i = n_1 X_1 = n_2 X_2 + \cdots + n_J X_J$$

then,

$$EK = \frac{C}{E\,\xi_1} + \frac{\text{Var}\ \xi_1}{2E^2\ \xi_1} - \frac{1}{2}$$

$$E\,\xi_1 = E\,n_1\,E\,X_1 + \cdots + E\,n_J\,E\,X_J$$

and

$$\text{Var}\ \xi_1 = \text{Var}\ n_1\ \text{Var}\ X_1 + \cdots + \text{Var}\ n_J\ \text{Var}\ X_J\ .$$

An experiment could be designed to estimate $C$ from fixed loads with $n_i$ fixed, and all possible $X_J$'s. For example, with two different loads which produce mean extensions $\mu_1$ and $\mu_2$, we would apply the first load $\bar{n}_1$ times and the second $\bar{n}_2$ times and measure the cycles-to-failure, $\bar{K}$. Then, we would estimate $\mu_i/C$ by ignoring the term with $\text{Var}\ \xi_1$ and apply individual loads to obtain

$$\bar{K}_1 = \frac{C}{\bar{n}_1\mu_1} - \frac{1}{2} \quad \text{and} \quad \bar{K}_2 = \frac{C}{\bar{n}_2\mu_2} - \frac{1}{2}$$

giving

$$E\,K = \frac{1}{\dfrac{1}{\bar{K}_1 + \frac{1}{2}} + \dfrac{1}{\bar{K}_2 + \frac{1}{2}}} .$$

Under random, nonidentical, but grouped loading the number of groups to failure would be estimated by

$$E\,K = \frac{1}{a\,\dfrac{\mu_1}{C} + b\,\dfrac{\mu_2}{C}} + \frac{c\sigma_1^2 + d\sigma_2^2}{2(a\mu_1 + b\mu_2)^2} - \frac{1}{2}$$

where $a = E\,n_1$, the average number of cycles of load one in a group, $B = E\,n_2$, $c = \text{Var}\ n_1$ and $d = \text{Var}\ n_2$.

Ignoring all but the first term and assuming a basic flight load is typically $\Sigma_{i=1}^{n}\ a_i X_i$ where $X_i$ is the $i^{th}$ type of load and $a_i$ is its number of cycles, one would find the average number of flight loads-to-failure to be

$$E\,K = \frac{C}{\Sigma_{i=1}^{n}\ E\,a_i\ E(X_i)} .$$

Instead of testing a metal component at a fixed load to determine the constant $C$, existing data could be used to fit data from variable flight conditions to the above equation in order to determine C.

## 6.13 A Model That Considers Dependence

Let, as before, $N = \inf \{ n : \Sigma_{i=1}^{n} X_i \geq C \}$. We have

$$E\,N = \sum_{n=1}^{\infty} P(S_n \leq C) .$$

We can rewrite E N as

$$E\,N = P(S_1 \leq C) + \sum_{n=2}^{\infty} P(S_n \leq C)$$

$$= P(S_1 \leq C) + \sum_{n=2}^{\infty} \int_0^C P(S_{n+1} + X_n \leq t \mid S_{n-1} = x) \cdot dP(S_{n-1} \leq x)$$

and

$$E\,N = P(S_1 \leq C) + \sum_{n=2}^{\infty} \int_0^C P(X_n \leq t - x \mid S_{n-1} = x)\, dP(S_{n-1} \leq x) .$$

Assuming that the distribution of crack growth, given the previous crack length,

$$P(X_n \leq y \mid S_{n-1} = x) = F_n(y,x)$$

is not a function of $n$, but depends only on $x$ and $y$, say, $F(y,x)$, we then obtain

$$E\,N = F(t,0) + \int_0^C F(C-x,x)\, d\left( \sum_{n=2}^{\infty} P(S_{n-1} \leq x) \right) .$$

Consider $E\,N$ as a function of $C$ to get

$$E\,N_C = F(C,0) + \int_0^C F(C-x,x)\, dE\,N_x \quad .$$

If the dependence is of the form

$$F(y,x) = H(x+y)$$

then

$$M(t) = H(t) + H(t)\, M(t)$$

where we have written $t$ in place of $C$ to place this in the context of renewal theory. Solving for $M(t)$ we get

$$M(t) = \frac{H(t)}{1 - H(t)} \quad .$$

In particular, if

$$H(t) = \frac{\frac{t}{\mu}}{1 + \frac{t}{\mu}}$$

then $E\,N = C/\mu$, as in the independent situation. In

general, this form, which corresponds to Miner's rule, will not occur. As an example, assume that

$$F(y,x) = 1 - e^{-\lambda y - \mu x} .$$

Then we have

$$M(t) = \frac{\lambda}{\mu}(e^{\mu t} - 1)$$

and, if $\lambda = \mu$

$$H(t) = 1 - e^{-\lambda t}$$

for

$$M(t) = \frac{1 - e^{-\lambda t}}{e^{-\lambda t}} = e^{\lambda t} - 1$$

for which $M(t) \approx \lambda t$ for small $t$; but this is in contradiction to the renewal theorem that

$$\frac{M(t)}{t} \longrightarrow \lambda \quad \text{as} \quad t \longrightarrow \infty .$$

By choosing a variety of conditional "growth" distributions $P(X_n \leq y \mid X_{n-1} = x) = F(y,x)$, the renewal equation

$$M(t) = F(t,0) + \int_0^t F(t-x,x)\, dM(x)$$

may be solved either exactly or numerically for $M(C)$, the average number of cycles-to-failure, with failure occurring when the crack length reaches $C$. As the above simple example shows, the average may behave quite differently from the $\lambda C$ form predicted by the analysis of independent loads that corresponds to Miner's rule. Yet, as discussed by McMillan and Pelloux [137], crack growth appears to depend on the previous load, not necessarily the previous crack length. A relation can be found if the equation relating load to crack growth is known.

## 6.14 Basic Conclusions and Suggestions for Future Research Based on Actual In-Flight Airframe Structure Data

Prediction of fatigue life with statistical confidence for full scale structures, such as helicopters and aircraft, is currently an unsolved problem. Even in the laboratory, with small test specimens, methods for the prediction of fatigue life and even explanations of the mechanism of fatigue failure are unknown. What is known is summarized by Murthy and Swartz in [157]. In the previous section a mathematical model which utilized available physical theories of fatigue crack growth was given. It was shown, under the hypothesis of independence of crack growth on the previous load, that the expected cycles-to-failure agreed with Miner's rule and the variance of the number of cycles-to-failure was obtained. This was accomplished without reference to the physically nonexistent quantity called "damage." It was also shown that under load dependence (and it is well verified that crack growth is dependent on previous loads) widely different equations for the average expected life could occur. A mathematical method was developed for investigating the resulting dependent renewal process; however, without further physical investigation into the effect of load dependence and into the initiation stage, a reasonable model cannot be developed.

The application of a single-element model to a complex structure represents further unsolved difficulties. The development of a theory of fatigue-life prediction which would calculate the full cumulative probability distribution, the expected life, the variance of the expected life and confidence bands for estimation purposes, and which is based entirely on the physical principle underlying damage appears to be a long way off. Research in this area must, however, continue.

There is, fortunately, another approach which has

been used in the investigation of complex systems of economics, urbanization, medicine, behavior and pattern recognition. The methods of time-series analysis, covariance analysis, and factor analysis, when used on large scale computing systems that incorporate man-machine interaction, allowing a skilled data analyst to make judgments on various displays have been successful.

The definition of time-to-failure, when applied to aircraft, will mean the time until a crack grows to a certain length. The crack length will depend considerably on the load history of the aircraft. An overall analysis, applicable to a class of aircraft, would be based on the worst case-load history and this would lead to conservative estimates for the entire class. A potentially more useful approach would be to model crack growth as an autoregressive integrated moving average process (ARIMA) based on its actual load history. This would permit individual control -- such as overhaul time -- based on the aircraft's load history. Techniques for modeling with an ARIMA process are discussed by Box and Jenkins, in Time Series Analysis, and have, for simple cases, been applied to economic studies. The process is nonstationary and, therefore, can account for the continually increasing crack length.

Let $\ell(t)$ be either the length of the dominant crack, or an index number of accumulated fatigue. Assume that $\ell(t)$ is related to past load history and current load in the following way:

$$\ell(t) = a\ell(t - \Delta t) + b_j h_j(t) + \varepsilon_t$$

where $\Delta t$ is a time interval, $h_j(t)$ is the instantaneous hostility of type $j$ during the time between $t$ and $t + \Delta t$ with $1 \leq j \leq M$ and $\varepsilon_t$ is a random variable with zero mean and constant variance, independent of $\varepsilon_t$ for $t' \neq t$.

The hostilities $h_1$, $h_2$ and $h_3$ that will be considered in the first model will be due to the take-off mission phase, maneuver-mission phase, and the landing-mission phase. Let the time interval be one unit and denote by $R_j(h)$ the probability that a hostility of type $h_j$ will exceed $h$ in one unit of time. Assume that the load peaks arrive with an exponential interarrival time $1/\lambda$ ($\lambda$ per unit of time). The hostility, then, has a compound Poisson distribution with mean $\lambda\, E\, R_j$ where $E\, R_j$ denotes the mean peak value of hostility type $j$. The product $\lambda\, E\, R_j$ is then the cumulative number of positive peaks in one unit of time. To relate this to the

C-141 data, notice that $\lambda R(h)$ is the cumulative number of positive peaks which exceed $h$ in the time period. From the C-141A data on the Take-Off Mission Phase we crudely estimate that

$$R(h) = \frac{1}{\lambda} e^{-32.73h}$$

and the gross averages give $\lambda$ as, roughly, $725/5.8 = 125.0$ peaks per hour. The incremental load factor $h$ ranges between 0 and 1 and is proportional to g-force.

Making similar estimates for $h_2$ and $h_3$, we have

$$R_2(h) = \frac{1}{\lambda_2} e^{-18.42h}, \qquad \lambda_2 \quad \text{unknown}$$

$$R_3(h) = \frac{1}{\lambda_3} e^{-1.38h}, \qquad \lambda_3 = 122.0 \text{ per hr.}$$

as shown in Figures 8 and 20 of [ ].

These estimates were made by noting that the plot of the cumulative number of positive peaks exceeding $h$ was, approximately, a straight line when plotted on log paper. One point on each graph was used to find $a$, where

$$\log_{10} \lambda R(h) = ah \quad .$$

Then

$$R(h) = \frac{1}{\lambda} e^{-2.30ah} \quad .$$

For the purpose of Model 1 this rough estimate is satisfactory. The average number of occurrences per unit time, in this case one hour, was computed by dividing the reported number of occurrences by the time period over which they were measured. These data were not given for the maneuver portion. The proper method of collecting, organizing and making statistical estimates will be discussed below.

These hostilities occur over disjoint time intervals $(0,T_1)$, $(T_1,T_2)$ and $(T_2,T_3)$ with length $\tau_1$, $\tau_2$ and $\tau_3$, respectively. These lengths are random variables with certain distribution. However, the data necessary for estimation of the intervals is not reported in the C141-A study.

If data on crack length, of some index of fatigue damage were recorded along with the hostility measurements, it would be possible to estimate $a$ and $b_j$ by multivariate analysis. Those data were not available. We will show what can occur for various constants $a$ and $b_j$.

Since data are collected at discrete instants of time, we will index the variable by $n$ instead of continuous time $t$. The model can be written as:

$$\ell_n = \begin{cases} a\ell_{n-1} + b_1 h_{1n} + \varepsilon_n & \text{for} \quad 1 \le n \le N_1 \\ a\ell_{n-1} + b_2 h_{2n} + \varepsilon_n & \text{for} \quad N_1 < n \le N_2 \\ a\ell_{n-1} + b_3 h_{3n} + \varepsilon_n & \text{for} \quad N_2 < n \end{cases}$$

where $N_1$, $N_2$ and $N_3$ are the lengths of time spent in mission phase 1, 2 and 3, respectively. The coefficients $a$, $b_1$, $b_2$ and $b_3$ are constants which are to be estimated.

Taking expected values, we have

$$E\ell_n = a\ell E_{n-1} + b_1\mu_1, \qquad n \le N_1 \;,$$

$$E\ell_n = a\ell E_{n-1} + b_2\mu_2, \qquad N_1 < n < N_2 \;,$$

$$E\ell_n = a\ell E_{n-1} + b_3\mu_3, \qquad N_2 < n \;.$$

Since $E\ell_0 = 0$, we can determine $E\ell_{N_1}$ iteratively as

$$E\ell_{N_1} = \left( \frac{1 - a^{N_1}}{1 - a} \right) b_1\mu_1 \;.$$

The proof is by induction; $E\ell_1 = b_1\mu_1$. If

$$E\,\ell_1 = \left( \sum_{j=0}^{n-1} a^j \right) b_1\mu_1$$

then

$$E\,\ell_{n+1} = \left( \sum_{j=0}^{n-1} a^j \right) b_1\mu_1 \cdot a + b\mu_1$$

$$= \left( \sum_{n=0}^{n} a^j \right) b_1\mu_1$$

which proves the statement.

Continuing to the second phase, we have

$$E\,\ell_{N_2} = a^{N_2-N_1} \left( \frac{1 - a^{N_1}}{1 - a} \right) b_1\mu_1 + \left( \frac{1 - a^{N_2-N_1}}{1 - a} \right) b_2\mu_2 \; .$$

Again, the proof is by induction:

$$E\,\ell_{N_1+1} = a \left( \frac{1 - a^{N_1}}{1 - a} \right) b_1\mu_1 + b_2\mu_2$$

which agrees with the above when $N_2 - N_1 = 1$. Assume the formula is true for $\ell_n$, $n > N_1$, then

$$E\,\ell_{n+1} = a \left( a^{n-N_1} \left( \frac{1 - a^{N_1}}{1 - a} \right) b_1\mu_1 \right.$$

$$\left. + \left( \frac{1 - a^{n-N_1}}{1 - a} \right) b_2\mu_2 \right) =$$

$$= a^{n+1-N_1}\left( \frac{1 - a^{N_1}}{1 - a} \right) b_1\mu_1 + \left( a\left( \frac{1 - a^{n-N_1}}{1 - a} \right) + 1 \right) b_2\mu_2 \ ,$$

which is the desired form.

Finally, at the end of the third phase we have

$$E\,\ell_{N_3} = a^{N_3-N_1}\left( \frac{1 - a^{N_1}}{1 - a} \right) b_1\mu_1 + a^{N_3-N_2}\left( \frac{1 - a^{N_2-N_1}}{1 - a} \right) b_2\mu_2$$

$$+ \frac{1 - a^{N_3-N_2}}{1 - a}\ b_3\mu_3 \ .$$

The proof is, again, by induction and is very similar to the previous proof.

If $L$ is the critical crack length or damage that the aircraft can sustain before failure, then the number of missions before failure is $L/E\,\ell_{N_3}$, assuming that all missions are of a similar type.

This model can be put in the form of Miner's rule when $a = 1$. Since $b_i\mu_i$ is the crack growth due to hostility $i$, $i = 1,2,3$, acting above (in application, it is not possible to let hostility $i$ act alone until failure), letting $M_i$ be the cycles-to-failure for the i-type load only, then $L$, being the total cycles-to-failure, is equal to $M_i \cdot b_i \cdot \mu_i$. For $a \to 1$ the ratio

$$\frac{1 - a^N}{1 - a} \longrightarrow N$$

and the above equation reduces to

$$L = \frac{1}{\frac{(N_3 - N_2)}{M_3} + \frac{(N_2 - N_1)}{M_2} + \frac{N_1}{M_1}} .$$

When $a < 1$, the ratio $(1 - a^N)/(1 - a)$ converges to $1/(1 - a)$, which implies that the crack stabilizes at a fixed length, contrary to physical theory. Hence, only $a > 1$ will be considered.

For a near one and for large $N$ we can write $a = 1 + \alpha$ and use the approximation $(1 + \alpha)^N = 1 + N\alpha$. The equation then becomes

$$E\,\ell_{N_3} = [1 + (N_3 - N_1)\alpha]N_1 b_1 \mu_1 + [1 + (N_3 - N_2)\alpha](N_2 - N_1)b_2\mu_2 + (N_3 - N_2)b_3\mu_3 .$$

If the hostility $\mu_i$ is applied until failure at $L$ cycles, then $b_i\mu_i = L/M_i(\alpha)$ where $M_i(\alpha)$ is a coefficient for hostility $i$ and is dependent on $\alpha$. The average number of cycles-to-failure becomes

$$N = \frac{1}{k_1 \dfrac{N_1}{M_1(\alpha)} + k_2 \dfrac{N_2 - N_1}{M_2(\alpha)} + \dfrac{N_3 - N_2}{M_3(\alpha)}}$$

where

$$k_1 = 1 + (N_3 - N_1)\alpha \quad \text{and} \quad k_2 = 1 + (N_3 - N_2)\alpha \ .$$

For example, with $N_1 = 10$, $N_2 = 1000$ and $N_3 - N_2 = 100$ with load $\mu$, $2\mu$ and $3\mu$, we have

$E\,\ell_{N_3} = 8{,}960\mu$ when the load sequence is high, medium and low.

We compute

$E\,\ell_{N_3} = 12{,}720\mu$ and

$E\,\ell_{N_3} = 4{,}960\mu$ when the load sequence is low, high, medium and high, low and medium, respectively.

The exact equation relating the coefficient $M_i(\alpha)$ to $TN_i$, the number of cycles-to-failure at hostility $i$, is

$$M_i(\alpha) = \left( a^{2TN_i} + a^{TN_i} + 1 \right)\left( \frac{a^{TN_i} - 1}{a - 1} \right)$$

$$\doteq 3\left(1 + \alpha\, TN_i\right)TN_i$$

for a near 1 where $\alpha = a - 1$.

To utilize the above model it is necessary to take simultaneous measurements on hostilities, duration of hostilities, and either crack length or an index of fatigue damage. The model, including the variable duration of hostilities is

$$\ell_n = a\ell_{n-1} + b_1 h_{1n} I_{1n} + b_2 h_{2n} I_{2n} + b_3 h_{3n} I_{3n} + \varepsilon_n ,$$

where $I_{in}$ is an indicator function which is 1 if the flight is in phase i and 0 otherwise; i.e.

$$I_{in} = \begin{cases} 1 & \text{if} \quad N_{i-1} < n \leq N_i \\ 0 & \text{otherwise} \end{cases}$$

where $N_0 = 1$.

The hostility would be a particular force component, or possibly a linear combination of forces. $h_{in}$ would be the number of peaks exceeding a certain level over the past unit of time. For purposes of characterizing the distribution of each hostility, the interarrival times between peaks exceeding the specified level should be measured, as well as the magnitude of the peak. In the initial phase of validating the model, hostilities are assumed to be pulse trains of height $h_t$, arriving with interarrival time T with $h_n$ the sume of the peaks over the unit time period. The model should be validated by using a portion of the data to estimate the coefficient and the remaining data as a test of the adequacy of the model. Once it is validated it will be possible to use the statistical description of hostilities for particular flight paths and conditions to estimate, without measurement, the amount of damage accumulated on each mission. At this time, due to the demonstrated inadequacy of Miner's rule, statistical descriptions of the hostilities cannot be applied to estimate fatigue damage or to predict fatigue life.

### 6.14.1 Summary

Through a summarization of the literature surveyed in [157] and based on the knowledge of fatigue failure uncovered in that survey, a stochastic model of fatigue failure has been proposed. Under the assumption of independence of load history and fatigue the model gives, for the mean number of cycles-to-failure, the usual Miner's rule and, in addition, the variance and in some cases the exact distribution. The model is extended to account for load history by allowing dependence on the previous crack growth. It was shown that the mean number of cycles-to-failure can depart radically from the Miner's rule in functional form. In order to model actual fatigue on single bar test specimens, additional information as to the nature of crack growth dependence on the previous load is required. To investigate statistically the applicability of the model to large-scale structures, an autoregressive integrated moving average process is proposed and the results of previous parameters have been shown. To develop the model fully and to validate the model requires that data on hostility measurements and an index of fatigue damage be simultaneously obtained. Development of this type of model would permit individual control of damage inspection, based on actual load history.

# CHAPTER 7. THE SUPERPOSITION OF ARBITRARY POINT PROCESSES

The important parameter known as the variance/time curve, which is the variance of the number of points or events that would have happened by a designated time, $t$, as a function of $t$, was investigated in Chapter 2. Also, the two-dimensional version of this parameter and the corresponding estimation problems, as extended by Warren [210], were presented in Chapter 5. In this chapter we will consider the superposition of an arbitrary number of renewal processes. This problem was primarily motivated by applications in neurophysiology (see Coleman and Gatsworth [36], Fatt and Katz [67], Greenwood and Yule [88], Moore, et. al. [145], Srinivasan and Rajamannar [199], and others). Evidently, there are other applications, as are referenced in the bibliography. This chapter, verbatim, follows the development of Cox and Smith [44] in their paper entitled "On the Superposition of Renewal Processes."

Suppose that a number of neurons send discrete pulses, independently, to a common central nerve cell. We investigate herein the relation between the statistical properties of the sequence of impulses from an individual neuron and the properties of the corresponding combined sequence of pulses at the central cell. A similar problem arose in the study by Fatt and Katz [67] of spontaneous subthreshold activity at motor nerve endings, in which it was found that at the tips of certain many-branching nerve endings, there are a large number of "active spots," each giving rise to localized electrical pulses in the muscle fiber with which they make common contact. The statistical problem here is to infer as much as possible, from observations on the sequence of pulses in the muscle fiber, about the individual "active spots." Figure 5, below, is a diagram of such pooling of outputs.

The problem can be stated, formally, as follows: Suppose there are a number of sources, at each of which, events occur from time to time and that the outputs of the sources are combined into one pooled output, as illustrated in Figure 5. The events are indicated by short vertical lines and the outputs of the sources, $S_1$, $S_2$ and $S_3$ are combined into one pooled output P. In general, the output of the $i^{th}$ source is defined by an increasing sequence, $[t_j^{(i)}]$, where $[t_j^{(i)}]$ is the time at which the $j^{th}$ event occurs at the $i^{th}$ source. By rearranging the $t_j^{(i)}$ into

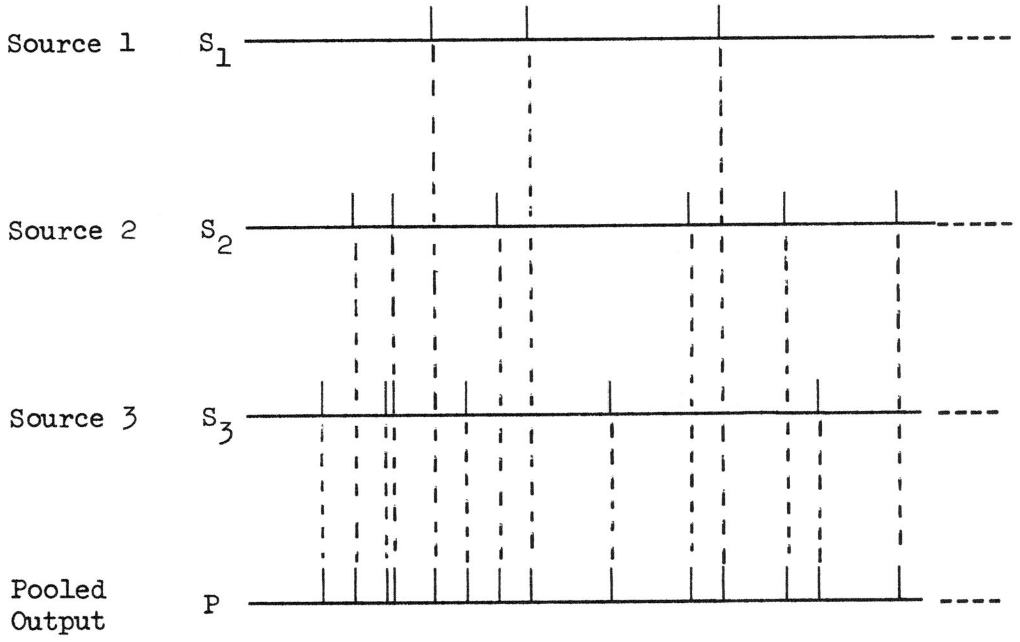


FIGURE 5

THE POOLING OF OUTPUTS

properties of the separate sequences $[t_j^{(i)}]$ in order to determine the statistical properties of the pooled output.

Cox and Smith [44] examined what happens when the individual sequences $S_i$ are strictly periodic, i.e., when $S_i$ is $[\theta_i, 2\theta_i, 3\theta_i, \ldots]$. We shall suppose that the intervals between successive events on any one source are independent random variables, all having the same distribution, and that random variables associated with the different sources are independent. Thus, the output of one source forms a renewal process of the type that has been investigated extensively by Feller [70].

In Sections 7.1 and 7.2 we will give some properties of single renewal process and in 7.3 we will develop the main properties of the pooled output. In 7.4, we investigate the limiting behavior as the number of sources becomes large, while in 7.5 we describe a numerical application to experimental data.

## 7.1 The Delay Distribution for a Single Source

Let the intervals between successive events be a sequence $[X_n]$ of independent identically distributed random variables, all with an absolutely continuous distribution function $F(x)$ and a frequency function $f(x)$. The

$n^{th}$ event occurs at time $Z_n = X_1 + \cdots + X_n$, and if $f_n(x)$ is the frequency function of $Z_n$, we have

$$(7.1.1) \qquad h(x) = \sum_{n=1}^{\infty} f_n(x)$$

which is the total density of events at $x$, irrespective of serial number.

Set a time $t$ and define the delay $Y(t)$ to be the time measured from $t$ back to the immediately preceding event. The frequency function $g(y;t)$ of $Y(t)$ will be called the delay function at $t$. Since the total density of events at $x$ is $h(x)$, and the chance that the interval between events exceeds $y$ is

$$(7.1.2) \qquad F_c(y) = 1 - F(y) ,$$

we have

$$(7.1.3) \qquad g(y;t) = h(t - y)\, F_c(y) .$$

Since we are concerned with the behavior a long time from the start of the process, we must consider

$$(7.1.4) \qquad g(y) = \lim_{t \to \infty} g(y;t) .$$

It is well known that under weak conditions (see Feller [70], Tacklind [203], Cox and Smith [44], and Smith, [195]) that

$$\lim_{x \to \infty} h(x) = \frac{1}{\mu} \quad \text{where} \quad \mu = E(X_n) , \tag{7.1.5}$$

thus, proving that the limit (Equation 7.1.4) exists and that

$$g(y) = \frac{F_c(y)}{\mu} . \tag{7.1.6}$$

We call $g(y)$ the equilibrium delay function, corresponding to the parent distribution $f(x)$. Conversely, given $g(y)$, $f(x)$ is determined by

$$f(x) = - \frac{1}{y(0)} \frac{dg(x)}{dx} . \tag{7.1.7}$$

The derivation of (7.1.6) and, hence, also of (7.1.7) depends only on the assumptions that

(i) the distribution function of the intervals between successive events is $F(x)$; and

(ii) the density of events at $t$ tends to $1/\mu$ as $t$ tends to infinity.

No use is made of the independence of successive

intervals, other than in the proof of (ii). Later, (7.1.7) will be applied when conditions (i) and (ii) can be verified, although successive intervals are not independent.

It is intuitively obvious, and can be proved, that the equilibrium frequency function of the time interval, measured forward from a fixed point to the next succeeding event is the same as that of the equilibrium delay (see Doob [52] for a discussion of the residual lifetime and the delay and forward interval, which are the same as two quantities defined by Smoluchowski in Bartlett [14].)

Moments of the delay may be expressed in terms of the moments of the parent distribution to show that the mean delay is $(\sigma^2 + \mu^2)/2\mu$, where $\mu$ and $\sigma$ are the mean and standard deviation of the parent distribution.

## 7.2 The Number of Events in Intervals of a Given Length

This section is concerned with the probability distribution and variance of the number of events falling in intervals of a given length $t$. Here, we shall deal mainly with the equilibrium behavior for intervals which are situated a long way from the origin, i.e., with the limiting behavior for intervals, $(u,u + t)$, as $u$ tends to infinity. The principal result is that, if $V(t)$ is the variance of the number of events in an interval $t$, then

$$V(t) \sim \frac{C^2 t}{\mu} \quad \text{as} \quad t \to \infty , \tag{7.2.1}$$

where $C$ is the coefficient of variation for the parent distribution. Further terms in the expansion of $V(t)$ will be obtained. Feller [70] proved the above equation in his well-known paper on recurrent events. The main differences between the work described herein and that of Feller's is that Feller considered discrete, not continuous time, and our problem is simpler, since it is concerned with equilibrium behavior.

A heuristic proof of (7.2.1) follows easily from two equations in sequential analysis (see Wolfowitz [216]). If $Z_n = X_1 + \cdots + X_n$ is the cumulative sum when sampling stops, after $n$ events, we have

$$E(Z_n) = E(n)\mu \quad \text{and} \quad E(Z_n - n\mu)^2 = E(n)\sigma^2 . \tag{7.2.2}$$

$Z_n$ is the time up to the $n^{th}$ renewal. If sampling is stopped after a long time $t$, $Z_n \simeq t$, where $n$ is the number of events occurring in $t$, and hence

$$E(n) \simeq \frac{t}{\mu} \quad \text{and} \quad E(t - n\mu)^2 \simeq \frac{\sigma^2 t}{\mu} ,$$

i.e.

$$\text{(7.2.3)} \qquad \text{Var } (n) \simeq \frac{C^2 t}{\mu} .$$

A similar argument from Wald's fundamental identity of sequential analysis is given by Bartlett [15].

A different approach is needed to obtain more precise results. Let $p_k^u(t)$ be the probability that $k$ events occur in the interval, $(u,u + t)$, so that, in particular, $p_k^0(t)$ is the probability of $k$ events in $(0,t)$. Then

$$\text{(7.2.4)} \qquad p_k^u(t) = \int_0^t g(y;u)\, p_k^0(t - y)dy .$$

By (7.1.3) and (7.1.5), $g(y;u)$ is, for sufficiently large $u$, bounded in $0 \leq y \leq t$; also, $0 \leq p_{k-1}^0(t) \leq 1$. Therefore, the theorem of bounded convergence gives

$$\lim_{u \to \infty} \int_0^t g(y;u)\, p_{k-1}^0(t - y)dy$$

$$= \int_0^t g(y)\, p_{k-1}^0(t - y)dy ,$$

thus, proving the existence of a limit for $p_k^u(t)$ as

$u \to \infty$. We write

$$p_k^e(t) = \lim_{u \to \infty} p_k^u(t) \quad , \tag{7.2.5}$$

and call $p_k^e(t)$ the equilibrium distribution of events. By (7.1.6) and (7.2.5)

$$p_k^e(t) = \frac{1}{\mu} \int_0^t \{p_{k-1}^0(\eta) - F(t-\eta)\, p_{k-1}^0(\eta)\} d\eta \quad .$$

But

$$\int_0^t p_k^0(\eta) d\eta = \int_0^t d\eta \int_0^\eta f(\eta - \xi)\, p_{k-1}^0(\xi) d\xi$$

$$= \int_0^t F(t - \eta)\, p_{k-1}^0(\eta) d\eta \quad ,$$

so that

$$p_k^e(t) = \frac{1}{\mu} \int_0^t \{p_{k-1}^0(\eta) - p_k^0(\eta)\} d\eta \quad . \tag{7.2.6}$$

If we define the moment-generating functions by

$$\begin{cases} M^0(\Theta,t) = \sum_{k=0}^{\infty} d^{k\Theta}\, p_k^0(t) \\ M^e(\Theta,t) = \sum_{k=0}^{\infty} e^{k\Theta}\, p_k^e(t) \end{cases} \tag{7.2.7}$$

then (7.2.6) leads to

$$(7.2.8)\quad M^e(\theta,t) = 1 - \frac{(1-e^{\theta})}{\mu}\int_0^t M^0(\theta,\eta)d\eta \quad .$$

Let $m_1^u(t), m_2^u(t), \ldots,$ be the moments about zero of the distribution $p_k^u(t)$, where $u = 0, e.$ From (7.2.8) we deduce that when the appropriate quantities exist

$$(7.2.9)\qquad m_1^e(t) = \frac{t}{\mu} \quad ,$$

$$(7.2.10)\qquad m_2^e(t) = \frac{t}{\mu} + \frac{2}{\mu}\int_0^t m_1^0(\eta)d\eta \quad .$$

If $v^e(t)$ is the equilibrium variance, then (7.2.9) and (7.2.10) give

$$(7.2.11)\qquad v^e(t) = \frac{1}{\mu}\int_0^t \psi(\eta)d\eta \quad ,$$

where

$$(7.2.12)\qquad \psi(t) = 1 + 2m_1^0(t) - \frac{2t}{\mu} \quad .$$

We denote the Laplace transform of a function by the corresponding bold symbol, ~, for example

$$(7.2.13)\qquad \boldsymbol{\psi}(s) = \int_0^\infty e^{-st}\,\psi(t)dt \quad .$$

Then is may be shown from (7.2.12) that

$$(7.2.14) \qquad \bar{\psi}(s) = \frac{1}{s} + \frac{2\bar{f}(s)}{s[1 - \bar{f}(s)]} - \frac{2}{\mu s^2} .$$

Let $\mu, \mu_2, \ldots,$ be the moments about zero of $f(x)$ and let $C$ be the coefficient of variation, $C^2 = (\mu_2 - \mu^2)/\mu^2$. Then, expansion of (7.2.14), as $s$ tends to zero, gives

$$(7.2.15) \qquad \bar{\psi}(s) \sim \frac{C^2}{s} + \frac{3\mu_2^2 - 2\mu\mu_3}{6\mu^3} .$$

This suggests that, as $t \to \infty$

$$(7.2.16) \qquad V^e(t) = \frac{1}{\mu} \int_0^t \psi(\eta) d\eta$$

$$\sim \frac{C^2 t}{\mu} + \frac{3\mu_2^2 - 2\mu\mu_3}{6\mu^4} ,$$

a rigorous proof of the above equation may be derived, under general conditions, from results in renewal theory; see, for example, Owen [160] and Smith [195]. A similar formula has been shown by Feller [70].

Equation (7.2.16) shows the behavior of $V^e(t)$ for large $t$. We also require the behavior for small $t$, which may be obtained as follows. By (7.2.11) we have

$$(7.2.17) \qquad V^e(t) = \frac{t}{\mu} + 2 \int_0^t \left\{ m_1^0(\eta) - \frac{\eta}{\mu} \right\} d\eta ,$$

and it is easy to show from this that, if as $t$ tends to

zero

$$(7.2.18) \qquad \int_0^t f(x)dx = O(t^{\beta}), \qquad \beta > 0 ,$$

then

$$(7.2.19) \qquad V^e(t) = \frac{t}{\mu} + O(t) .$$

Thus, near $t = 0$, the variance/time curve behaves like that of a completely random series.

If $f(x)$ is given explicitly, it may be possible to obtain more precise results than that of (7.2.16) and (7.2.19). For example, if $f(x)$ is of the $\chi^2$ type, with $2\nu$ degrees of freedom, then $C^2 = 1/\nu$ and (7.2.16) becomes

$$(7.2.20) \qquad V^e(t) \sim \frac{t}{\nu\mu} + \frac{1}{6}\left(1 - \frac{1}{\nu^2}\right) \text{ as } t \to \infty .$$

We may, of course, find $V^e(t)$ exactly, although the calculation is tedious for large $\nu$. As an example, if $f(x)$ is of the $\chi^2$ type, with 6 degrees of freedom and mean 3,

$$\underset{\sim}{f}(s) = \frac{1}{(1 + s)^3}$$

and (7.2.13) and (7.2.14) lead to

$$(7.2.21) \qquad V^e(t) = \frac{t}{9} + \frac{4}{27}\left( 1 - e^{-\frac{3}{2}t} \cos \frac{\sqrt{3}t}{2} \right) .$$

This may be compared with

$$(7.2.22) \qquad V^e(t) \sim \frac{t}{9} + \frac{4}{27}$$

which is obtained from (7.2.20).

## 7.3 The Pooling of Outputs

Suppose that, the outputs of $N$ sources are pooled in the manner described in the introduction to this chapter. We shall assume that the outputs of the individual sources are of the type considered in Sections 7.1 and 7.2, that different sources are independent, and finally, for convenience, that all the sources have the same parent distribution $F(x)$. We shall consider, throughout, the equilibrium behavior a long time after the start of the process.

Our first step is to calculate the frequency distribution of the interval between successive events in the pooled output. For each source we define the delay random variables, $Y_i$, where $Y_i$ is the time from a fixed epoch back to the immediately preceding event on the $i^{th}$ source. If $Y$ is the corresponding random variable for the pooled output, then

$$Y = \min(Y_1, \ldots, Y_N) ,$$

so that, since the N sources are independent

$$(7.3.1) \qquad P(Y \geq y) = \left[ \int_y^\infty g(x)dx \right]^N$$

$$= \left[ \int_y^\infty \frac{F_c(x)}{\mu} dx \right]^N .$$

Therefore, the delay function for the pooled output is, on differentiating

$$\frac{N F_c(y)}{\mu} \left[ \int_y^\infty \frac{F_c(x)}{\mu} dx \right]^{N-1} .$$

It follows from Equation (7.1.7) that the frequency function of the interval between successive events on the pooled output is

$$(7.3.2) \qquad f_p(y) = -\frac{d}{dy} \left\{ F_c(y) \left[ \int_y^\infty \frac{F_c(x)}{\mu} dx \right]^{N-1} \right\} .$$

For example, if $f(y) = e^{-y}$, then (7.3.2) gives

$$f_p(y) = N e^{-Ny} ,$$

expressing the obvious fact that, if the separate outputs are completely random, so is the pooled output. As another example, suppose that the parent distributions are rectangular over (0,1). Then (7.3.2) gives

$$f_p(y) = (2N - 1)(1 - y)^{2N-2} ,$$

and, as $N \to \infty$,

$$f_p(y) \sim 2N\, e^{-2Ny} . \qquad (7.3.3)$$

In Section 4 it will be shown that the limiting form is exponential, in general.

The equilibrium distribution for the number of events falling in an interval of length $t$ may be found by convoluting the distributions for the individual sources, so that in particular, the moment-generating function is

$$[M^e(\theta,t)]^N , \qquad (7.3.4)$$

and the equilibrium variance of the number of events in an interval is

$$V_p(t) = N\, V^e(t) . \qquad (7.3.5)$$

Thus,

$$(7.3.6) \qquad V_p(t) \sim \frac{NC^2 t}{\mu} = C^2 t\lambda \quad \text{as} \quad t \to \infty \ ,$$

where $\lambda^{-1} = \mu/N$ is the mean interval between events on the pooled output. Also,

$$(7.3.7) \qquad V_p(t) \sim t\lambda \quad \text{as} \quad t \to 0 \ ,$$

and the intercept of the asymptote is, if $f(x)$ is of the $\chi^2$ form,

$$\frac{N}{6}(1 - C^4) \ .$$

Thus, if we are given the $V_p(t)$ curve for a pooled output of the type we are considering, $C$ may be estimated by

$$(7.3.8) \qquad \hat{C}^2 = \text{Slope of asymptote} \times \text{Mean interval between events.}$$

To estimate $N$, some further assumption is required about the parent distribution $f(x)$. For example, if an estimate is calculated from the intercept of the asymptote, the third moment of $f(x)$ must be known. The simplest procedure is to assume that $f(x)$ is of the $\chi^2$ type, when

$$(7.3.9) \qquad \hat{N} = \frac{6 \times \text{Intercept of asymptote}}{1 - \hat{C}^4}$$

is a suitable estimate. If $C$ is appreciably less than one, the estimate is insensitive to changes in the form of $f(x)$.

## 7.4 Large Number of Sources

We now consider, briefly, the form of the pooled output when the number of sources is large. We assume the weak condition (7.2.18) on the parent distribution, namely, that there exists $\beta$, $0 < \beta < 1$, such that for small $t$

$$(7.4.1) \qquad \int_0^t f(x)dx = O(t^\beta) .$$

It follows that

$$(7.4.2) \qquad M^0(\theta,t) = 1 + O(t^\beta) ,$$

so that, by (7.2.8) we obtain

$$(7.4.3) \qquad M^e(\theta,t) = 1 - \frac{(1 - e^\theta)}{\mu} \{t + O(t^{1+\beta})\} .$$

We express $t$ as a multiple of the mean interval on the pooled output by putting

$$t = \frac{\tau\mu}{N} .$$

Then we have, for the moment-generating function of the

pooled output, using (7.3.4)

$$(7.4.4) \qquad \left\{ M^e \left( \theta , \frac{\mu\tau}{N} \right) \right\}^N$$

$$= \left\{ 1 - (1 - e^{\theta}) \left[ \frac{\tau}{N} + 0 \quad \frac{\tau^{1+\beta}}{N^{1+\beta}} \right] \right\}^N$$

$$\sim \; e^{-\tau(1-e^{\theta})} \quad .$$

Therefore, the number of events falling in an interval of length, $\mu\tau/N$, tends to be distributed in a Poisson distribution as $N$ tends to infinity. In particular, the interval between successive events tends to be distributed in an exponential distribution, as can also be proved directly from (7.3.2). It does not follow from (7.4.4) that pairs of intervals tend to be independent, although this is, in fact, true. We omit the proof.

Thus, for large $N$, the pooled output is " locally random" in the sense that it has the properties of a completely random series, provided that we consider the behavior over intervals $t$, small, compared with the individual mean recurrence times $\mu$. This result may be expected to hold for a large number of independent sources, irrespective of the precise nature of the output of the single sources. A further particular case has been considered by

Cox and Smith [44]. The local approach to complete randomness is of general interest, because there are numerous practical applications of stochastic processes in which complete randomness is customarily assumed, in situations where a pooled output is being considered. For instance, the sequence of calls at a telephone exchange is the pooled output of the calls originating from individual subscribers. Hence, the overall sequence may be expected to be locally random.

## 7.5 Application

We will now consider the practical application of our results. Fatt and Katz, in [67], obtained a sequence of over 800 pulses, being the "pooled output" of a number of active spots. They showed that the distribution of intervals, between successive pulses, was fitted satisfactorily by the exponential curve, to be expected for a completely random sequence, although they were careful to point out that the exponential curve was consistent with strictly periodic individual outputs.

We consider three possible structures for the sequence:

(i) the individual sources, and hence, also the pooled output, are completely random;

(ii) the sequence is the pooled output of $N$ strictly periodic sources; or

(iii) the sequence is the pooled output of $N$ independent sources of the type considered in this chapter.

It is necessary to determine which possibility holds, in case (ii) to estimate the number, $N$, of active spots, and in case (iii) to estimate both $N$ and the coefficient of variation, $C$, of intervals on one source.

To do this, we use the variance/time curve, $V(t)$. If the sequence is completely random, then

$$V(t) = t\lambda \quad , \tag{7.5.1}$$

where $\lambda^{-1}$ is the mean interval between successive events in the pooled output. In case (ii), $V(t)$ has been shown by Cox and Smith [44] to oscillate for large $t$, about an average of $\frac{1}{6}N$. In case (iii) we have shown by (7.3.6) that

$$V(t) \sim C^2 t\lambda \quad \text{for large} \quad t \quad , \tag{7.5.2}$$

and that $C^2$ and $N$ can be estimated from the slope and

intercept of the asymptote. In all three cases

$$(7.5.3) \qquad V(t) \sim t\lambda \quad \text{for small} \quad t .$$

The estimation of $V(t)$ from experimental data has been described in a paper of Cox and Smith [44]. The experimental series is divided into sections of length $\tau$ and the number of events in each section counted. (A suitable choice for $\tau$ is approximately one-half the smallest value for which $V(t)$ is required.) From the discrete time series so formed, an estimate $\hat{V}(r\tau)$ of $V(r\tau)$ may be calculated by a process of successive addition and squaring, not described in this chapter. When the sequence is completely random, $\hat{V}(r\tau)$ is an unbiased estimate of $V(r\tau)$ and its standard error may be calculated.

For the data given by Fatt and Katz, we find the values given in Table I and illustrated in Figure 6. The mean interval between events is $\hat{\lambda}^{-1} = 0.220$ sec. The period of observation is 174 sec., so that, for example, $t = 32$ sec. is an appreciable proportion of the series available for analysis. This is why the standard error of $\hat{V}(32)$ is very large. In no case does $\hat{V}(t)$ differ from its value $\hat{\lambda}t$ for a completely random series by much more than its standard error, so that there is no evidence that the series is not completely random.

If the number of sources were large, or the coefficient of variation were near 1, our method would be insensitive. As examples, we have drawn on Figure 6, theoretical curve for

(a) 100 strictly periodic sources (approximate curve); and

(b) 100 stochastic sources with $C = 1/\sqrt{3}$, the intervals on any source being proportional to $\chi^2$ variables, with six degrees of freedom.

If the method were to be used extensively, it would be worth-while investigating the distribution of $\hat{V}(t)$ for the alternative sequences of types (ii) and (iii), hence, developing methods of determining confidence intervals for N and C.

| t (sec.) | $\hat{V}(t)$ | S.E. of $V(t)$ | $\hat{\lambda}t$ |
|---|---|---|---|
| 2 | 11.2 | 1.41 | 11.0 |
| 4 | 23.1 | 3.45 | 22.0 |
| 8 | 39.9 | 9.39 | 44.1 |
| 16 | 54.1 | 26.80 | 88.1 |
| 32 | 83.4 | 79.40 | 176.2 |
| 48 | 189.7 | 154.00 | 264.3 |

TABLE I

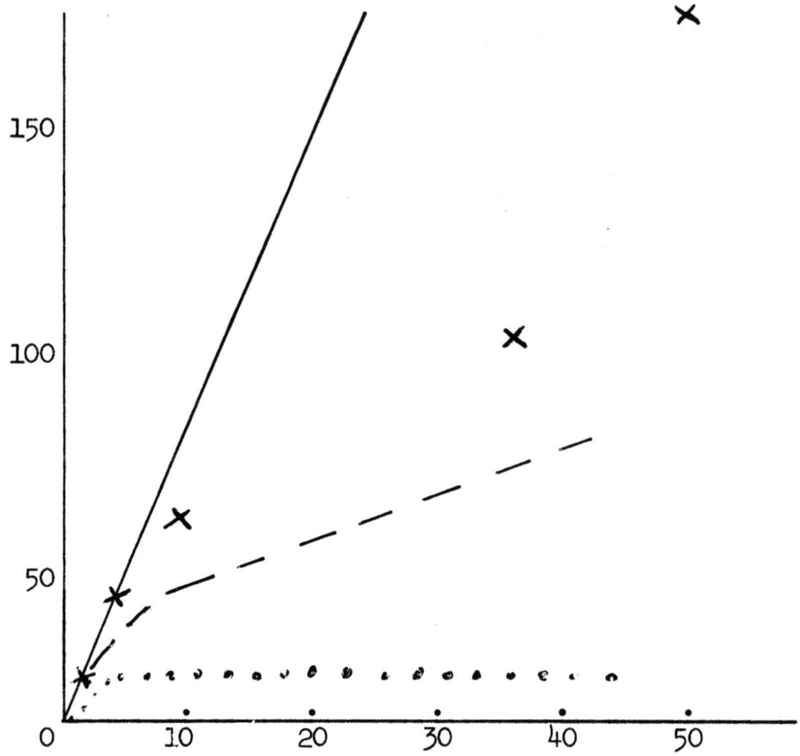


× × × × Experimental Values

———— Theoretical for completely random series

······· Theoretical for 100 strictly periodic sources

------- Theoretical for 100 stochastic sources, $C = 1/\sqrt{3}$ .

FIGURE 6

It has been empirically demonstrated by many authors that the number of arbitrary renewal processes needed to achieve the Poisson process approximately, are only about five or six. Thus, it is interesting, if not astonishing, that the superposition of as few as five arbitrary renewal processes is already a Poisson process.

# CHAPTER 8. APPLICATIONS OF THE THEORY OF THE GENERAL POINT PROCESS TO LIFE TEST DATA

## 8.1 Introduction

In this chapter we concern ourselves with the problem of obtaining the distribution of the number of failures, $N_t$, by any specified observation time $t$, when failures happen according to a given (or assumed or established) law, as characterized by the distribution function of time-to-failure. The statistic, $N_t$, being the observed number of failures by a specified time, $t$, is the so-called renewal statistic which can equivalently be defined by

$$N_t = \sup_k \{S_k \leq t\}$$

where

$$S_k = x_1 + x_2 + \cdots + x_k ,$$

with the convention that $N_t = 0$ if $x_1 > t$ and $x_1, x_2, \ldots$ are the times-to-failure of identical items assumed to be independently, identically distributed random variables with a common distribution function, say, $F(x) = P\{x \leq X\}$. The sequence of random variables (in this case nonnegative, being observed values of times-to-failure) is then called a point process [149]. If the nonnegativity condition of the variables is relaxed, then the sequence of random variables is called an extended point process. For the purpose of the problems dealt with in this chapter, we will consider only the nonnegative case. If we augment the sequence $x_1, x_2, \ldots,$ by another random variable, say $x_0$, which is not necessarily distributed the same as the $x_j$'s, $j = 1,2,\ldots,$ the sequence $x_0, x_1, x_2, \ldots,$ is called a General Point Process [149]. Feller [70] calls the augmented process a delayed point process, in that the augmenting variable $x_0$ could be in practice the residual lifetime of a piece of equipment already under test. It may be mentioned that the so-called "equilibrium point process" which one encounters in reality and is discussed at length in the following section, is a particular case of a General Point Process, where the distribution function, say $K(x)$, of the residual life is characterized in a unique way by the distribution function of the rest of the variables, $F(x)$, in accordance with the "equilibrium" criteria.

A good part of early work in the theory of reliability concerned itself with establishing several life quality parameters like the so-called reliability, which is the probability that the item survives a specified period of time, mean time before failure, hazard rate, etc., under the assumption that failures occur at random, or equivalently, the underlying law of failures is exponential. Also, in the exponential case, and only in the exponential case, can one obtain an exact sampling theory for estimates of the life quality parameters [195] and [ 65 ], as well as the exact distribution of the corresponding renewal statistic, $N_t$. However, inadequacy of the exponential assumption stems from the fact that the corresponding failure rate is constant for all times, in other words, no matter how long an item or piece of equipment has survivied, the associated failure rate remains the same. In many realistic situations this instantaneous failure rate does, in fact, depend on the time the item has survived.

Empirical studies reveal that the gamma- and log-normal distribution functions are plausible specifications for the underlying failure law and each one of the above two distributions imposes certain types of dependence for the hazard rate, as a function of time, wiich might in some situations take care of the actual dependence of hazard rate and time.

Other work in obtaining the distribution of the

number of failures by time, t, has mainly consisted of Monte Carlo techniques, or using a normal approximation. The latter assumes that

$$\frac{N_t - \frac{t}{\mu}}{\frac{\sigma\sqrt{t}}{\mu^{3/2}}}$$

is an asymptotically normal random variable with zero mean and unit variance [70]. This method, however, is only valid when the time t is very large, compared to the average time-to-failure of the item under life test. The method presented in this chapter is valid when t is small, as well as large, in comparison to the average failure time. In fact, the distribution function obtained by the method presented herein will approach the normal as $t \to \infty$.

Under each heading, viz., namely log-normal and gamma-type specifications for the underlying failure law, we derive the first four moments of the number of failures, $N_t$, by any specified time t, for both ordinary and equilibrium point processes. We then seek the appropriate Pearson-type approximation for the sampling distribution of the statistic, $N_t$. Having established the sampling distribution of $N_t$, one can actually assess or test the significance of the specification itself. Another important by-product is confidence statements on the expected number of failures for any assigned time $t$, in accordance with the underlying failure distribution.

The method offered here is perfectly general and it could be carried out to other plausible failure distributions, including even mixtures of distributions for the underlying failure law. An example is worked which completely illustrates the method offered herein.

It may not be out of place to mention here, a couple of problems which can actually arise in this connection and which remain to be explained. To test of randomness of the underlying failure phenomena, we have established in Chapter 2 the consistency and asymptotic normality of an estimate of the variance of the number of failures, $N_t$, observed in any specified time period, $t$. To substantiate Smith's claim that the test based on the variance time curve for randomness is better than all other existing tests for randomness, in the sense of power (Type II error), one needs to establish the non-null (not exponential) distribution of the statistic which presumably is also asumptotically normal.

A point process is a sequence of nonnegative,

independently, identically distributed random variables which are all nonzero with probability one. As an example, consider a light bulb put to a life test. Say it lasts $x_1$ units of time and then fails. Imagine that it is instantaneously replaced by an exactly identical bulb and let $x_2$ denote the time-to-failure of the second bulb. Imagine this process continues. Then, $x_1, x_2, \ldots, x_n, \ldots,$ are the observed values of the failure times and are i.i.d. random variables with distribution function $F(x)$, i.e., the sequence $\{x_n\}$ is a point process.

One is interested in the random variables, $N_t$, defined by the maximum suffix $k$, for which

$$S_k = x_1 + x_2 + \cdots + x_k \leq t$$

subject to the condition $N_t = 0$, if $x_1 > t$.

In particular, if the $x_i$'s denote times-to-failure of identical items, $N_t$ is clearly the number of failures by time $t$. The theory of point processes concerns itself with the study of the random variable $N_t$.

If one augments the sequence $\{x_n\}$, $n = 1,2,\ldots,$ by a random variable $x_0$, where $x_0$ is independent of the $x_i$'s, $i = 1,2,\ldots,$ but the distribution of $x_0$, say

$K(x)$, being not necessarily equal to $F(x)$, the common distribution function of the $x_i$'s, then the augmented sequence $x_0, x_1, x_2, \ldots, x_n, \ldots,$ is called a General Point Process. In practice, $x_0$ could be the residual lifetime of an item already under test.

Now consider a point process which has been in progress for a long time. Fix a point $t$ on the time axis. (It is not necessary that the event $E$, e.g., failure of the item under test, of the point process happen at the arbitrarily chosen point $t$ on the time axis.) Let us denote by $Y(t)$ the time that elapses from $t$ on to the next succeeding event of the point process. Let $K_t(x)$ denote the distribution function of $Y(t)$. What we now observe, from the instant $t$ onwards, is a General Point Process whose "residual lifetime" distribution is $K_t(x)$; the intervals between events being independently, identically distributed random variables with the same distribution function $F(x)$. Cox and Smith [44] have shown that

$$(8.1.1) \quad \lim_{t \to \infty} K_t(x) = \frac{1}{\mu_1'} \int_0^x [1 - F(y)]dy = K(x) .$$

In other words, if a point process with distribution function $F(x)$ of the intervals between successive events, has been in progress a long time since, and if observations are made starting from an arbitrary origin $t$, then what we are actually observing is a General Point Process whose "residual lifetime" distribution is given by $K(x)$ of (8.1.1). This particular General Point Process is called the "Equilibrium Process."

Now suppose $x_1, x_2, \ldots, x_n$ are the times-to-failure of $n$ items subjected to life test, and suppose these times-to-failure are independent and distributed in either a log-normal or gamma-, or any other plausible distribution, then, the following procedure can be used to estimate the distribution of the number of failures in time $t$.

Step One

Using the failure data, estimate the parameters of the underlying distribution from the following equation:

$$E(x) = \frac{1}{n} \sum_{i=1}^{n} x_i$$

or

$$E(x^2) = \frac{1}{n} \sum_{i=1}^{n} x_i^2 .$$

Step Two

Using the estimates of the parameters from step one and the time $t$, calculate $E(N_t)$, Var $(N_t)$, $\mu_3(N_t)$ and $\mu_4(N_t)$ for the applicable point process (ordinary or equilibrium):

$$E(N_t) = E(N_t) ,$$

$$\text{Var}\ (N_t) = E(N_t - E(N_t))^2 ,$$

$$\mu_3(N_t) = E(N_t - E(N_t))^3 ,$$

$$\mu_4(N_t) = E(N_t - E(N_t))^4 .$$

Step Three

Use the moments from Step Two to determine the type of Pearson curve best suited. Calculate $\beta_1, \beta_2$ and $K$ (see Section 8.5).

$$\beta_1 = \frac{\mu_3^2(N_t)}{\mu_2^3(N_t)} ,$$

$$\beta_2 = \frac{\mu_4(N_t)}{\mu_2^3(N_t)} ,$$

$$K = \frac{\beta_1(\beta_2 + 3)^2}{4[2\beta_2 - 3\beta_1 - 6](4\beta_2 - 3\beta_1)} .$$

Step Four

Calculate the constants for the Pearson curve. The curve obtained is the probability density function of the number of failures in time $t$.

## 8.2 Moments

In this section we will calculate the first four moments of the number of points $(N_t)$ for both the ordinary point process and the equilibrium point process. Using these moments, the mean, variance and third and fourth central moments will be determined for the point processes, when the underlying failure distribution is

i) log normal, and

ii) gamma.

THEOREM 13: (Smith [196]). Let $x_1, x_2, \ldots,$ be a point process. Let $F(\cdot)$ be the distribution function of $x$ and $\mu'_r = E(x^r)$ $(\leq \infty)$. Let $S_k = x_1 + x_2 + \cdots + x_k$ and $F_k(\cdot)$ be the distribution function of $S_k$. Write $\mathfrak{F}$ for the class of distribution functions $F(\cdot)$ for which $F_k(\cdot)$, for some finite $k$, has an absolutely continuous component.

*If* $F(\cdot) \in \mathfrak{F}$ *and* $\mu'_{n+p+1} < \infty$, $p \geq 0$, *then there exists constants* $\alpha_n$ *and* $\beta_n$ *such that the* $n^{th}$ *cumulant of* $N_t$ *is given by*

$$\alpha_n t + \beta_n + \frac{\lambda(t)}{(1+t)^p}$$

*where* $\lambda(t)$ *is of bounded total variation, is* $O(1)$ *as* $t \to +\infty$, *satisfies the condition*

$$\lambda(t) - \lambda(t-\delta) = O(t^{-1})$$

*as* $t \to \infty$ *for every fixed* $\delta > 0$, *and when* $p \geq 1$ *has the additional property that* $\lambda(t)/(1+t)$ *belongs to the class* $L_1$.

THEOREM 14. (Murthy [149]). *Let* $x_0, x_1, \ldots,$ *be a General Point Process. Let* $\nu'_r = E(x_0^r)$.

*If* $F(\cdot) \in \mathfrak{F}$ *and* $\mu'_{n+p+1} < \infty$, $p > 0$, *then there exists constants* $\tilde{\alpha}_n$ *and* $\tilde{\beta}_n$ *such that the* $n^{th}$ *cumulant of* $N_t$ *is given by*

$$\tilde{\alpha}_n t + \tilde{\beta}_n + \frac{\lambda(t)}{(1+t)^p}.$$

Based on Theorem 13, Smith obtained the cumulants of $N_t$ and actually tabulated the first eight. Murthy, using

Theorem 14, extended Smith's results to the case of a General Point Process and, in particular, extended Smith's table of the first eight cumulants, and as a special case also derived the first eight cumulants of an equilibrium process.

For the ordinary point process:

$$\alpha_1 = \frac{1}{\mu_1'} ,$$

$$\alpha_2 = \frac{\mu_2}{\mu_1'} ,$$

$$\alpha_3 = \frac{1}{\mu_1'} (3\mu_2^2 - \mu_3) ,$$

$$\alpha_4 = \frac{1}{\mu_1'} (\mu_4 - 10\mu_2\mu_3 + 15\mu_2^3) .$$

$$\beta_1 = \frac{1}{2} \mu_2 ,$$

$$\beta_2 = -\frac{2}{3} \mu_3 + \frac{5}{4} \mu_2^2 ,$$

$$\beta_3 = \frac{3}{4} \mu_4 - 5\mu_2\mu_3 + \frac{11}{3} \mu_2^3 ,$$

$$\beta_4 = -\frac{4}{5} \mu_5 + \frac{17}{2} \mu_2\mu_4 + \frac{16}{3} \mu_3^2 - 44\mu_2^2\mu_3 + \frac{279}{8} \mu_2^4 ,$$

where

$$\mu_r = E\left(\frac{x^r}{\mu_1'^r}\right) \quad \text{and} \quad \mu_r' = E(x^r) \quad .$$

The cumulants of the ordinary point process are:

$$\psi_i(t) = \alpha_i t + \beta \quad ,$$

$$\psi_1 = \frac{t}{\mu_1'} + \frac{1}{2}\mu_2 \quad ,$$

$$\psi_2 = \frac{\mu_2}{\mu_1'} t + \frac{5}{4}\mu_2^2 - \frac{2}{3}\mu_3 \quad ,$$

$$\psi_3 = \frac{1}{\mu_1'}(3\mu_2^2 - \mu_3)t + \frac{3}{4}\mu_4 - 5\mu_2\mu_3 + \frac{11}{3}\mu_2^3 \quad ,$$

$$\psi_4 = \frac{1}{\mu_1'}(\mu_4 - 10\mu_2\mu_3 + 15\mu_2^3)t - \frac{4}{5}\mu_5 + \frac{17}{2}\mu_2\mu_4 + \frac{16}{3}\mu_3^2 - 44\mu_2^2\mu_3 + \frac{279}{8}\mu_2^4 \, .$$

For the equilibrium point process:

$$\tilde{\alpha}_1 = \frac{1}{\mu_1'} \quad ,$$

$$\tilde{\alpha}_2 = \frac{\mu_2}{\mu_1'} \quad ,$$

$$\tilde{\alpha}_3 = \frac{1}{\mu_1'}(3\mu_2^2 - \mu_3) \quad ,$$

$$\tilde{\alpha}_4 = \frac{1}{\mu_1'}(\mu_4 - 10\mu_2\mu_3 + 15\mu_2^3) \quad .$$

$$\tilde{\beta}_1 = 1 ,$$

$$\tilde{\beta}_2 = -\frac{1}{3}\mu_3 + \frac{1}{2}\mu_2^2 + 1 ,$$

$$\tilde{\beta}_3 = \frac{1}{2}\mu_4 - 3\mu_2\mu_3 + 3\mu_2^3 + 2 ,$$

$$\tilde{\beta}_4 = -\frac{3}{5}\mu_5 + 6\mu_2\mu_4 + \frac{11}{3}\mu_3^2 - 29\mu_2^2\mu_3 + \frac{87}{4}\mu_2^4 + 6 .$$

The cumulants of the equilibrium process are:

$$\tilde{\psi}_i(t) = \tilde{\alpha}_i t + \tilde{\beta}_i ,$$

$$\tilde{\psi}_1 = \frac{t}{\mu_1'} + 1 ,$$

$$\tilde{\psi}_2 = \frac{\mu_2}{\mu_1'} + \frac{1}{2}\mu_2^2 - \frac{1}{3}\mu_3 + 1 ,$$

$$\tilde{\psi}_3 = \frac{1}{\mu_1'}(3\mu_2^2 - \mu_3)t + \frac{1}{2}\mu_4 - 3\mu_2\mu_3 + 3\mu_2^3 + 2 ,$$

$$\tilde{\psi}_4 = \frac{1}{\mu_1'}(\mu_4 - 10\mu_2\mu_3 + 15\mu_2^3)t - \frac{3}{5}\mu_5 + 6\mu_2\mu_4 + \frac{11}{3}\mu_3^2 - 29\mu_2^2\mu_3 + \frac{87}{4}\mu_2^4 + 6 .$$

From Kendall [120] the factorial moments can be expressed as functions of the cumulants.

$$\varphi_k(t) = E(N_t + 1)(N_t + 2) \cdots (N_t + k) ,$$

$$\varphi_1(t) = \psi_1(t) \quad ,$$

$$\varphi_2(t) = \psi_2(t) + \psi_1^2(t) \quad ,$$

$$\varphi_3(t) = \psi_3(t) + 3\psi_1(t)\,\psi_2(t) + \psi_1^3(t) \quad ,$$

$$\varphi_4(t) = \psi_4(t) + 4\psi_1(t)\,\psi_3(t) + 3\psi_2^2(t) + 6\psi_1^2(t)\,\psi_2(t) + \psi_1^4(t) \quad .$$

For the ordinary point process:

$$\varphi_1(t) = \frac{t}{\mu_1'} + \frac{\mu_2}{2} \quad ,$$

$$\varphi_2(t) = \frac{2\mu_2}{\mu_1'}\,t + \left(\frac{3}{2}\mu_2^2 - \frac{2}{3}\mu_3\right) + \frac{t^2}{\mu_1'^2} \quad ,$$

$$\varphi_3(t) = \left(9\mu_2^2 - 3\mu_3\right)\frac{t}{\mu_1'} + \left(\frac{3}{4}\mu_4 - 6\mu_2\mu_3 + \frac{17}{3}\mu_2^3\right) + \frac{9\mu_2}{2\mu_1'^2}\,t^2 + \frac{t^3}{\mu_1'^3} \quad ,$$

$$\varphi_4(t) = \left(4\mu_4 - 40\mu_2\mu_3 + \frac{158}{3}\mu_2^3\right)\frac{t}{\mu_1'} + \left(10\mu_2\mu_4 - \frac{4}{5}\mu_5 - 60\mu_2^2\mu_3 + \frac{20}{3}\mu_3^2 + \frac{155}{3}\mu_2^4\right) + \left(30\mu_2^2 - 8\mu_3\right)\frac{t^2}{\mu_1'^2} + \frac{8\mu_2}{\mu_1'^3}\,t^3 + \frac{t^4}{\mu_1'^4} \quad .$$

For the equilibrium point process:

$$\tilde{\varphi}_1(t) = \frac{t}{\mu_1'} + 1$$

$$\tilde{\varphi}_2(t) = (\mu_2 + 2)\frac{t}{\mu_1'} + \left(2 - \frac{1}{3}\mu_3 + \frac{1}{2}\mu_2^2\right) + \frac{t^2}{\mu_1'^2}$$

$$\tilde{\varphi}_3(t) = \left(\frac{9}{2}\mu_2^2 - 2\mu_3 + 6\right)\frac{t}{\mu_1'}$$

$$+ \left(\frac{1}{2}\mu_4 - 3\mu_2\mu_3 + 3\mu_2^3 - \mu_3 + \frac{3}{2}\mu_2^2 + 6\right)$$

$$+ \left(3\mu_2 + 3\right)\frac{t^2}{\mu_1'^2} + \frac{t^3}{\mu_1'^3}$$

$$\tilde{\varphi}_4(t) = \left(3\mu_4 - 24\mu_2\mu_3 + 30\mu_2^3 - 8\mu_3 + 18\mu_2^2 + 12\mu_2 + 24\right)\frac{t}{\mu_1'}$$

$$+ \left(-\frac{3}{5}\mu_5 + 2\mu_4 - 4\mu_3 + 4\mu_3^2 + \frac{45}{2}\mu_2^4 + 12\mu_2^3 + 6\mu_2^2\right.$$

$$\left. + 6\mu_2\mu_4 - 30\mu_2^2\mu_3 - 12\mu_2\mu_3 + 24\right)$$

$$+ \left(-6\mu_3 + 18\mu_2^2 + 12\mu_2 + 12\right)\frac{t^2}{\mu_1'^2}$$

$$+ \left(4 + 6\mu_2\right)\frac{t^3}{\mu_1'^3} + \frac{t^4}{\mu_1'^4} .$$

Finally, Smith [196] has expressed the natural moments of $N_t$ in terms of the factorial moments.

$$E(N_t) = \varphi_1(t) - 1$$

$$E(N_t^2) = \varphi_2(t) - 3\varphi_1(t) + 1$$

$$E(N_t^3) = \varphi_3(t) - 6\varphi_2(t) + 7\varphi_1(t) - 1$$

$$E(N_t^4) = \varphi_4(t) - 10\varphi_3(t) + 25\varphi_2(t) - 15\varphi_1(t) + 1$$

For the ordinary point process:

$$E(N_t) = \frac{t}{\mu_1'} + \frac{\mu_2' - 2\mu_1'^2}{2\mu_1'^2}$$

$$E(N_t^2) = \frac{2\mu_2' - 3\mu_1'^2}{\mu_1'^3}\,t + \frac{9\mu_2'^2 - 4\mu_1'\mu_3' - 9\mu_1'^2\mu_2' + 6\mu_1'^4}{6\mu_1'^4} + \frac{t^2}{\mu_1'^2}$$

$$E(N_t^3) = \left(\frac{9\mu_2' - 3\mu_1'\mu_3' - 12\mu_1'^2\mu_2' + 7\mu_1'^4}{\mu_1'^5}\right)t$$

$$+ \left(\frac{9\mu_1'^2\mu'_4 - 72\mu_1'\mu_2'\mu'_3 + 48\mu_1'^3\mu_3' + 42\mu_1'^4\mu_2' - 108\mu_1'\mu_2'^2 + 68\mu_2'^3 - 12\mu_1'^6}{12\mu_1'^6}\right)$$

$$+ \left(\frac{9\mu_2' - 12\mu_1'^2}{2\mu_1'^4}\right)t^2 + \frac{t^3}{\mu_1'^3}$$

$$E(N_t^4) = \left(\frac{12\mu_1'^2\mu_4' + 90\mu_1'^3\mu_3' + 150\mu_1'^4\mu_2' - 120\mu_1'\mu_2'\mu_3' - 270\mu_1'^2\mu_2'^2 + 158\mu_2'^3 - 45\mu_1'^6}{3\mu_1'^7}\right)t$$

$$+ \Bigg[\left(\frac{-24\mu_1'^3\mu_5' - 225\mu_1'^4\mu_4' - 500\mu_1'^5\mu_3' - 225\mu_1'^6\mu_2' + 300\mu_1'^2\mu_2'\mu_4'}{30\mu_1'^8}\right)$$

$$+ \left( \frac{1800\mu_1'^3\mu_2'\mu_3' - 1800\mu_1'\mu_2'^2\mu_3' + 200\mu_1'^2\mu_3'^2 + 1125\mu_1'^4\mu_2'^2 - 1700\mu_1'^2\mu_2'^3}{30\mu_1'^8} \right)$$

$$+ \left( \frac{1550\mu_2'^4 + 30\mu_1'^8}{30\mu_1'^8} \right) \Bigg] + \left( \frac{-8\mu_1'\mu_3' - 45\mu_1'^2\mu_2' + 30\mu_2'^2 + 25\mu_1'^4}{\mu_1'^6} \right) t^2$$

$$+ \left( \frac{8\mu_2' - 10\mu_1'^2}{\mu_1'^5} \right) t^3 + \frac{t^4}{\mu_1'^4}$$

For the equilibrium point process:

$$\tilde{E}(N_t) = \frac{t}{\mu_1'}$$

$$\tilde{E}(N_t^2) = \left( \frac{\mu_2' - \mu_1'^2}{\mu_1'^3} \right) t + \left( \frac{3\mu_2'^2 - 2\mu_1'\mu_3'}{6\mu_1'^4} \right) + \frac{t^2}{\mu_1'^2}$$

$$\tilde{E}(N_t^2) = \left( \frac{2\mu_1'^4 + 9\mu_2'^2 - 6\mu_2'\mu_1'^2 - 4\mu_3'\mu_1'}{2\mu_1'^5} \right. t$$

$$+ \left( \frac{\mu_4'\mu_1'^2 + 6\mu_1'\mu_2'\mu_3' + 6\mu_2'^3 + 2\mu_1'^3\mu_3' - 3\mu_3'^2\mu_1'^2}{2\mu_1'^6} \right)$$

$$+ \left( \frac{3\mu_2' - 3\mu_1'^2}{\mu_1'^4} \right) t^2 + \frac{t^3}{\mu_1'^3}$$

$$= \left( \frac{3\mu_4'\mu_1'^2 - 24\mu_1'\mu_2'\mu_3' + 30\mu_2'^3 + 27\mu_1'^2\mu_2'^2 + 7\mu_1'^4\mu_2' - \mu_1'^6}{\mu_1'^6} \right) t$$

$$+ \Bigg[ \left( \frac{-18\mu_5'\mu_1'^3 - 90\mu_1'^4\mu_4' - 70\mu_1'^5\mu_4' + 120\mu_1'^2\mu_3'^2 + 675\mu_2'^4 - 540\mu_1'^2\mu_2'^3}{30\mu_1'^8} \right)$$

$$+\left(\frac{105\mu_1'^4\mu_2'^2+180\mu_1'^2\mu_2'\mu_4'-900\mu_1'\mu_2'^2\mu_3'+540\mu_1'^3\mu_2'\mu_3'}{30\mu_1'^8}\right)\Bigg]$$

$$+\left(\frac{-6\mu_1'\mu_3'+18\mu_2'^2-18\mu_1'^2\mu_2'+7\mu_1'^4}{\mu_1'^6}\right)t^2$$

$$+\left(\frac{6\mu_2'-6\mu_1'^2}{\mu_1'^6}\right)t^3+\frac{t^4}{\mu_1'^4}$$

## 8.3 Point Processes with a Common Log Normal Distribution

The function

$$f(x) = \frac{1}{\sqrt{2}\,\pi\sigma x}\, e^{-\frac{1}{2\sigma^2}(\log x-\mu)^2}$$

is known as the log-normal distribution. There are two properties of the log-normal distribution which make it quite useful.

The first is that statistical problems connected with the log-normal are often easily solved by a log transformation. If $x$ is distributed log-normally, then $\log x$ is distributed normally with mean $\mu$ and variance $\sigma^2$.

The second property relates to the instantaneous

failure rate, $f(x)/(1-F(x))$, where $F(x)$ is the cumulative probability distribution and $f(x)$ is the probability density function, $F'(x)$. For the log-normal distribution, the instantaneous failure rate has a maximum.

Figure 7 shows the distribution for various cases.

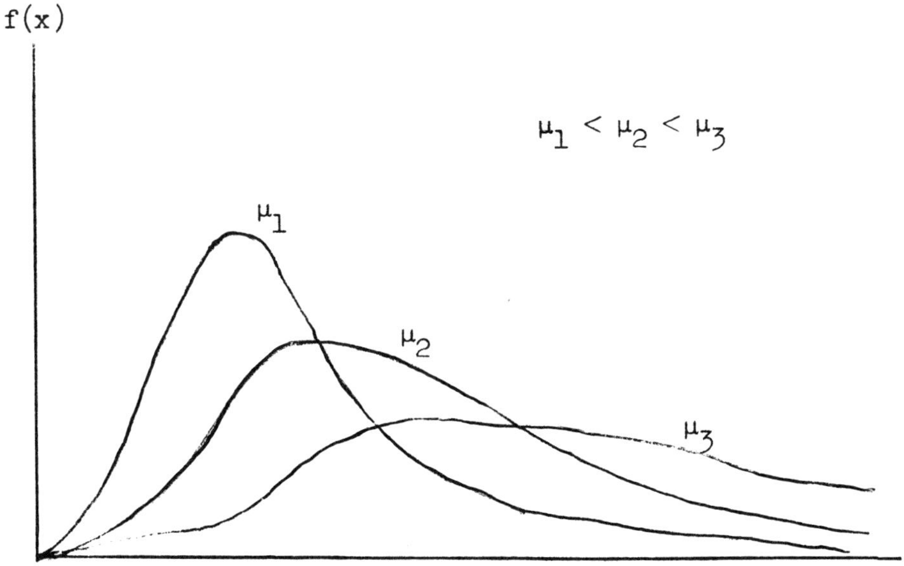


FIGURE 7

LOG-NORMAL DISTRIBUTION

The moments of the log-normal are

$$\mu_r' = E(x^r) = e^{r\mu + (r^2\sigma^2/2)}$$

and

$$\mu_r = E\left( \frac{x^r}{\mu_1'^r} \right) = e^{(r^2\sigma^2/2)-(r\sigma^2/2)} .$$

For the ordinary point process:

$$E(N_t) = e^{-\mu^2\sigma^2/2}\, t + \frac{e^{\sigma^2} - 2}{2}$$

$$E(N_t^2) = \left( 2e^{-\mu+(\sigma^2/2)} - 3e^{-\mu-(\sigma^2/2)} \right) t$$

$$+ \left( \frac{3}{2} e^{2\sigma^2} - \frac{2}{3} e^{3\sigma^2} - \frac{3}{2} e^{\sigma^2} + 1 \right) + e^{-2\mu-\sigma^2} t^2$$

$$E(N_2^3) = \left( - 3e^{3\sigma^2} + 9e^{2\sigma^2} - 12e^{\sigma^2} + 7 \right) e^{-\mu-(\sigma^2/2)}\, t$$

$$+ \left( \frac{3}{4} e^{6\sigma^2} - 6e^{4\sigma^2} + \frac{29}{3} e^{3\sigma^2} - 9e^{2\sigma^2} + \frac{7}{2} e^{\sigma^2} - 1 \right)$$

$$+ \left( \frac{9}{2} e^{\sigma^2} - 6 \right) e^{-2\mu-\sigma^2} t^2 + e^{-3\mu-(3\sigma^2/2)} t^3$$

$$E(N_t^4) = \left( 4e^{6\sigma^2} - 40e^{4\sigma^2} + \frac{248}{3} e^{3\sigma^2} - 90e^{2\sigma^2} + 50e^{\sigma^2} - 15 \right)$$

$$\cdot\, e^{-\mu-\sigma(\sigma^2/2)}\, t$$

$$+ \left( - \frac{4}{5} e^{10\sigma^2} + 10e^{7\sigma^2} - \frac{5}{6} e^{6\sigma^2} - 60e^{5\sigma^2} + \frac{335}{3} e^{4\sigma^2} \right.$$

$$\left. - \frac{220}{3} e^{3\sigma^2} + \frac{75}{2} e^{2\sigma^2} - \frac{15}{2} e^{\sigma^2} + 1 \right) +$$

$$+\left( -8e^{3\sigma^2} + 30e^{2\sigma^2} - 45e^{\sigma^2} + 25 \right) e^{-2\mu-\sigma^2} t^2$$

$$+\left( 8e^{\sigma^2} - 10 \right) e^{-3\mu-(3\sigma^2/2)} t^3 + e^{-4\mu-2\sigma^2} t^4 \quad .$$

$$E(N_t - E(N_t))^2$$
$$= \left( e^{\sigma^2} - 1 \right) e^{-\mu-(\sigma^2/2)} t + \left( \frac{5}{4} e^{2\sigma^2} - \frac{2}{3} e^{3\sigma^2} + \frac{1}{2} e^{\sigma^2} \right)$$

$$E(N_t - E(N_t))^4$$
$$= \left( - e^{3\sigma^2} + 3e^{2\sigma^2} - 3e^{\sigma^2} + 1 \right) e^{-\mu-(\sigma^2/2)} t$$

$$+ \left( \frac{3}{4} e^{6\sigma^2} - 5e^{4\sigma^2} + \frac{17}{3} e^{3\sigma^2} - \frac{15}{4} e^{2\sigma^2} + \frac{1}{2} e^{\sigma^2} \right)$$

$$E(N_t - E(N_t))^4$$
$$= \left( e^{6\sigma^2} - 14e^{4\sigma^2} + \frac{65}{2} e^{3\sigma^2} - \frac{57}{2} e^{2\sigma^2} + 10e^{\sigma^2} - 1 \right)$$

$$\cdot\, e^{-\mu-(\sigma^2/2)} t$$

$$+ \left( -\frac{4}{5} e^{10\sigma^2} + \frac{17}{2} e^{7\sigma^2} + \frac{13}{6} e^{6\sigma^2} - 49e^{5\sigma^2} \right.$$
$$\left. + \frac{3571}{48} e^{4\sigma^2} - \frac{365}{12} e^{3\sigma^2} + \frac{19}{2} e^{2\sigma^2} - \frac{1}{2} e^{\sigma^2} \right)$$

$$+ 3\left( e^{2\sigma^2} - 2e^{\sigma^2} + 1 \right) e^{-2\mu-\sigma^2} t^2 \quad .$$

For the equilibrium point process:

$$\tilde{E}(N_t) = e^{-\mu-(\sigma^2/2)}\ t$$

$$\tilde{E}(N_t^2) = \left(e^{\sigma^2} - 1\right) e^{-\mu-(\sigma^2/2)}\ t + \left(-\frac{1}{3}e^{3\sigma^2} + \frac{1}{2}e^{2\sigma^2}\right)$$

$$+\ e^{-2\mu-\sigma^2}\ t^2$$

$$\tilde{E}(N_2^3) = \left(-2e^{3\sigma^2} + \frac{9}{2}e^{2\sigma^2} - 3e^{\sigma^2} + 1\right)e^{-\mu-(\sigma^2/2)}\ t$$

$$+\left(\frac{1}{2}e^{6\sigma^2} - 3e^{4\sigma^2} + 4e^{3\sigma^2} - \frac{3}{2}\right) + 3\left(e^{\sigma^2} - 1\right)e^{-2\mu-\ \sigma^2}\ t^2$$

$$+\ e^{-3\mu-(3\sigma^2/2)}\ t^3$$

$$\tilde{E}(N_t^4) = \left(3e^{6\sigma^2} - 24e^{4\sigma^2} + 42e^{3\sigma^2} + 27e^{2\sigma^2} + 7e^{\sigma^2} - 1\right)e^{-\mu-(\sigma^2/2)}\ t$$

$$+\left(-\frac{3}{5}e^{10^{\sigma^2}} + 6e^{7\sigma^2} + e^{6\sigma^2} - 30^{5\sigma^2} + \frac{81}{2}e^{4\sigma^2} - \frac{61}{3}e^{3\sigma^2} + \frac{7}{2}e^{2\sigma^2}\right)$$

$$+\left(-6e^{3\sigma^2} + 18e^{2\sigma^3} - 18e^{\sigma^2} + 7\right)e^{-2\mu-\sigma^2}\ t^2$$

$$+\left(6e^{\sigma^2} - 6\right)e^{-3\mu-(3\sigma^2/2)}\ t^3 + e^{-4\mu-2\sigma^2}\ t^4$$

$$E(N_t - E(N_t))^2 = \left(e^{\sigma^2} - 1\right)e^{-\mu-(\sigma^2/2)}\ t + \left(-\frac{1}{3}e^{3-^2} + \frac{1}{2}e^{2\sigma^2}\right)$$

$$E(N_t - E(N_r))^3 = \left(-e^{3\sigma^2} + 3e^{2\sigma^2} - 3e^{\sigma^2} + 1\right)e^{-\mu-(\sigma^2/2)}\ t$$

$$+\left(\frac{1}{2}e^{6\sigma^2} - 3e^{4\sigma^2} + 4e^{3\sigma^2} - \frac{3}{2}e^{2\sigma^2}\right)$$

$$E(N_t - E(N_t))^4$$

$$= \left(e^{6\sigma^2} - 12e^{4\sigma^2} + 26e^{3\sigma^2} - 21e^{2\sigma^2} + 7e^{\sigma^2} - 1\right)e^{-\mu-(\sigma^2/2)}\ t\ +$$

$$+\left( -\frac{3}{5} e^{10\sigma^2} + 6e^{7\sigma^2} + e^{6\sigma^2} - 30e^{5\sigma^2} + \frac{81}{2} e^{4\sigma^2} - \frac{61}{3} e^{3\sigma^2} + \frac{7}{2} e^{2\sigma^2} \right)$$

$$+ 3\left( e^{2\sigma^2} - 2e^{\sigma^2} + 1 \right) e^{-2\mu-\sigma^2} t^2$$

## 8.4 Point Processes with a Gamma Distribution

The function

$$f(x) = \frac{1}{\alpha!\ \beta^{\alpha+1}} x^{\alpha} e^{-x/b}, \qquad x > 0$$

is called the gamma distribution. The distribution finds extensive application in the field of reliability, since many empirical distributions can be represented, at least roughly, by a suitable choice of the parameters $\alpha$ and $\beta$. Also, the relative simplicity of the distribution makes it most useful.

The distribution becomes exponential when $\alpha = 0$.

When the limit is taken as $\alpha \to \infty$ and $\beta \to \infty$, with the mean $(\alpha + 1)\beta$ fixed, the distribution is asymptotically normal about the mean.

When $\beta = 2$ and $\alpha + 1 = b/2$, where $b$ is an

integer, the distribution is known as the $\chi^2$ distribution with b degrees of freedom

The function is plotted in Figure 8 for several values of $\alpha$ with $\alpha = 1$.

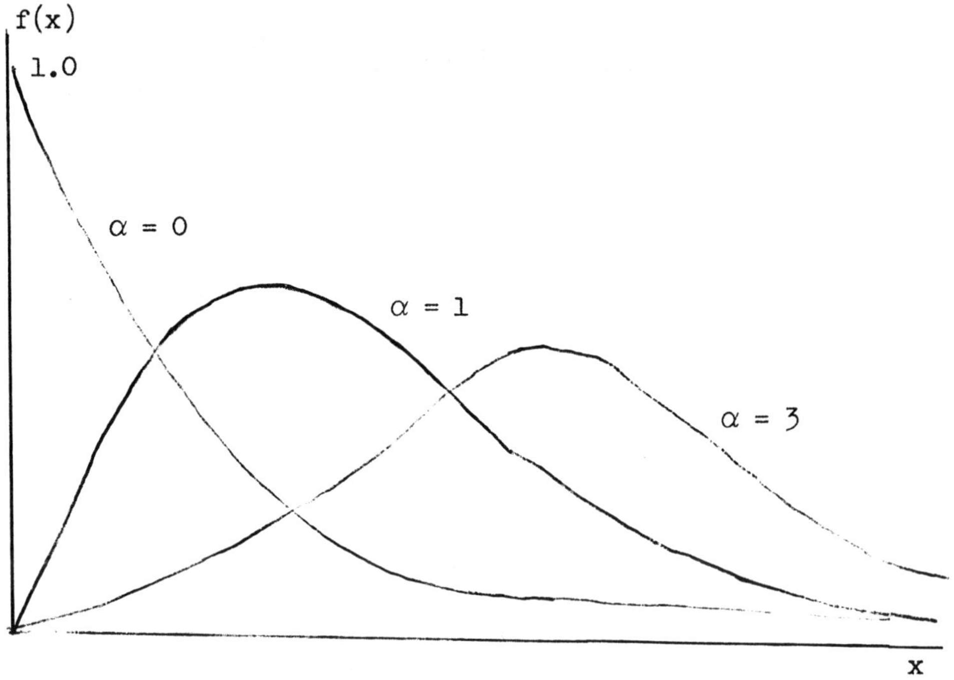


FIGURE 8

GAMMA DISTRIBUTION FUNCTION

The moments of the gamma distribution are given by:

$$\mu_r' = E(x^r) = \beta^r(\alpha+1)(\alpha+2)\cdots(\alpha+r), \quad r = 1,2,\ldots,$$

and

$$\mu_r(x) = E\left(\frac{x^r}{\mu_1'^{\,r}}\right) = \frac{(\alpha+2)\cdots(\alpha+r)}{(\alpha+1)^{r-1}}, \quad r = 2,3,\ldots,$$

For the ordinary point process:

$$E(N_t) = \frac{t}{\beta(\alpha+1)} - \frac{\alpha}{2(\alpha+1)}$$

$$E(N_t^2) = \frac{1-\alpha}{\beta(\alpha+1)}t + \frac{2\alpha^2+\alpha}{6(\alpha+1)^2} + \frac{t^2}{\beta^2(\alpha+1)^2}$$

$$E(N_2^3) = \frac{\alpha^2-\alpha+1}{\beta(\alpha+1)^3}t - \frac{25\alpha^3+135\alpha^2+264\alpha+176}{12(\alpha+1)^3}$$

$$+\left(\frac{6-3\alpha}{2\beta^2(\alpha+1)^3}\right)t^2 + \frac{t^3}{\beta^3(\alpha+1)^3}$$

$$E(N_t^4) = -\left(\frac{25\alpha^3+129\alpha^2+267\alpha+173}{3\beta(\alpha+1)^4}\right)t$$

$$+\left(\frac{531\alpha^4+3659\ ^3+9311\alpha^2+10199\alpha+4000}{30(\alpha+1)^4}\right)$$

$$+\left(\frac{2\alpha^2-5\alpha+7}{\beta^2(\alpha+1)^4}\right)t^2 + \left(\frac{6-2\alpha}{\beta^3(\alpha+1)^4}\right)t^3$$

$$+\frac{t^4}{\beta^4(\alpha+1)^4}$$

$$E(N_t - E(N_t))^2 = \frac{1}{\beta(\alpha+1)^2}t + \frac{\alpha^2+2}{12(\alpha+1)^2}$$

$$E(N_t - E(N_t))^3 = \frac{1}{\beta(\alpha+1)^3}t - \frac{22\alpha^3+132\alpha^2+264\alpha+176}{12(\alpha+1)^3}$$

$$\mathbf{E}(N_t - E(N_t))^4 = \frac{\alpha^2 + 2\alpha + 2}{2\beta(\alpha+1)^4}\, t + \frac{3}{\beta^2(\alpha + 1)^3}\, t^2$$
$$\frac{6646\alpha^4 + 47864\alpha^3 + 127856\alpha^2 + 149104\alpha + 64000}{480(\alpha + 1)^4} .$$

For the equilibrium point process:

$$\tilde{E}(N_t) = \frac{t}{\beta(\alpha + 1)}$$

$$\tilde{E}(N_t^2) = \frac{t}{\beta(\alpha + 1)^2} + \frac{\alpha^2 + 2\alpha}{6(\alpha + 1)^2} + \frac{t^2}{\beta^2(\alpha + 1)^2}$$

$$\tilde{E}(N_t^3) = \left( \frac{\alpha^2 + 2\alpha + 2}{2\beta(\alpha+1)^3} \right) t + \frac{3t^2}{\beta^2(\alpha + 1)^3} + \frac{t^3}{\beta^3(\alpha + 1)^3}$$

$$\tilde{E}(N_t^4) = \frac{t}{\beta(\alpha + 1)^2} + \frac{2\alpha^4 + 8\alpha^3 + 7\alpha^2 - 2\alpha}{30(\alpha + 1)^4}$$
$$+ \left( \frac{\alpha^2 + 2\alpha + 7}{\beta^2(\alpha+1)^3} \right) t^2 + \frac{6t^3}{\beta^3(\alpha + 1)^4} + \frac{t^4}{\beta^4(\alpha + 1)^4}$$

$$\tilde{E}(N_t - E(N_t))^2 = \left( \frac{1}{\beta(\alpha + 1)^2} \right) t + \frac{\alpha^2 + 2\alpha}{6(\alpha + 1)^2}$$

$$\tilde{E}(N_t - E(N_t))^3 = \left( \frac{1}{\beta(\alpha + 1)^3} \right) t$$

$$\tilde{E}(N_t - E(N_t))^4 = \left( \frac{1}{\beta(\alpha + 1)^2} \right) t + \frac{2\alpha^4 + 8\alpha^3 + 7\alpha^2 - 2\alpha}{30(\alpha + 1)^4}$$
$$+ \frac{3}{\beta^2(\alpha + 1)^3}\, t^2 .$$

## 8.5 Pearsonian Frequency Distributions as Possible Candidates

This section presents a summarization of the salient features of the Pearsonian frequency curves.

This family of curves originates from the differential equation

$$\frac{1}{y}\frac{dy}{dx} = \frac{x + a}{b_0 + b_1 x + b_2 x^2} \quad . \tag{8.5.1}$$

It is readily seen that Equation (8.5.1) has the basic characteristics of most frequency distributions. It starts at zero, reaches a maximum at some value of $x$, and then falls off to zero.

Writing Equation (8.5.1) in the form

$$(b_0 + b_1 x + b_2 x^2)\frac{dy}{dx} = y(x + a) \quad ,$$

and then, multiplying both sides by $x^n$ and integrating with respect to $x$, we obtain

(8.5.2)

$$x^n(b_0 + b_1 x + b_2 x^2)y$$

$$- \int |n\, b_0 x^{n-1} + (n+1)b_1 x^n + (n+2)b_2 x^{n+1}|y\, dx =$$

$$= \int y\, x^{n+1}\, dx + \int y\, ax^n\, dx \quad .$$

Since, at the ends of the curve the expression

$$x^n(b_0 + b_1 x + b_2 x^2)y$$

vanishes, (8.5.2) becomes

$$(8.5.3) \quad - n\, b_0 \mu'_{n-1} - (n + 1)b_1 \mu'_n - (n + 2)b_2 \mu'_{n+1} = \mu'_{n+1} + a\mu'_n$$

where

$$\mu'_n = \int y\, x^n\, dx \quad .$$

The constants $a, b_0, b_1$ and $b_2$ can be obtained in terms of the moments by putting $n = 0,1,2$ and $3$.

$$(8.5.4) \quad \begin{aligned} a\mu'_0 + \phantom{2b_0\mu'_0} + b_1\mu'_0 + 2b_2\mu'_1 &= - \mu'_1 \\ a\mu'_1 + b_0\mu'_0 + 2b_1\mu'_1 + 3b_2\mu'_2 &= - \mu'_2 \\ a\mu'_2 + 2b_0\mu'_1 + 3b_1\mu'_2 + 4b_2\mu'_3 &= - \mu'_3 \\ a\mu'_3 + 3b_0\mu'_2 + 4b_1\mu'_3 + 5b_2\mu'_4 &= - \mu'_4 \quad . \end{aligned}$$

If we replace the natural moments by the central moments and let $\mu'_0 = 1$, we obtain from (8.5.4), the following system of equations for the constants $a, b_0, b_1$ and $b_2$:

(8.5.5)

$$\begin{aligned} a + b_1 &= 0 \\ b_0 + 3b_2\mu_2 &= -\mu_2 \\ a\mu_2 + 3b_1\mu_2 + 4b_2\mu_3 &= -\mu_3 \\ a\mu_3 + 3b_0\mu_2 + 4b_1\mu_3 + 5b_2\mu_4 &= -\mu_4 . \end{aligned}$$

By substitution of the solution of (8.5.5) into (8.5.1) one obtains

(8.5.6)

$$\frac{1}{y}\frac{dy}{dx} = - \frac{x + \dfrac{\mu_3(\mu_4 + 3\mu_2^2)}{10\mu_2\mu_4 - 18\mu_2^3 - 12\mu_3^2}}{\dfrac{\mu_2(4\mu_2\mu_4 - 3\mu_3^2)}{10\mu_2\mu_4 - 18\mu_2^3 - 12\mu_3^2} + \dfrac{\mu_3(\mu_4 + 3\mu_3^2)}{10\mu_2\mu_4 - 18\mu_2^3 - 12\mu_3^2}x + \dfrac{2\mu_2\mu_4 - 3\mu_3^2 - 6\mu_2^3}{10\mu_2\mu_4 - 18\mu_2^3 - 12\mu_3^2}x^2}$$

The final form of (8.5.1) is obtained by letting $\beta_1 = \mu_3^2/\mu_2^3$, $\beta_2 = \mu_4/\mu_2^2$ and $\sigma = \sqrt{\mu_2}$ .

(8.5.7)

$$\frac{1}{y}\frac{dy}{dx} = -\frac{x + \dfrac{\sigma\sqrt{\beta_1}(\beta_2+3)}{2(5\beta_2 - 6\beta_1 - 9)}}{\dfrac{\sigma^2(4\beta_2 - 3\beta_1) + \sigma\sqrt{\beta_1}(\beta_2+3)x + (2\beta_2 - 3\beta_1 - 6)x^2}{2(5\beta_2 - 6\beta_1 - 9)}}.$$

Two comments should be noted at this point. One, the denominator of the right-hand side of Equation (8.5.1) could have had higher order terms in $x$. The gain, however, would be small since, in addition to the added work, the higher moments needed to calculate the additional constants are considered untrustworthy.

The second comment pertains to the integration of Equation (8.5.7). It is possible to substitute the values of the moments from the data into (8.5.7) and then integrate. This would not, however, give a graduation in the same form as that in the original data ($y$ rather than $(1/y)(dy/dx)$). It is, therefore, necessary to integrate Equation (8.5.7) first.

The integration of (8.5.7) depends on the coefficients of $x$ in the denominator. To be specific, on the nature of the roots of the denominator. Looking at the denominator in the general form of Equation (8.5.1) we have:

$$b_0 + b_1x + b_2x^2$$

$$= b_2 \left[ x - \frac{-b_1 + \sqrt{b_1^2 - 4b_0b_2}}{2b_2} \right] \left[ x - \frac{-b_1 - \sqrt{b_1^2 - 4b_0b_2}}{2b_2} \right]$$

whose roots will depend on $b_1^2/(4b_0b_2)$, or in the form of (8.5.7).

$$(8.5.8) \qquad \frac{\beta_1(\beta_2 + 3)^2}{4(2\beta_2 - 3\beta_1 - 6)(4\beta_2 - 3\beta_1)} = K \ .$$

If

$K < 0$ the curve is a Pearsonian Type I

$0 < K < 1$ the curve is a Pearsonian Type IV

$K > 1$ the curve is a Pearsonian Type VI .

These three, represent the main types of curves, though others occur at the transition points.

See Elderton [60] for a complete discussion of Pearsonian curves.

<u>Type I</u>

$$y = y_0 \left( 1 + \frac{x}{a_1} \right)^{m_1} \left( 1 - \frac{x}{a_2} \right)^{m_2} ,$$

with the origin at the mode, and where:

$$r = \frac{6(\beta_2 - \beta_1 - 1)}{6 + 3\beta_1 - 2\beta_2},$$

$$a_1 + a_2 = \frac{1}{2}\left(\text{Var }(N_t)\sqrt{\beta_1(r+2)^2 + 16(r+1)}\right)^{1/2},$$

and the m's are given by:

$$\frac{1}{2}\left\{r - 2 \pm r(r+2)\sqrt{\frac{\beta_1}{\beta_1(r+2)^2 + 16(r+1)}}\right\}$$

where

$m_1$ is the positive root when $\mu_3(N_t)$ is negative ,

$m_2$ is the positive root when $\mu_3(N_t)$ is positive .

$$y_0 = \frac{1}{a_1 + a_2} \frac{m_1^{m_1} m_2^{m_2}}{(m_1 + m_2)^{m_1 + m_2}} \frac{\Gamma(m_1 + m_2 + 2)}{\Gamma(m_1 + 1)\,\Gamma(m_2 + 1)}.$$

$$\text{Mode} = \text{Mean} - \frac{1}{2}\frac{\mu_3(N_t)}{\text{Var }(N_t)}\left(\frac{r+2}{r+1}\right),$$

and

$$\frac{m_1}{a_1} = \frac{m_2}{a_2}.$$

## Type IV

We have

$$y = y_0 \left( 1 + \frac{x^2}{a^2} \right)^{-m} e^{-\nu \tan^{-1}(x/a)}$$

$$r = \frac{6(\beta_2 - \beta_1 - 1)}{2\beta_2 - 3\beta_1 - 6}$$

$$m = \frac{1}{2}\left( r + 2 \right)$$

$$\nu = \frac{r(r - 2)\sqrt{\beta_1}}{\sqrt{16(r - 1) - \beta_1(r - 2)^2}}$$

$$a = \left( \frac{\text{Var }(N_t)}{16} \sqrt{16(r - 1) - \beta_1(r - 2)^2} \right)^{1/2}$$

and

$$y_0 = \frac{1}{a\,F(r,\nu)} \quad ,$$

The $\log F(r,\nu)$ may be found in "Tables for Statisticians and Biometricians" [ 162 ].

If $r$ is large

$$y_0 \cong \frac{1}{a} \sqrt{\frac{r}{2\pi} \frac{e^{\frac{\cos^2 \varphi}{3r} - \frac{1}{12r} - \varphi\nu}}{(\cos\,\mu)^{r+1}}}$$

where $\tan \varphi = \nu/r$.

$$\text{Mode} = \text{Mean} - \frac{1}{2}\frac{\mu_3(N_t)(r-2)}{\text{Var}\,(N_t)(r+2)}$$

$$\text{Origin} = \text{Mean} \pm \frac{\nu a}{r} .$$

Use $+$ when $\mu_3(N_t)$ is negative.

Type VI

We have

$$y = y_0(x-a)^{q_2}\, x^{-q_1} .$$

$$r = \frac{6(\beta_2 - \beta_1 - 1)}{6 + 3\beta_1 - 2\beta_2}$$

$$a = \frac{1}{2}\left( \text{Var}\,(N_t)\sqrt{\beta_1(r+2)^2 + 16(r+1)}\right)^{1/2} .$$

The $q_2$ and $-q_1$ are given by:

$$\frac{r-2}{2} \pm \frac{r(r+2)}{2}\sqrt{\frac{\beta_1}{\beta_1(r+2)^2 + 16(r+1)}} .$$

Then

$$\text{Origin} = \text{Mean} \pm \frac{a(q_1 - 1)}{q_1 - q_2 - 2} ,$$

and using + when $\mu_3(N_t)$ is positive

$$\text{Mode} = \text{Mean} - \frac{1}{2} \frac{\mu_3(N_t)}{\text{Var } (N_t)} \frac{r + 2}{r - 2} .$$

## 8.6 An Example

The Problem:

It is desired to send a space probe to the planet Mars to analyze its atmosphere. To insure receiving all of the data obtained by the probe , its transmitting equipment must function properly for a period of 300 minutes. To be specific, the Space Agency requires that the transmitting equipment have a reliability of 0.99 for 300 minutes.

A manufacturer of the required equipment has developed a new transmitter which can repair itself after a failure. Through the use of redundant circuits, the transmitter can switch to a new circuit after a failure has occurred. The manufacturer wishes to determine how many circuits are needed to achieve an 0.99 probability of 300 minutes of operation.

To determine the number of circuits, the distribution of the number of failures in 300 minutes must be calculated.

The Solution:

One hundred circuits were tested to failure. The individual times-to-failure were found to be approximately log-normal. From the data (see Table II), estimates of the log-normal distribution parameters $\mu$ and $\sigma$ were made.

We have

$$\sum_{i=1}^{100} x_i = 6,088 \quad \text{and} \quad \sum_{i=1}^{100} x_i^2 = 473,610 .$$

Then

$$\hat{\mu}_1' = e^{\hat{\mu} + \frac{\hat{\sigma}^2}{2}} = \sum_{i=1}^{100} \frac{x_i}{100} = 60.88$$

$$\hat{\mu}_2' = e^{2\hat{\mu}+2\hat{\sigma}^2} = \sum_{i=1}^{100} \frac{x_i^2}{100} = 4736.1$$

where $x_i$ = circuit time to failure, $i = 1,\ldots,100$.

TABLE II

Circuit Time to Failure (Minutes)

| | | | | | | | |
|---|---|---|---|---|---|---|---|
| 1. | 43.0 | 26. | 25.0 | 51. | 38.0 | 76. | 104.0 |
| 2. | 44.0 | 27. | 45.5 | 52. | 34.0 | 77. | 32.5 |
| 3. | 58.5 | 28. | 49.0 | 53. | 56.0 | 78. | 36.0 |
| 4. | 33.5 | 29. | 79.0 | 54. | 71.5 | 79. | 114.0 |
| 5. | 47.5 | 30. | 38.0 | 55. | 59.5 | 80. | 27.0 |
| 6. | 20.5 | 31. | 86.0 | 56. | 76.0 | 81. | 61.0 |
| 7. | 42.5 | 32. | 78.0 | 57. | 66.5 | 82. | 30.5 |
| 8. | 87.0 | 33. | 22.5 | 58. | 30.0 | 83. | 45.5 |
| 9. | 77.5 | 34. | 61.0 | 59. | 47.0 | 84. | 117.0 |
| 10. | 40.5 | 35. | 48.5 | 60. | 50.5 | 85. | 61.0 |
| 11. | 45.0 | 36. | 73.5 | 61. | 84.5 | 86. | 83.0 |
| 12. | 72.0 | 37. | 44.5 | 62. | 120.0 | 87. | 82.0 |
| 13. | 42.0 | 38. | 41.5 | 63. | 69.5 | 88. | 84.0 |
| 14. | 133.0 | 39. | 53.5 | 64. | 97.0 | 89. | 22.0 |
| 15. | 120.0 | 40. | 57.5 | 65. | 36.5 | 90. | 64.0 |
| 16. | 34.5 | 41. | 75.0 | 66. | 36.5 | 91. | 109.0 |
| 17. | 137.0 | 42. | 46.5 | 67. | 31.5 | 92. | 51.0 |
| 18. | 95.0 | 43. | 59.0 | 68. | 54.5 | 93. | 114.0 |
| 19. | 35.0 | 44. | 31.0 | 69. | 46.0 | 94. | 32.5 |
| 20. | 20.5 | 45. | 89.0 | 70. | 39.0 | 95. | 48.5 |
| 21. | 97.5 | 46. | 68.0 | 71. | 38.0 | 96. | 40.5 |
| 22. | 61.5 | 47. | 58.0 | 72. | 41.5 | 97. | 77.5 |
| 23. | 49.0 | 48. | 66.5 | 73. | 79.0 | 98. | 66.0 |
| 24. | 62.5 | 49. | 60.0 | 74. | 110.0 | 99. | 44.0 |
| 25. | 55.5 | 50. | 39.0 | 75. | 205.0 | 100. | 72.0 |

$$\hat{\mu} + \frac{\hat{\sigma}^2}{2} = \ln \quad 60.88$$

$$2\hat{\mu} + 2\hat{\sigma}^2 = \ln 4736.1 \quad .$$

The estimates are:

$$\hat{\mu} = 3.99$$

$$\hat{\sigma}^2 = 0.24 \quad .$$

Using $\hat{\mu}$ and $\hat{\sigma}^2$, we calculate $E(N_t)$, Var $(N_t)$, $\mu_3(N_t)$ and $\mu_4(N_t)$ for the ordinary point process associated with the log-normal probability distribution.

We have

$$E(N_t) = e^{-\mu - \frac{\hat{\sigma}^2}{2}} t + \frac{e^{\hat{\sigma}^2} - 2}{2}$$

$$= e^{-3.99 - \frac{0.24}{2}} (300) + \frac{e^{0.24} - 2}{2}$$

$$= 4.558 \quad .$$

$$\text{Var } (N_t) = (e^{\hat{\sigma}^2} - 1)e^{-\hat{\mu} - \frac{\hat{\sigma}^2}{2}} t + \frac{5}{4} e^{2\hat{\sigma}^2} - \frac{2}{3} e^{3\hat{\sigma}^2} - \frac{1}{2} e^{\hat{\sigma}^2}$$

$$= (0.2712)(0.01641)300 + 2.020 - 1.370 - 0.635$$

$$= 1.347.$$

$$\mu_3(N_t) = (-e^{3\hat{\sigma}^2} + 3e^{2\hat{\sigma}^2} - 3e^{\hat{\sigma}^2} + 1)e^{-\hat{\mu}-\frac{\hat{\sigma}^2}{2}} t$$

$$+ \frac{3}{4} e^{6\hat{\sigma}^2} - 5e^{4\hat{\sigma}^2} + \frac{17}{3} e^{3\hat{\sigma}^2} - \frac{15}{4} e^{2\hat{\sigma}^2} + \frac{1}{2} e^{\hat{\sigma}^2}$$

$$= (-2.0544 + 4.8483 - 3.8136 + 1)(0.01641)(300)$$

$$+ 3.165 - 13.065 + 11.625 - 6.060 + 0.635$$

$$= -3.80.$$

$$\mu_4 = \left(e^{6\hat{\sigma}^2} - 14e^{4\hat{\sigma}^2} + \frac{65}{2} e^{3\hat{\sigma}^2} - \frac{57}{2} e^{2\hat{\sigma}^2} + 10^{\hat{\sigma}^2} - 1\right) e^{-\hat{\mu}-\frac{\hat{\sigma}^2}{2}} t$$

$$+ 3(e^{2\hat{\sigma}^2} - 2e^{\hat{\sigma}^2} + 1)e^{-2\hat{\mu}-\hat{\sigma}^2} t^2 - \frac{4}{5} e^{10\hat{\sigma}^2} + \frac{17}{2} e^{7\hat{\sigma}^2}$$

$$+ \frac{13}{6} e^{6\hat{\sigma}^2} - 49e^{5\hat{\sigma}^2} + \frac{3571}{48} e^{4\hat{\sigma}^2} - \frac{365}{12} e^{3\hat{\sigma}^2} + \frac{19}{2} e^{2\hat{\sigma}^2} - \frac{e^{\hat{\sigma}^2}}{2}$$

$$= (4.2207 - 36.5638 + 66.7670 - 46.0589 + 12.7120 - 1) \cdot (0.01641)300$$

$$+ 3(1.6161 - 2.5424 + 1)(0.01641)^2 (300) - 8.818 + 45.604$$

$$+ 9.085 - 162.765 + 194.400 - 62.498 + 15.354 - 0.595$$

$$= 34.49.$$

We next determine the type of Pearsonian Frequency Curve best suited. The Pearsonian criterion, K, is calculated, using the renewal moments.

$$\beta_1 = \frac{\mu_3^2(N_t)}{\mu_2^3(N_t)} = \frac{(-3.80)^2}{(1.347)^3} = 5.90$$

$$\beta_2 = \frac{\mu_4(N_t)}{\mu_2^2(N_t)} = \frac{34.49}{(1.347)^2} = 19.05$$

$$K = \frac{\beta_1(\beta_2 + 3)^2}{4(2\beta_2 - 3\beta_1 - 6)(4\beta_2 - 3\beta_1)}$$

$$= \frac{5.90(19.05 + 3)^2}{4[2(19.05) - 3(5.90) - 6][4(19.05) - 3(5.90)]}$$

$$= 0.85 \quad .$$

For $0 < K < 1$, Type IV is the proper curve to select. However, since $K$ is close to unity, the Type V curve was selected due to its simpler form. A complete description of Pearsonian Curves can be found in Elderton [60].

The Pearson Type V curve is

$$y = y_0 \, x^{-p} \, e^{-\gamma/x}$$

where

$$p = 4 + \frac{8 + 4\sqrt{4 + \beta_1}}{\beta_1}$$

$$\gamma = (p - 2)\sqrt{\sigma_x^2(p - e)}$$

$$y_0 = \frac{\gamma^{p-1}}{\Gamma(p - 1)} ,$$

with

$$\text{Origin} = \text{Mean} \pm \frac{\gamma}{p - 2}$$

$$\text{Mode} = \text{Mean} \pm \frac{2\gamma}{p(p - 2)} ,$$

using + when $\mu_3(N_t)$ is negative, and - when $\mu_3(N_t)$ is positive.

For this example

$$p = 4 + \frac{8 + 4\sqrt{4 + 5.9}}{5.9} = 7.50$$

$$\gamma = (7.50 - 2)\sqrt{1.347(7.50 - 3)} = 13.55$$

$$y_0 = \frac{(13.55)^{6.50}}{\Gamma(7.5 - 1)} = \frac{2.28 \times 10^7}{287.5} = 7.93 \times 10^4$$

$$\text{Origin} = 4.558 + \frac{13.55}{7.5 - 2} = 7.024$$

$$\text{Mode} = 4.558 + \frac{2(13.55)}{7.5(7.5 - 2)} = 5.216 ,$$

Therefore

$$f(N_t) = 79300(7.024 - N_t)^{-7.5} e^{-\gamma/(7.024-N_t)} .$$

Figure 9, shows a plot of the probability density function, $f(N_t)$, of the number of failures $N_t$. From the figure, the probability of exceeding 5 failures ($N_t > 5.5$) is about 0.14, and that of exceeding 6 failures ($N_t > 6.5$) is zero. The number of circuits required is, therefore, 7.

It was mentioned at the beginning of this chapter that when $t$ is large enough, the variable

$$N_t^* = \frac{N_t - \frac{t}{u}}{\frac{\sigma\sqrt{t}}{\mu^{3/2}}}$$

becomes asymptotically, normally distributed with zero means and unit variance; $\mu$ and $\sigma^2$ being the mean and variance of the underlying failure distribution.

The dashed line in Figure 9 shows the resulting distribution function if the above assumption were made. Based on this curve, 9 circuits would be required.

FIGURE 9

Distribution of the Number of Failures
doe t = 300 Minutes

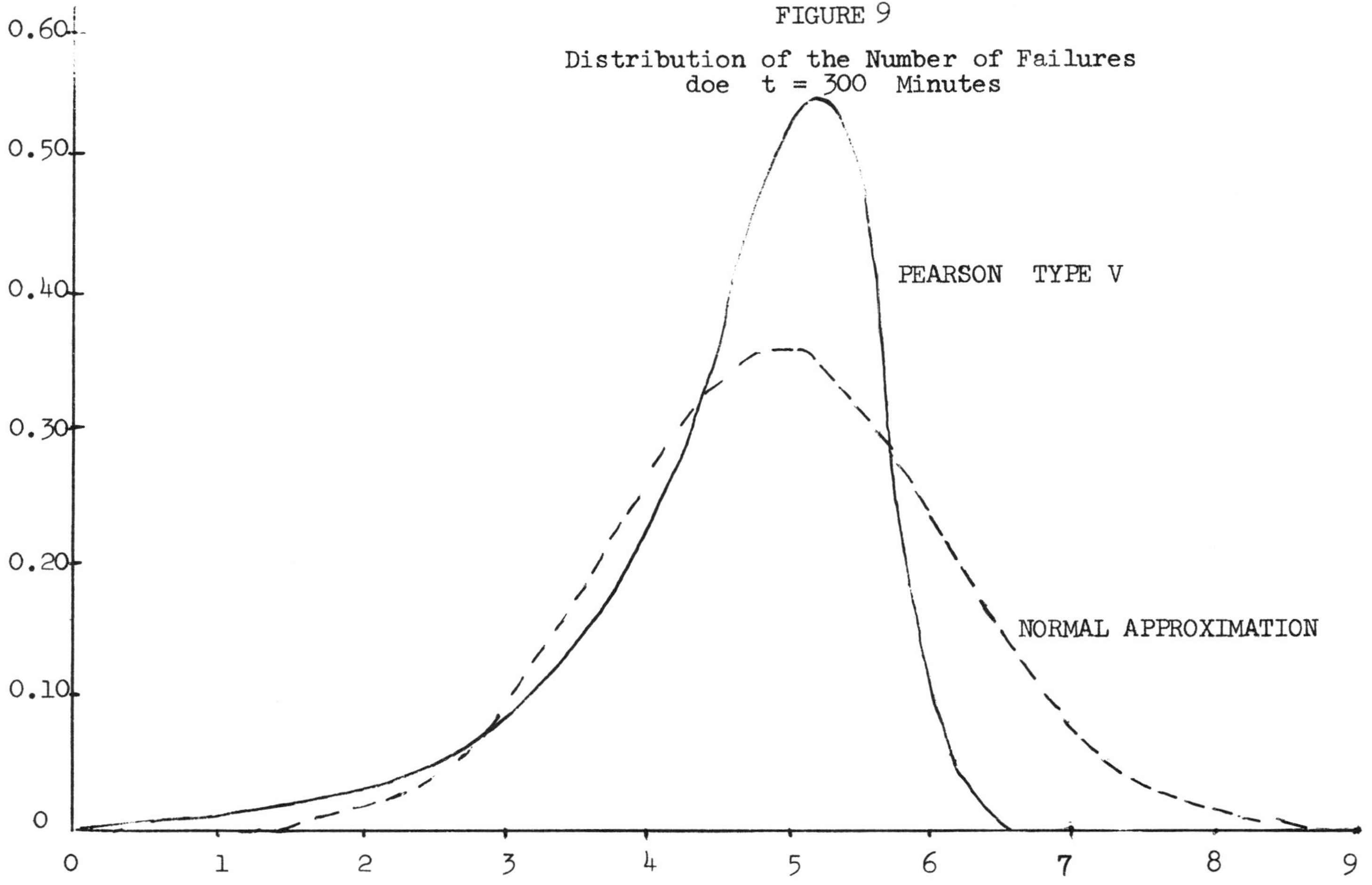

In the next chapter, widely used appropriate distributions, are found as candidates for the inter-event distribution, $F(x)$, that characterizes the underlying point processes, will be considered. In order to apply the general theory, we have developed so far in the first few chapters, one needs to know the "best" estimates of the parameters which a specific effect might involve. We have, therefore, considered the statistical problems dealing with the estimation of these parameters and their properties are discussed at length.

# CHAPTER 9. APPROPRIATE DISTRIBUTIONS FOR THE INTER-EVENT INTERVALS FOR THE POINT DAMAGE PROCESSES AND THEIR ESTIMATION PROBLEMS

## 9.1 The Problem and Proposed Solution

In the design of any industrial product, be it a complex piece of electronic equipment or a simple nut and bolt, there is usually a requirement that the component in question perform a specified function for a specified period of time under a specified environment. Generally, the useful life or time of operation for any particular item cannot be predicted exactly. The only statement that can be made is that there is some probability, $R(T)$, that an item will not fail by time $T$. This probability is called the "reliability" of the item. Design requirements for component useful life are thus usually stated in terms of the probability of operation for a specified time $T$, i.e., in terms of component reliability.

If the underlying failure distribution of a particular component, or product, can be specified as some probability density function, $f(t)$, then the reliability, $R(T)$, of the component can be expressed mathematically as:

$$R(T) = 1 - \int_0^T f(t)dt \quad . \tag{9.1.1}$$

Another parameter of interest is known as the instantaneous failure rate, or hazard rate; this is essentially the probability that an item which has not failed while operating for time $T$, will fail in the next instant of operation. Mathematically, the hazard rate, $Z(T)$, can be expressed as the limit of the ratio of the conditional probability of failure, occurring in $(T, T + \Delta T)$, given that it has not occurred previously, and $\Delta T$ as $\Delta T \to 0^+$. Thus

$$Z(T) \triangleq \lim_{\Delta T \to 0^+} \frac{P(T < t \leq T + \Delta T \mid T < t)}{\Delta T} \quad . \tag{9.1.2}$$

where $P$ stands for probability and $\triangleq$ means "equals by definition." For any two events $A$ and $B$

$$P(A \mid B) = \frac{P(A \cap B)}{P(B)} \quad . \tag{9.1.3}$$

In our case, the event $(T < t : T + \Delta T \cap T < t)$ is the same as the event $(T < t \leq T + \Delta T)$. Thus

$$(9.1.4) \quad Z(T) = \lim_{\Delta T \to 0^+} \frac{P(T < t \leq T + \Delta T)}{\Delta T} \; \frac{1}{P(T < t)}$$

or

$$(9.1.5) \qquad Z(T) = \frac{f(T)}{R(T)} \; .$$

Hazard rate and reliability determine each other uniquely; however, in many applications it is more convenient to deal with hazard rate than reliability. Hazard rate is particularly useful if one wants to study the nature of the underlying failure law. For example, if the hazard rate, $Z(T)$, is increasing with time, there is positive aging. That is, the older the component, the more likely is immediate failure. If $Z(T)$ is decreasing with time, there is negative aging. That is, the older the component, the less likely is immediate failure. For many types of components, the chance of immediate failure is high at the beginning of life due to the presence of defectives, then levels off through middle life and, finally, goes up late in life due to wear-out. Since the hazard rate represents the probability of immediate failure, it is also very useful in developing replacement strategies. Some examples of its use, along these lines, are given in

Chapter 11 of [10].

In many cases, the reliability of a given component is unknown until it is subjected to life test and data in the form of times-to-failure are collected in accordance with a designated sampling scheme. The problem then becomes one of estimating the component reliability, given the results of the life test, i.e., the times-to-failure and the sampling scheme.

An exact statistical treatment, like confidence estimation and testing for significance of the life-quality parameters reliability and hazard rate, is now available only when the underlying probability distribution function of time-to-failure is exponential. Thus, there exists a whole variety of other possible specifications of failure distributions for which there is no available exact statistical treatment.

In the absence of an exact statistical treatment, one might think of the best possible sample (asymptotic) treatment.

If the mathematical form of the underlying failure distribution is known, except for the specification of certain unknown parameters, a method is advocated by Neyman in [159] which leads to the best asymptotic normal estimates, which provide the asymptotically shortest confidence intervals, on the average, for the several parameters that occur in the specification of the failure law. Since each of the life quality parameters reliability and hazard rate can be easily expressed in terms of the unknown parameters occurring in the failure distribution, the use of Neyman's "Best Asymptotically Normal" theory (B.A.N.), at once provides B.A.N. estimates for the reliability and hazard rate, both individually and simultaneously.

Murthy in [151] has carried out a complete analysis of the Weibull failure distribution for random sampling, applying the Best Asymptotically Normal theory of Neyman. The object of this chapter is to extend the above mentioned results for the Weibull to Type I and Type II censored sampling schemes and to also extend these results to another important distribution, the log-normal distribution. The method presented herein is not limited to the particular distributions analyzed. It can be applied whenever the mathematical form of the underlying distribution is known, except for the specification of certain unknown parameters. The method is not applicable when any of the unknown parameters are of function of the time-to-failure, and the reason for this will be shown in Section 9.2 which follows.

Also, for the method to be applicable, the estimation problem for the unknown parameters must make sense, i.e., the problem must be identifiable. This last problem might arise in the case of mixtures of distributions.

## 9.2 Best Asymptotically Normal Estimates of Reliability and Hazard Rate

Best asymptotically normal estimates have the property of being normally distributed with finite variances about the "true" parameter value for large sample size, where "true" parameter refers to the population value of the parameters $\theta_1,\ldots,\theta_\ell$, occurring in the specification of the probability density function $f(t,\theta_1,\ldots,\theta_\ell)$. Furthermore, no other asymptotically normally distributed estimate can have a smaller variance, according to Neyman [159]. They also have the property that the probability goes to 1 that the estimated value of the parameter converges to the "true" value of the parameter as the sample size gets large [159]. In other words, the estimate of a parameter converges in probability to the "true" value of the parameter. B.A.N. estimates are a generalization of the widely used Maximum Likelihood Estimates.

It is assumed that the underlying failure distribution has a probability density function that can be specified as $f(t,\theta_1,\ldots,\theta_\ell)$, where $\theta_1,\ldots,\theta_\ell$ are unknown population parameters to be estimated from the sample. Best asymptotically normal estimates $\hat{\theta}_1,\ldots,\hat{\theta}_\ell$ of $\theta_1,\ldots,\theta_\ell$ can be obtained by using the method of maximum likelihood. This consists of solving for those estimates $\hat{\theta}_1,\ldots,\hat{\theta}_\ell$ of $\theta_1,\ldots,\theta_\ell$ which maximize the likelihood, L, of the set of observations obtained in the sample. The likelihood function L is proportional to the probability density function of the observations, the constant of proportionality being independent of the estimated parameters.

Since $\hat{\theta}_1,\ldots,\hat{\theta}_\ell$ are B.A.N. estimates of $\theta_1,\ldots,\theta_\ell$ the best asymptotically normal estimates of component reliability and hazard rate are given by

$$(9.2.1)\qquad \hat{R}(T,\theta_1,\ldots,\theta_\ell) \triangleq 1 - \int_0^T f(t,\hat{\theta}_1,\ldots,\hat{\theta}_\ell)dt$$

and

$$(9.2.2)\qquad \hat{Z}(T,\theta_1,\ldots,\theta_\ell) \triangleq \frac{f(T,\hat{\theta}_1,\ldots,\hat{\theta}_\ell)}{\hat{R}(T,\theta_1,\ldots,\theta_\ell)} .$$

In order to compute confidence limits for the "true"

reliability and hazard rate the following two theorems are used.

THEOREM 15: <u>The maximum likelihood estimates $\hat{\theta}_1,\ldots,\hat{\theta}_\ell$ for the parameters of a density function $f(x,\theta_1,\ldots,\theta_\ell)$ from samples of size $N$, for large $N$, converge in distribution to the multivariate normal distribution with means $\theta_1,\ldots,\theta_\ell$ and with covariance $[\sigma^{ij}]$, $i = 1,\ldots,\ell$ and $j = 1,\ldots,\ell$, where</u>

(9.2.3) $$\sigma^{ij} \triangleq |\sigma_{ij}|^{-1}$$

<u>and</u>

(9.2.4) $$\sigma_{ij} \triangleq \left[ - \frac{\partial^2 \log L(\theta_1,\ldots,\theta_\ell)}{\partial\theta_i \, \partial\theta_j} \right] .$$

<u>Proof</u>: For a proof of Theorem 15 see [45], pages 208-212.

Employing the above theorem and the one that follows, confidence intervals for the "true" reliability and hazard rate of an item can be calculated.

THEOREM 16: <u>Suppose that the joint distribution of</u>

*the statistics,* $T_1, T_2, \ldots, T_k$ *tends to the* $k$ *-variate normal form with mean values* $\theta_1, \ldots, \theta_k$ *and covariance matrix* $\Sigma \triangleq \sigma^{ij}$, *where* $\sigma^{ij}$ *are finite and* $N$ *is the sample size. Then, the random vector,*

$$(T_1 - \theta_1), (T_2 - \theta_2), \ldots, (T_k - \theta_k)$$

*converges in distribution as* $N$ *gets large, to a* $k$*-variate normal distribution with zero mean vector and covariance matrix* $\Sigma \triangleq \sigma^{ij}$. *Furthermore, if* $g(T_1, \ldots, T_k)$ *is a continuous function, with continuous first-partial derivatives, then the random variable*

$$u \triangleq g(T_1, T_2, \ldots, T_k) - g(\theta_1, \theta_2, \ldots, \theta_k)$$

*converges in distribution for large* $N$ *to a normal distribution with zero mean and variance*

$$\sum_i \sum_j \sigma^{ij} \left( \frac{\partial g}{\partial \theta_i} \right) \left( \frac{\partial g}{\partial \theta_j} \right) . \qquad (9.2.5)$$

*Proof*: For proof of Theorem 16 see [45], pages 207-208.

Before preceding further, it must be noted that in order for Theorem 14 to be valid, it must be permissible to interchange the operations of integrations with respect to t, and differentiation with respect to $\theta_i$, $i = 1, \ldots, \ell$, for the function $\log f(t, \theta_1, \ldots, \theta_\ell)$. Thus, the methods as presented herein are not valid if any of the parameters are a function of the time-to-failure.

Theorems 15 and 16 can be used to obtain the large sample variances of the estimates $\hat{R}(T, \theta_1, \ldots, \theta_\ell)$ and $\hat{Z}(T, \theta_1, \ldots, \theta_\ell)$. Once the variances of the estimates have been obtained, it is possible to construct confidence intervals for the estimates for the case of large samples.

In general, one-sided and two-sided confidence intervals can be constructed. However, for the sake of illustration, only lower confidence intervals for the true reliability and upper confidence intervals for the true hazard rate have been calculated. There is also some practical justification for this, since, generally, it is important to insure that component reliability be greater than some specified requirement and that the hazard rate be less than some specified requirement.

Thus, based on the above two theorems, for a given confidence coefficient, the $100(1 - \alpha)$ percent lower confidence interval for the true reliability of an item $R(T, \theta_1, \ldots, \theta_\ell)$ is given by

$$R(T,\theta_1,\ldots,\theta_\ell) - h_\alpha \sqrt{\text{Var } \hat{R}(T,\theta_1,\ldots,\theta_\ell}\quad ,$$

where $P(h > h_\alpha) = \alpha$ and $h_\alpha$ is a standard normal deviate.

Thus,

$$(9.2.6)\quad \text{Prob.} \left[R(T,\theta_1,\ldots,\theta_\ell) \geq \hat{R}(T,\theta_1,\ldots,\theta_\ell) - h_\alpha \sqrt{\text{Var } \hat{R}(T,\theta_1,\ldots,0_\ell)}\right] = 1 - \alpha \ .$$

The upper confidence limit of the hazard rate of an item, for a given $\alpha$-confidence coefficient is given by

$$(9.2.7)\quad \hat{Z}(T,\theta_1,\ldots,\theta_\ell) + h_\alpha \sqrt{\text{Var } \hat{Z}(T,\theta_1,\ldots,\theta_\ell)}\quad ,$$

where $h_\alpha$ is the standard normal deviate corresponding to the $\alpha$ portion of the normal curve from the upper tail.

Thus,

$$(9.2.8)\quad \text{Prob.} \left[Z(T,\theta_1,\ldots,\theta_\ell) \leq \hat{Z}(T,\theta_1,\ldots,\theta_\ell) + h_\alpha \sqrt{\text{Var } \hat{Z}(T,\theta_1,\ldots,\theta_\ell)}\right] = 1 - \alpha.$$

It is also interesting to note that the variances of $\hat{R}(T,\theta_1,\ldots,\theta_\ell)$ and $\hat{Z}(T,\theta_1,\ldots,\theta_\ell)$ as given by the two theorems stated in this section, and using maximum likelihood estimates of $\theta_1,\ldots,\theta_\ell$ are equivalent to the minimum variances obtainable, as given by [45], page 146, thus illustrating one of the important properties of the B.A.N.-estimates of reliability and hazard rate, i.e., that of asymptotic efficiency.

9.3 Sampling Schemes Used

The following is a brief discussion of each of the sampling schemes considered in the analysis.

The first case considered is that of random sampling. In this case it is assumed that $N$ identical components have been subjected to life test and they have all failed. There are thus $N$ times-to-failure, $t_1,\ldots,t_N$, which constitute a random sample of size $N$ from the given population of times-to-failure with probability density function $f(t,\theta_1,\ldots,\theta_\ell)$. The likelihood function for this sampling scheme is given by:

$$L = \prod_{i=1}^{N} f(t_i,\theta_1,\ldots,\theta_\ell) \tag{9.3.1}$$

and the maximum likelihood estes $\hat{\theta}_1,\ldots,\hat{\theta}_\ell$ of $\theta_1,\ldots,\theta_\ell$, satisfy the set of $\ell$ equations given by

$$(9.3.2) \qquad \frac{\partial \log L}{\partial\theta_1} = 0 \,,\, \frac{\partial \log L}{\partial\theta_2} = 0 \,,\ldots,\, \frac{\partial \log L}{\partial\theta_\ell} = 0 \;.$$

The second sampling scheme used is that of Type I censored samples. The term censoring of samples refers to the case for which N identical components are subjected to life testing, but several are removed from the test prior to failure. "Progressively censored" samples refers to the case where the censoring or removing of components, prior to failure occurs in several stages. In many applications of life testing, components are removed from the test prior to failure for use as test objects in related experimentation. Also, progressively censored samples result if test facilities are limited and prolonged tests are too expensive. The early censoring of the sample frees part of the facilities for other uses, while items which are allowed to continue "on test" until subsequent failure, permit the observation of extreme values.

Type I censoring, as is usually defined, refers to the case in which the censoring occurs in several stages, and the times of censoring are predetermined; that is, at predetermined times, $T_1, T_2, \ldots, T_k$, a predetermined number of components, $r_1, r_2, \ldots, r_k$, are removed from the test prior to failure. Type II censoring, which will be discussed later in this section, refers to the case when the censoring occurs at a time when the number of survivors drops to predetermined levels. In both Type I and Type II censoring the number of objects removed during each stage of censoring is predetermined.

In developing the likelihood function for censored samples, the function of interest is the likelihood of all items being removed from the sample as a function of time. There are two possible reasons for removel:

1. an item is removed because of failure; and
2. an item is removed because of censoring.

Let the total sample size be denoted by N, and the number of components that fail at times $t_1, \ldots, t_n$ be denoted by n. If all items are tested until removal or failure, then the total sample consists of those items that failed, plus those that are removed prior to failure, Thus,

$$N = \sum_{i=1}^{k} r_i + n \quad . \tag{9.3.3}$$

For Type I censoring, components are removed in sets of $r_i$, at times $T_i$, due to censoring, or are removed in sets of one or more at times $t_j$, due to failure of the component or components. The probability that an items fails during $\Delta t$ at time $t_j$ is $f(t_j, \theta_1, \ldots, \theta_\ell)\Delta t$, whereas, the probability that $r_i$ components have not failed and can be removed at time $T_i$ is

$$(9.3.4) \qquad [1 - F(T_i, \theta_1, \ldots, \theta_\ell)]^{r_i}$$

where

$$(9.3.5) \qquad F(T_i, \theta_1, \ldots, \theta_\ell) \triangleq \int_0^{T_i} f(t, \theta_1, \ldots, \theta_\ell) dt \ .$$

Thus, the likelihood function for Type I censoring is defined by:

$$(9.3.6) \qquad L \triangleq C \prod_{j=1}^{n} f(t_j, \theta_1, \ldots, \theta_\ell) \cdot \prod_{i=1}^{k} [1 - F(T_i, \theta_1, \ldots, \theta_\ell)]^{r_i} ,$$

and the maximum likelihood estimates, $\hat{\theta}_1, \ldots, \hat{\theta}_\ell$ of $\theta_1, \ldots, \theta_\ell$, satisfy the set of $\ell$ simultaneous equations in (9.3.2).

The third category of sample schemes, Type II censoring, as is usually defined, refers to the case where the censoring occurs when the number of survivors drops to predetermined levels. Thus, the times at which censoring occurs, correspond to the times of component failures and are random variables. In the most general case, when a member of the sample fails at time $t_i$, $r_i$ additional members which have not yet failed are removed from the sample. It is assumed that a total of $n$ items fail during the test, and, therefore,

$$N - n = \sum_{i=1}^{n} r_i \tag{9.3.7}$$

items are removed prior to failure.

The likelihood, as given by [ ] for Type II case is:

$$L \triangleq \prod_{i=1}^{n} G_i \; f(t_i,\theta_1,\ldots,\theta_\ell)[1 - F(t_i,\theta_1,\ldots,\theta_\ell)]^{r_i}, \tag{9.3.8}$$

where

$$G_i \triangleq N - \sum_{j=1}^{i-1} r_j - i + 1 \tag{9.3.9}$$

and $N$ is as given in (9.3.3).

The maximum likelihood estimates, $\hat{\theta}_1,\ldots,\hat{\theta}_\ell$ of $\theta_1,\ldots,\theta_\ell$, satisfy the set of $\ell$ simultaneous equations given by (9.3.2).

## 9.4 The Log-Normal Distribution

We will now apply the method previously outlined to the case where the underlying failure distribution is log-normal.

The log-normal distribution arises in many practical applications. A fairly extensive work on this distribution may be found in [ 1 ]. An example of its application is in the aerospace industry, where it is assumed in many reliability studies that batteries fail according to a log-normal law. Figure 10 is a graph of the distribution for various values of $\sigma$, for the case where $\mu = 1$.

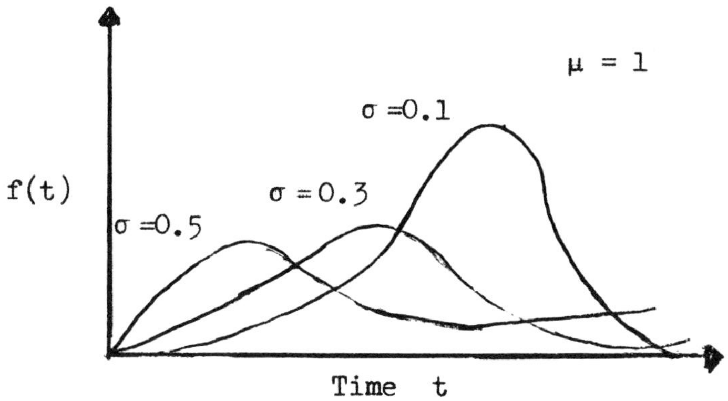


FIGURE 10

THE LOG-NORMAL DISTRIBUTION

The log-normal case arises when the natural logarithms of the times-to-failure are distributed normally. Thus, is $x$ is a normal random variable, $N:(\mu,\sigma^2)$, we have

$$(9.4.1) \qquad f(x) \triangleq \frac{1}{\sqrt{2\pi}\sigma} e^{-\frac{1}{2}\left(\frac{x-u}{\sigma}\right)^2}, \quad -\infty < x \leq \infty ,$$

then, the distribution of $t \triangleq e^x$ is called the log-normal distribution, where

$$x = \log t$$

then

$$(9.4.2) \qquad g(t) = \frac{1}{\sqrt{2\pi}\sigma} e^{-\frac{1}{2}\left(\frac{\log t-\mu}{\sigma}\right)^2} \left| \frac{dx}{dt} \right| ,$$

where $0 < t \leq \infty$. Thus, the log-normal distribution is given by

$$(9.4.3) \qquad g(t) \triangleq \begin{cases} \dfrac{1}{\sqrt{2\pi}\sigma} e^{-\frac{1}{2}\left(\frac{\log t-\mu}{\sigma}\right)^2} \dfrac{1}{t} , \\ \\ 0 \quad \text{everywhere else} . \end{cases}$$

It is shown below, that $g(t)$ satisfies the relation of the zero$^{th}$ moment, i.e.,

$$\int_{-\infty}^{\infty} g(t)dt = 1 \qquad (9.4.4)$$

for

$$\int_{-\infty}^{\infty} g(t)dt = \int_{0}^{\infty} \frac{1}{\sqrt{2\pi}\sigma} e^{-\frac{1}{2}\left(\frac{\log t-\mu}{\sigma}\right)^2} \frac{1}{t}\, dt \quad . \qquad (9.4.5)$$

Let

$$h \triangleq \frac{\log t - \mu}{\sigma}$$

when $t = 0$, $h = -\infty$ and when $t = \infty$, $h = \infty$, with

$$dh = \frac{1}{t\sigma}\, dt$$

then

$$\frac{1}{\sqrt{2\pi}} \int_{0}^{\infty} e^{-\frac{1}{2}\left(\frac{\log t-\mu}{\sigma}\right)^2} \frac{1}{t}\, dt \qquad (9.4.6)$$

$$= \frac{1}{\sqrt{2\pi}} \int_{-\infty}^{\infty} e^{-\frac{h^2}{2}} dh = 1 \quad .$$

The natural moments of the log-normal distribution are derived as follows: We have for the First Moment:

Let

$$h \triangleq \frac{\log t - \mu}{\sigma} ,$$

when $t = 0$, $h = -\infty$, and when $t = \infty$, $h = \infty$, with

$$dh = \frac{1}{t\sigma} dt .$$

Also, $\log(t) \equiv h\sigma + \mu$ where $t \equiv e^{h\sigma} + \mu$, then

$$(9.4.8)\quad E(t) = \int_{-\infty}^{\infty} \frac{1}{\sqrt{2\pi}} e^{-\frac{1}{2}h^2} e^{h\sigma} e^{\mu} dh$$

$$= \frac{1}{\sqrt{2\pi}} e^{\mu} \int_{-\infty}^{\infty} e^{-\frac{1}{2}(h^2-2h\sigma+\sigma^2-\sigma^2)} dh$$

$$= \frac{1}{\sqrt{2\pi}} e^{\mu+(\sigma^2/2)} \int_{-\infty}^{\infty} e^{-\frac{1}{2}(h-\sigma)^2} dh .$$

Let $z \triangleq h - \sigma$ with $dz = dh$, then when $h = \infty$, $z = \infty$, and when $h = -\infty$, $z = -\infty$, and we have

$$(9.4.10)\quad E(t) = \frac{1}{\sqrt{2\pi}} e^{\mu+(\sigma^2/2)} \int_{-\infty}^{\infty} e^{-\frac{z^2}{2}} dz$$

$$= e^{\mu+(\sigma^2/2)} .$$

In a similar way, the $n^{th}$ natural moment can be derived. Thus

$$(9.4.11)\quad E(t^n) = \int_{-\infty}^{\infty} t^n\, g(t)dt$$

$$= \int_{-\infty}^{\infty} t^n \frac{1}{\sqrt{2\pi}\sigma} e^{-\frac{1}{2}\left(\frac{\log t-\mu}{\sigma}\right)^2} \frac{1}{t}\, dt$$

$$= e^{n\mu+(n^2\sigma^2/2)} \quad .$$

The log-normal distribution has the self-reproductive properties under multiplication that the normal distribution has under addition. Thus, if the independent random variables, $x_1,\ldots,x_n$, are log-normally distributed, the product

$$(9.4.12)\qquad y = \prod_{i=1}^{n} x_i$$

is also log-normally distributed. Also, the log-normal possesses the limiting properties for the products of random variables, that the normal possesses for sums. For example, an analogous form of the Liapounoff version of the central limit theorem for the log-normal is as follows [ 1]:

Let $|x_j|$ be a sequence of independent, positive random variables such that

$$(9.4.13)\qquad \begin{cases} E\left\{\log x_j\right\} \overset{\Delta}{=} \mu_j \\ \mathrm{Var}\left\{\log x_j\right\} \overset{\Delta}{=} \sigma_j^2 \\ E\left\{\left|\log x_j - {}_j\right|^2\right\} = \omega_j^3 \end{cases}$$

all exist for every $j$. Then, if

$$(9.4.14)\qquad \begin{cases} \mu(n) = \sum_{j=1}^{n} \mu_j \\ \sigma^2(n) = \sum_{j=1}^{n} \sigma_j^2 \\ \omega^3(n) = \sum_{j=1}^{n} \omega_j^3 \end{cases}$$

the product $\Pi_{j=1}^{n} x_j$ is asymptotically log-normally distributed with parameters $\mu = \mu(n)$ and $\sigma^2 = \sigma^2(n)$, provided that $\omega(n)/(\sigma(n)) \to 0$ as $n \to \infty$.

From the previous analysis, it can be seen that the log-normal distribution might apply to processes for which the outcome is determined by the product of a large number of random variables.

## 9.5 The Random Sample

We will now estimate the values of population, $\mu, \sigma$, as a function of the random sample, $t_1, t_2, \ldots, t_N$, of failure times, by the method of maximum likelihood.

(9.5.1)
$$L = \prod_{i=1}^{N} \frac{1}{\sqrt{2\pi}\sigma} e^{-\frac{1}{2}\left(\frac{\log t_i - \mu}{\sigma}\right)^2} \frac{1}{t_i} .$$

Then

(9.5.2)
$$\text{Log } L = \sum_{i=1}^{N} \left[\log \left(\frac{1}{2\pi}\right)^{1/2} + \log \left(\frac{1}{\sigma}\right) - \frac{1}{2}\left(\frac{\log t_i - \mu}{\sigma}\right)^2 + \log \frac{1}{t_i}\right]$$

$$= \log \left(\frac{1}{2\pi}\right)^{N/2} - N \log \sigma - \frac{1}{2\sigma^2} \sum_{i=1}^{N} (\log t_i - \mu)^2$$

$$+ \sum_{i=1}^{N} \log \frac{1}{t_i} ,$$

where

(9.5.3)
$$\frac{\partial \log L}{\partial \sigma} = -\frac{N}{\sigma} + \frac{1}{\sigma^3} \sum_{i=1}^{N} (\log t_i - \mu)^2 = 0$$

and

$$(9.5.4) \qquad \hat{\sigma} = \sqrt{\Sigma_{i=1}^{N} \frac{(\log t_i - \mu)^2}{N}}$$

and when

$$(9.5.5) \quad \frac{\partial \log L}{\partial \mu} = -\frac{1}{2\sigma^2} \sum_{i=1}^{N} 2(\log t_i - \mu)(-1) = 0$$

we have

$$(9.5.6) \qquad \hat{\mu} \triangleq \sum_{i=1}^{N} \frac{\log t_i}{N} .$$

From the definition of the log-normal distribution, $\log t_i \triangleq x_i$ where $x_i$ is normally distributed with mean $\mu$ and variance $\sigma^2$.

Then

$$(9.5.7) \qquad \hat{\mu} = \sum_{i=1}^{N} \frac{\log t_i}{N} = \sum_{i=1}^{N} \frac{x_i}{N} = \bar{x}$$

and

$$(9.5.8) \qquad \hat{\sigma}^2 = \sum_{i=1}^{N} \frac{(\log t_i - \hat{\mu})^2}{N}$$

$$= \sum_{i=1}^{N} \frac{(x_i - \bar{x})^2}{N} = s^2 .$$

It has been shown, in [ 1], that $(S^2N)/\sigma^2$ is Chi-square distributed with $N-1$ degrees of freedom. Thus, the $100(1-\alpha)$ percent conficence interval for $\sigma$ is given by

$$(9.5.9) \quad P\left( S\sqrt{\chi^{N/2}_{\alpha/2;N-1}} \leq \sigma \leq S\sqrt{\chi^{N/2}_{\alpha/2;N-1}} \right) = 1-\alpha .$$

The distribution of

$$(\bar{x}-\mu)\sqrt{\frac{N-1}{S}}$$

has been shown in [ 1] to have the $t$ distribution with $N-1$ degrees of freedom.

Thus, the $100(1-\alpha)$ percent confidence interval for $\mu$ is given by

$$(9.5.10) \quad P\left[\bar{x} - t_{\alpha/2;N-1}\left(\frac{S}{\sqrt{N-1}}\right) \leq \mu \leq \bar{x} + t_{\alpha/2;N-1}\left(\frac{S}{\sqrt{N-1}}\right)\right] = 1-\alpha .$$

To obtain the asymptotic covariance matrix of $\hat{\mu}$ and

$\hat{\theta}$ we use Theorem 15. By applying this theorem to the log-normal distribution in the case of random sampling, we get the following:

$$(9.5.11)\qquad B \triangleq \begin{pmatrix} \dfrac{\partial^2 \log L}{\partial \mu^2} & \dfrac{\partial^2 \log L}{\partial \mu \, \partial \sigma} \\ \\ \dfrac{\partial^2 \log L}{\partial \sigma \, \partial \mu} & \dfrac{\partial^2 \log L}{\partial \sigma^2} \end{pmatrix}$$

then

$$(9.5.12)\qquad \begin{cases} \dfrac{\partial^2 \log L}{\partial \mu^2} = - \dfrac{N}{\sigma^2} \\ \\ \dfrac{\partial^2 \log L}{\partial \mu \, \partial \sigma} = - \dfrac{2}{\sigma^3} \displaystyle\sum_{i=1}^{N} (\log t_i - \mu) \\ \\ \dfrac{\partial^2 \log L}{\partial \sigma^2} = \dfrac{N}{\sigma^2} - \dfrac{3}{\sigma^4} \displaystyle\sum_{i=1}^{N} (\log t_i - \mu)^2 \end{cases}$$

also,

$$(9.5.13)\qquad - E(B) \triangleq M = E|-b_{ij}|, \qquad i,j = 1,2$$

then

(9.5.14)

$$-E\left(\frac{\partial^2 \log L}{\partial \mu^2}\right)$$

$$= \int_0^\infty \cdots \int_0^\infty \frac{N}{\sigma^2}\, g(t_1 \cdots t_N)dt_1 \cdots dt_N = \frac{N}{\sigma^2} ,$$

(9.5.15)

$$-E\left(\frac{\partial^2 \log L}{\partial \mu\, \partial \sigma}\right)$$

$$= \int_0^\infty \cdots \int_0^\infty \frac{2}{\sigma^3}\left(\sum_{i=1}^{N} (\log t_i - \mu)\right) g(t_1 \cdots t_N)dt_1 \cdots dt_N$$

$$(9.5.16) \quad -E\left(\frac{\partial \log L}{\partial \mu\ \partial \sigma}\right) = \frac{2}{\sigma^2} \sum_{i=1}^{N} \int_0^\infty \log t_i\ g(t_i)dt_1$$

$$- \frac{2}{\sigma^3} \sum_{i=1}^{N} \int_0^\infty \mu\ g(t_i)dt_1 .$$

The $\log t_i \triangleq x_i$, where $x_i$ is a normal random variable with

$$(9.5.17) \quad f(x_i) \triangleq \frac{1}{\sqrt{2\pi}\sigma}\, e^{-\frac{1}{2}\left(\frac{x_i - \mu}{\sigma}\right)^2} , \quad -\infty < x_i < \infty,$$

thus, $E(\log t_i) = E(x_i) = \mu$, so

$$(9.5.18) \quad -E\left(\frac{\partial^2 \log L}{\partial\sigma\,\partial\mu}\right) = \frac{2}{\sigma^3}\sum_{i=1}^{N} \mu - \frac{2}{\sigma^3}\sum_{i=1}^{N} = 0 ,$$

(9.5.19)

$$-E\left(\frac{\partial^2 \log L}{\partial\sigma^2}\right)$$

$$= \int_0^\infty \cdots \int_0^\infty -\frac{N}{\sigma^2}\, g(t_1 \cdots t_N)dt_1 \cdots dt_N$$

$$+ \int_0^\infty \cdots \int_0^\infty \frac{3}{\sigma^4}\sum_{i=1}^{N} (\log t_i - \mu)^2\, g(t_1 \cdots t_N)dt_1 \cdots dt_N$$

$$= -\frac{N}{\sigma^2} + \frac{3}{\sigma^4}\sum_{i=1}^{N}\int_0^\infty (\log t_i - \mu)^2\, g(t_i)dt_i \ .$$

For the $\log t_i \overset{\Delta}{=} x_i$, where $x_i$ is distributed $N(\mu,\sigma^2)$, $E(\log t_i - \mu)^2 = \text{Var}(\log t_i) = \text{Var}(x_i) = \sigma^2$. Hence

$$(9.5.20) \quad -E\left(\frac{\partial^2 \log L}{\partial\sigma^2}\right) = -\frac{N}{\sigma^2} + \frac{3N\sigma^2}{\sigma^4} = \frac{2N}{\sigma^2} \ .$$

Thus,

$$(9.5.21) \qquad M = \begin{pmatrix} \frac{N}{\sigma^2} & 0 \\ 0 & \frac{2N}{\sigma^2} \end{pmatrix}$$

$$(9.5.22) \qquad M^{-1} = \frac{\begin{pmatrix} \frac{2N}{\sigma^2} & 0 \\ 0 & \frac{N}{\sigma^2} \end{pmatrix}}{\left(\frac{2N^2}{\sigma^4}\right)}$$

$$(9.5.23) \qquad M^{-1} = \begin{pmatrix} \frac{\sigma^2}{N} & 0 \\ 0 & \frac{\sigma^2}{2N} \end{pmatrix} .$$

Thus, $\hat{\mu}$ and $\hat{\sigma}$ are approximately normally distributed with mean $[\mu,\sigma]$ and covariance matrix

$$\Sigma \begin{pmatrix} \frac{\sigma^2}{N} & 0 \\ 0 & \frac{\sigma^2}{2N} \end{pmatrix} ,$$

## 9.6 The Type I Censored Sample

We will now estimate, by the method of maximum likelihood, the values of $\mu$ and $\sigma$ as a function of the predetermined times of censoring, $T_1,\ldots,T_k$, the predetermined numbers of components, $r_1 \cdots r_k$ (which are removed from the test prior to failure), and the random failure times, $t_1 \cdots t_n$.

From Section 9.3, the likelihood function for Type I censoring is given by:

$$(9.6.1) \quad L \triangleq C \prod_{j=1}^{n} f(t_j,\mu,\sigma) \prod_{i=1}^{k} |1 - F(t_i,\mu,\sigma)|^{r_i} \quad .$$

The maximum likelihood estimates $\hat{\mu}$ and $\hat{\sigma}$ of $\mu$ and $\sigma$ satisfy the pair of equations given by:

$$\frac{\partial \log L}{\partial \mu} = 0 \quad , \quad \frac{\partial \log L}{\partial \sigma} = 0 \quad .$$

Then

$$(9.6.2) \quad \text{Log } L = \log C + \sum_{j=1}^{n} \log f(t_j) + \sum_{i=1}^{k} r_i \log |1 - F(T_i)| \quad .$$

For the log-normal distribution

$$(9.6.3) \quad f(t_j) \triangleq \begin{cases} \dfrac{1}{\sqrt{2\pi}\sigma} e^{-\frac{1}{2}\left(\frac{\log t_j - \mu}{\sigma}\right)^2} \dfrac{1}{t_j}, & 0 \le t_j < \infty \\ \\ 0 & \text{otherwise} \end{cases} ,$$

$$(9.6.4)\quad F(T_i) \triangleq \begin{cases} \int_0^{T_i} \frac{1}{\sqrt{2\pi}\sigma} e^{-\frac{1}{2}\left(\frac{\log x-\mu}{\sigma}\right)^2} \frac{1}{x}\,dx\,, & 0 \le T_i \\ 0 & \text{otherwise} \end{cases} .$$

Thus

(9.6.5)

$$\text{Log } L = \log C + \sum_{j=1}^{n} \left[\log\left(\frac{1}{\sqrt{2\pi}}\right) - \log\sigma - \frac{1}{2\sigma^2}\left(\log t_j - \mu\right)^2 - \log t_j\right]$$

$$+ \sum_{i=1}^{k} \log\left[1 - \int_0^{T_i} \frac{1}{\sqrt{2\pi}\sigma} e^{-\frac{1}{2}\left(\frac{\log x-\mu}{\sigma}\right)^2} \frac{1}{x}\,dx\right]$$

$$(9.6.6)\quad \text{Log } L = \log C + n\log\frac{1}{\sqrt{2\pi}} - n\log\sigma$$

$$- \frac{1}{2\sigma^2}\sum_{j=1}^{n} (\log t_j - \mu)^2 - \sum_{j=1}^{n} \log t_j$$

$$+ \sum_{i=1}^{k} r_i \log\left[1 - \int_0^{T_i} \frac{1}{\sqrt{2\pi}} e^{-\frac{1}{2}\left(\frac{\log x-\mu}{\sigma}\right)^2} \frac{1}{x}\,dx\right]$$

The integral

$$(9.6.7) \quad \int_0^{T_i} \frac{1}{\sqrt{2\pi}\sigma} e^{-\frac{1}{2}\left(\frac{\log x-\mu}{\sigma}\right)^2} \frac{1}{x}\, dx$$

$$= \int_{-\infty}^{\left(\frac{\log T_i-\mu}{\sigma}\right)} \frac{1}{\sqrt{2\pi}} e^{-(u^2/2)}\, du \quad ,$$

with the substitution

$$u \triangleq \frac{\log x - \mu}{\sigma} \quad .$$

The maximum likelihood estimators $\hat{\mu}$ and $\hat{\sigma}$, by definition of maximum likelihood, satisfy the equations

$$\frac{\partial \log L}{\partial \mu} = 0 \quad , \quad \frac{\partial \log L}{\partial \sigma} = 0 \quad .$$

Also, if

$$(9.6.8) \qquad \varphi(u) \triangleq \int_{a(u)}^{b(u)} F(x,u)dx$$

then, by a theorem of calculus

$$(9.6.9) \quad \frac{\partial \varphi(u)}{\partial u} \triangleq \int_{a(u)}^{b(u)} \frac{\partial F}{\partial u}\, dx + F(b,u)\frac{db}{du} - F(a,u)\frac{da}{du} \quad .$$

Thus

$$(9.6.10)\quad \frac{\partial \log L}{\partial \mu} = 0 = -\frac{1}{2\sigma^2}\sum_{j=1}^{n} 2(\log t_j - \mu)(-1)$$

$$+ \sum_{i=1}^{k} r_i \frac{\frac{1}{\sqrt{2\pi}\sigma} e^{-\frac{1}{2}\left(\frac{\log T_i - \mu}{\sigma}\right)^2}}{1 - \int_{-\infty}^{\left(\frac{\log T_i - \mu}{\sigma}\right)} \frac{1}{\sqrt{2\pi}} e^{-\frac{1}{2}t^2}\, dt}$$

From the definition of $Z(T)$, let

$$(9.6.11)\qquad Z_i(\xi_i) \triangleq \frac{\frac{1}{\sqrt{2\pi}} e^{-\frac{1}{2}\xi_i^2}}{1 - \int_{-\infty}^{\xi_i} \frac{1}{\sqrt{2\pi}} e^{-\frac{1}{2}t^2}\, dt},$$

where

$$\xi_i \triangleq \frac{\log T_i - \mu}{\sigma}$$

so

$$(9.6.12)\quad \frac{\partial \log L}{\partial \mu} = 0 = \frac{1}{\sigma}\left[\sum_{j=1}^{n} \frac{(\log t_j - \mu)}{\sigma} \sum_{i=1}^{k} r_i Z_i\right].$$

Also

$$(9.6.13)\quad \frac{\partial L}{\partial \sigma} = 0 = -\frac{n}{\sigma} + \frac{2}{2\sigma^2} \sum_{j=1}^{n} (\log t_j - \mu)^2$$

$$+ \sum_{i=1}^{k} r_i \frac{\frac{1}{\sqrt{2\pi}} e^{-\frac{1}{2}\left(\frac{\log T_i - \mu}{\sigma}\right)^2} \left(\frac{\log T_i - \mu}{\sigma}\right) \frac{1}{\sigma}}{1 - \int_{-\infty}^{\left(\frac{\log T_i - \mu}{\sigma}\right)} \frac{1}{\sqrt{2\pi}} e^{-\frac{1}{2}t^2}\, dt}$$

and

$$(9.6.14)\quad \frac{\partial \log L}{\partial \sigma} = 0$$

$$= \frac{1}{\sigma}\left(-n + \frac{1}{\sigma^2} \sum_{j=1}^{n} (\log t_j - \mu)^2 + \sum_{i=1}^{k} r_i Z_i \xi_i\right)$$

Equations (9.6.12) and (9.6.14) must be solved by iterative (approximation) procedures for the estimators $\hat{\mu}$ and $\hat{\sigma}$. If we have approximate solutions $\mu_0$ and $\sigma_0$, we can use Newton's method, as given in [ 1 ]. Later, a method will be shown for obtaining values of $\mu_0$ and $\sigma_0$.

Let

$$\hat{\mu} \triangleq \mu_0 + h \quad , \quad \hat{\sigma} \triangleq \sigma_0 + k \quad ,$$

in which h and k are corrections to be determined by the

by the iterative process.

By Taylor's theorem, and neglecting powers of h and k above, the first

(9.6.15) $$h \frac{\partial^2 \log L}{\partial \mu_0^2} + k \frac{\partial^2 \log L}{\partial \mu_0 \, \partial \sigma_0} = - \frac{\partial \log L}{\partial \mu_0} ,$$

(9.6.16) $$h \frac{\partial^2 \log L}{\partial \mu_0 \, \partial \sigma_0} + k \frac{\partial^2 \log L}{\partial \sigma_0^2} = - \frac{\partial \log L}{\partial \sigma_0} .$$

The above are two linear equations (9.6.15) and (9.6.16) which can be solved for h and k. The process is then repeated, using the new values $\mu_1 \triangleq \mu_0 + h_1$ and $\sigma_1 \triangleq \sigma_0 + k_1$ as the approximate solutions. The iterative process is repeated until the desired accuracy is achieved.

In this case

(9.6.17)

$$\frac{\partial^2 \log L}{\partial \mu^2} = - \frac{n}{\sigma^2} + \sum_{i=1}^{k} r_i \times \frac{\frac{1}{\sqrt{2\pi}} e^{-\frac{1}{2}\left(\frac{\log T_i - \mu}{\sigma}\right)^2} - \frac{2}{2}\left(\frac{\log T_i - \mu}{\sigma}\right) - \frac{1}{\sigma}}{1 - \int_{-\infty}^{\left(\frac{\log T_i - \mu}{\sigma}\right)} \frac{1}{\sqrt{2\pi}} e^{-\frac{1}{2} t^2} dt} -$$

$$- \sum_{i=1}^{k} r_i \frac{\frac{1}{\sqrt{2\pi}\sigma} e^{-\frac{1}{2}\left(\frac{\log T_i - \mu}{\sigma}\right)^2} \frac{1}{\sqrt{2\pi}\sigma} e^{-\frac{1}{2}\left(\frac{\log T_i - \mu}{\sigma}\right)^2}}{\left(1 - \int_{-\infty}^{\left(\frac{\log T_i - \mu}{\sigma}\right)} e^{-\frac{1}{2}t^2} \, dt\right)^2}$$

$$(9.6.18) \quad \frac{\partial^2 \log L}{\partial \mu^2} = \frac{1}{\sigma^2}\left[ - n + \sum_{i} r_i Z_i(\xi_i - Z_i) \right]$$

Also

(9.6.19)

$$\frac{\partial^2 \log L}{\partial \mu \, \partial \sigma} = \frac{\partial^2 \log L}{\partial \sigma \, \partial \mu} = - \frac{2}{\sigma^3} \sum_{j=1}^{n} (\log t_j - \mu) + \sum_{i=1}^{k} r_i$$

$$\times \frac{\frac{1}{\sqrt{2\pi}\sigma^2} e^{-\frac{1}{2}\left(\frac{\log T_i - \mu}{\sigma}\right)^2} + \frac{1}{\sqrt{2\pi}\sigma} e^{-\frac{1}{2}\left(\frac{\log T_i - \mu}{\sigma}\right)^2} \frac{2}{2}\left(\frac{\log T_i - \mu}{\sigma}\right)^2 \frac{1}{\sigma}}{1 - \int_{-\infty}^{\left(\log T_i - \frac{\mu}{\sigma}\right)} \frac{1}{\sqrt{2\pi}} e^{-\frac{1}{2}t^2} \, dt}$$

$$\times \sum_{i=1}^{k} r_i \frac{\frac{1}{\sqrt{2\pi}\sigma} e^{-\frac{1}{2}\left(\frac{\log T_i - \mu}{\sigma}\right)^2} + \left(\frac{1}{\sqrt{2\pi}\sigma} e^{-\frac{1}{2}\left(\frac{\log T_i - \mu}{\sigma}\right)^2} \left(\frac{\log T_i - \mu}{\sigma}\right)\right)}{\left(1 - \int_{-\infty}^{\frac{\log T_i - \mu}{\sigma}} \frac{1}{\sqrt{2\pi}} e^{-\frac{1}{2}t^2} \, dt\right)^2}$$

(9.6.20)

$$\frac{\partial^2 \log L}{\partial\mu \; \partial\sigma} = \frac{1}{\sigma^2}\left[-\sum_{j=1}^{n}\frac{2(\log t_j-\mu)}{\sigma} + \sum_{i=1}^{k} r_i (Z_i\xi_i^2 - Z_i^2\xi_i - Z_i)\right].$$

(9.6.21)

$$\frac{\partial \log L}{\partial\sigma^2} = \frac{n}{\sigma^2} + \frac{3}{\sigma^4}\sum_{j=1}^{n} (\log t_j - \mu)^2 + \sum_{i=1}^{k} r_i$$

$$\times \frac{\left(\frac{1}{\sqrt{2\pi}} e^{-\frac{1}{2}\left(\frac{\log T_i-\mu}{}\right)^2}\left(\frac{\log T_i-\mu}{\sigma}\right)^3\frac{1}{\sigma^2} + \frac{1}{\sqrt{2\pi}}e^{-\frac{1}{2}\left(\frac{\log T_i-\mu}{\sigma}\right)^2} - \frac{2}{\sigma^2}\left(\frac{\log T_i-\mu}{\sigma}\right)\right)}{1-\int_{-\infty}^{\left(\frac{\log T_i-\mu}{\sigma}\right)}\frac{1}{\sqrt{2\pi}}e^{-\frac{1}{2}t^2}\,dt} - \sum_{i=1}^{k} r_i$$

$$\times \frac{\frac{1}{\sqrt{2\pi}} e^{-\frac{1}{2}\left(\frac{\log T_i-\mu}{\sigma}\right)^2}\frac{1}{\sqrt{2\pi}} e^{-\frac{1}{2}\left(\frac{\log T_i-\mu}{\sigma}\right)^2}\frac{1}{\sigma^2}\left(\frac{\log T_i-\mu}{\sigma}\right)^2}{\left(1-\int_{-\infty}^{\left(\frac{\log T_i-\mu}{\sigma}\right)}\frac{1}{\sqrt{2\pi}}e^{-\frac{1}{2}t^2}\,dt\right)^2}.$$

$$(9.6.22)\quad \frac{\partial \log L}{\partial\sigma^2} = \frac{1}{\sigma^2}\left[n - \frac{3}{\sigma^2}\sum_{j=1}^{n}(\log t_j - \mu)^2 + \sum_{i=1}^{k} r_i(Z_i\xi_i^3 - 2\xi_i Z_i - Z_i^2\xi_i^2)\right] .$$

We will now calculate the initial approximation of $\mu_0$ and $\sigma_0$ by use of the method of probits.

Let $f_i$ designate the number of failure observed between the times of censorship $T_i$ and $T_{i-1}$. Then, the total sample size is

$$(9.6.23)\qquad N = n + \sum_{i=1}^{k} r_i ,$$

where $r_i$ is the number of items removed from the sample at times $T_i$, and

$$n = \sum_{i=1}^{k} f_i .$$

If $f(t)$ is the probability density function of $t$, the conditional probability density, subject to the restriction that $t > T_i$, may be written as

$$f(t|t > T_i) = \frac{f(t)}{1 - F_i}$$

where

$$F_i \triangleq \int_0^{T_i} f(t)dt \quad . \tag{9.6.25}$$

Then, the expected frequencies in progressively censored samples, of the type considered, are as given:

$$\begin{cases} E(f_1) \triangleq N \int_0^{T_1} f(t)dt = N\, P_1 \\ E(f_2) \triangleq N \int_{T_1}^{T_2} f(t)dt - r_1 \int_{T_1}^{T_2} \frac{f(t)dt}{1 - F_1} \\ E(f_3) \triangleq N \int_{T_2}^{T_3} f(t)dt - r_1 \int_{T_2}^{T_3} \frac{f(t)dt}{1 - F_1} \\ \qquad\qquad - r_2 \int_{T_2}^{T_3} \frac{f(t)dt}{1 - F_2} \end{cases} \tag{9.6.26}$$

and, in general

$$E(f_i) \triangleq \left[ N - \sum_{1}^{i-1} \frac{r_j}{1 - F_j} \right] \int_{T_{i-1}}^{T_i} f(t)dt \quad . \tag{9.6.27}$$

Let

$$P_i \triangleq \int_{T_{i-1}}^{T_i} f(t)dt \quad ,$$

then

$$(9.6.27) \qquad E(f_i) = \left[ N - \sum_{j=1}^{i-1} - \frac{r_j}{1 - F_j} \right] P_i \quad .$$

Extimates of $P_i^*$ of $P_i$ may now be obtained as

$$(9.6.28) \begin{cases} P_1^* = \dfrac{f_1}{N} \\ P_i^* \triangleq \dfrac{f_i}{\left[ N - \Sigma_1^{i-1} \dfrac{r_j}{1 - F_j^*} \right]} , \quad i = 2,3,\ldots,k \end{cases}$$

where $F_i^*$ of $F_i$ are given by

$$(9.6.29) \qquad \begin{cases} F_1^* \triangleq P_1^* \\ F_i^* \triangleq F_{i-1}^* + P_i^*, \quad i = 2,3,\ldots,k \quad . \end{cases}$$

Then, using the value of $F_i^*$ and a table of the standard normal distribution, we can obtain an estimate of $\xi_i^*$ of

$$\xi_i \triangleq \frac{\log T_i - \mu}{\sigma} ,$$

where $\xi_i^*$ satisfied

(9.6.30) $$F_i^* = \int_{-\infty}^{\xi_i^*} \frac{1}{\sqrt{2\pi}} e^{-(u^2/2)} du .$$

Then, using the standard probit tranformation $y_i^* = 5 + \xi_i^*$, we can fit a straight line through the $(k-1)$-pair of values $(\log T_i y_i^*)$, $1 < i \leq k-1$. The straight line obtained will be of the form

$$y = 5 + \xi = 5 + \frac{\log T - \mu}{\sigma} .$$

The value of the $\log T$ when $y = 5$ is an approximate value $\mu_0$ of $\mu$, and the slope of the line is an approximate value $\sigma_0$ of $\sigma$. For the purposes of obtaining first values $\mu_0$ and $\sigma_0$, a graphical fit by eye will usually be satisfactory. More accurate results could be obtained by a least-squares fit, but this involves more computational effort. By Theorem 14, $(\hat{\mu},\hat{\sigma})$ are asymptotically normally distributed with mean $(\mu,\sigma)$ and covariance matrix $\Sigma$, where:

(9.6.31)

$$\Sigma = B^{-1} = \begin{bmatrix} -E\left(\dfrac{\partial^2 \log L}{\partial\mu^2}\right) & -E\left(\dfrac{\partial^2 \log L}{\partial\mu \; \partial\sigma}\right) \\ \\ -E\left(\dfrac{\partial^2 \log L}{\partial\sigma \; \partial\mu}\right) & -E\left(\dfrac{\partial^2 \log L}{\partial\sigma^2}\right) \end{bmatrix}^{-1} .$$

By Equation (9.6.18)

$$(9.6.32) \quad -E\left(\frac{\partial^2 \log L}{\partial\mu^2}\right) = \frac{1}{\sigma^2}\left[n - \sum_{i=1}^{k} r_i Z_i (\xi_i - Z_i)\right] .$$

By Equation (9.6.32)

$$(9.6.33) \quad -E\left(\frac{\partial^2 \log L}{\partial\mu \, \partial\sigma}\right) = E\left[\sum_{j=1}^{n} \frac{2(\log t_j - \mu}{\sigma^3}\right] - \frac{1}{\sigma^2}\sum_{i=1}^{k} r_i (Z_i \xi_i^2 - Z_i^2 \xi_i - Z_i) .$$

The $\log t_j \triangleq x_i$, where $x_i$ is a normal random variable $N:(\mu,\sigma^2)$

$$(9.6.34) \quad \begin{cases} E(\log t_j) = E(x_i) = \mu \\ \\ E(\log t_j - \mu)^2 = \text{Var}\,(x_i) = \sigma^2 \end{cases} .$$

Thus

$$E\left[\sum_{j=1}^{n} \frac{2}{\sigma^3}(\log t_j - \mu)\right] = 0 \quad ;$$

$$(9.6.35)\quad -E\left(\frac{\partial^2 \log L}{\partial\sigma^2}\right) = -\frac{1}{\sigma^2}\sum_{i=1}^{k} r_i(Z_i\xi_i^2 - Z_i^2\xi_i - Z_i) \quad .$$

By Equation (9.6.22)

$$(9.6.36)\begin{cases} -E\left(\frac{\partial^2 \log L}{\partial\sigma^2}\right) = E\left(\frac{3}{\sigma^4}\sum_{j=1}^{n}(\log t_j - \mu)^2\right) - \frac{n}{\sigma^2} \\ \qquad + \frac{1}{\sigma^2}\sum_{i=1}^{k} r_i\left(-Z_i\xi_i^3 + 2\xi_i Z_i + Z_i^2\xi_i^2\right) \\ -E\left(\frac{\partial^2 \log L}{\partial\sigma^2}\right) = \frac{3n}{\sigma^2} - \frac{n}{\sigma^2} \\ \qquad + \frac{1}{\sigma^2}\sum_{i=1}^{k} r_i\left(-Z_i\xi_i^3 + 2\xi_i Z_i + Z_i^2\xi_i^2\right) \\ -E\left(\frac{\partial^2 \log L}{\partial\sigma^2}\right) = \frac{2n}{\sigma^2} + \frac{1}{\sigma^2} \\ \qquad \times \sum_{i=1}^{k} r_i\left(-Z_i\xi_i^3 + 2\xi_i Z_i + Z_i^2\xi_i^2\right) \quad . \end{cases}$$

(9.6.37)

$$\sum = \frac{\begin{bmatrix} -E\left( \dfrac{\partial^2 \log L}{\partial\sigma^2} \right) & E\left( \dfrac{\partial^2 \log L}{\partial\mu \;\; \partial\sigma} \right) \\ E\left( \dfrac{\partial^2 \log L}{\partial\mu \;\; \partial\sigma} \right) & -E\left( \dfrac{\partial^2 \log L}{\partial^{\;2}} \right) \end{bmatrix}}{\left[ E\left( \dfrac{\partial^2 \log L}{\partial\mu^2} \right) E\left( \dfrac{\partial \log L}{2\sigma^2} \right) - \left[ E\left( \dfrac{\partial^2 \log L}{\partial\mu \, \partial\sigma} \right) \right]^2 \right]} ,$$

$$(9.6.38) \qquad \sum = \frac{\begin{pmatrix} \dfrac{2n + C}{\sigma^2} & \dfrac{L}{\sigma^2} \\ \dfrac{L}{\sigma^2} & \dfrac{n - D}{\sigma^2} \end{pmatrix}}{\dfrac{2n^2 + nC - 2nD - DC - L^2}{\sigma^4}} ,$$

where

$$(9.6.39) \quad \begin{cases} C \triangleq \displaystyle\sum_{i=1}^{k} r_i(- Z_i\xi_i^3 + 2\xi_i Z_i + Z_i^2\xi_i^2) , \\ D \triangleq \displaystyle\sum_{i=1}^{k} r_i \; Z_i(\xi_i - Z_i) , \\ L = \displaystyle\sum_{i=1}^{k} r_i(Z_i\xi_i^2 - Z_i^2\xi_i - Z_i) . \end{cases}$$

(9.6.40)

$$\Sigma = \begin{bmatrix} \frac{\sigma^2}{n}\left(\frac{2+\frac{C}{n}}{2+\frac{C}{n}-\frac{2D}{n}-\frac{DC}{n^2}-\frac{L^2}{n^2}}\right) & \frac{\sigma^2}{n^2}\left(\frac{L}{2+\frac{C}{n}-\frac{2D}{n}-\frac{DC}{n^2}-\frac{L^2}{n^2}}\right) \\ \frac{\sigma^2}{n^2}\left(\frac{L}{2+\frac{C}{n}-\frac{2D}{n}-\frac{DC}{n^2}-\frac{L^2}{n^2}}\right) & \frac{\sigma^2}{n}\left(\frac{1-\frac{D}{n}}{2+\frac{C}{n}-\frac{2D}{n}-\frac{DC}{n^2}-\frac{L^2}{n^2}}\right) \end{bmatrix}$$

In practice, the final values of $(\partial^2 \log L)/(\partial\sigma^2)$, $(\partial^2 \log L)/(\partial\mu^2)$ and $(\partial^2 \log L)/(\partial\mu\, \partial\sigma)$ are calculated by the iteration technique (Equations (9.6.15) and (9.6.16)) and should approximately equal their expected values, (they converge in probability to their expected values), and may therefore be used to approximate $\Sigma$.

## 9.7 The Type II Censored Sample

We will now estimate, by the method of maximum likelihood, the values of $\mu$ and $\sigma$, as a function of the random time-of-failure and censoring time, setting $t_1 \cdots t_n$ and the predetermined number of components $r_1 \cdots r_n$ having been removed from the test prior to failure.

From Section 9.3, the likelihood function for Type II

censoring is given by:

$$(9.7.1) \qquad L \triangleq \prod_{i=1}^{n} D_i \, f(t_i) |1 - F(t_i)|^{r_i}$$

where

$$(9.7.2) \qquad D_i \triangleq N - \sum_{j=1}^{i-1} r_j - i + 1 \; .$$

The maximum likelihood estimates $\hat{\mu}$ and $\hat{\sigma}$ of $\mu$ and $\sigma$, by definition of maximum likelihood, satisfy the simultaneous equations given by:

$$\frac{\partial \log L}{\partial \mu} = 0 \quad , \quad \frac{\partial \log L}{\partial \sigma} = 0 \; .$$

Then

$$(9.7.3) \quad \text{Log } L = \sum_{i=1}^{n} \log D_i + \sum_{i=1}^{n} \log f(t_i) + \sum_{i=1}^{n} r_i \log |1 - F(t_i)|$$

$$(9.7.4)\quad 0 = \frac{\partial \log L}{\partial \mu}$$

$$= \sum_{i=1}^{n} \frac{\partial \log f(t_i)}{\partial \mu} + \sum_{i=1}^{n} \frac{\partial r_i \log |1 - F(t_i)|}{\partial \mu}$$

$$(9.7.5)\quad 0 = \frac{\partial \log L}{\partial \sigma}$$

$$= \sum_{i=1}^{n} \frac{\partial \log f(t_i)}{\partial \sigma} + \sum_{i=1}^{n} \frac{\partial r_i \log |1 - F(t_i)|}{\partial \sigma}.$$

These equations are the same as (9.6.12) and (9.6.14) for the Type I Censoring, with the exception that $t_i$ replaces $T_i$ and

$$\xi_i \triangleq \frac{\log t_i - \mu}{\sigma} .$$

Thus, the estimating equations for $\hat{\mu}$ and $\hat{\sigma}$ are:

$$(9.7.6)\quad \frac{\partial \log L}{\partial \mu} = 0$$

$$= \frac{1}{\sigma} \left[ \sum_{i=1}^{n} \left( \frac{\log t_i - \mu}{\sigma} + r_i Z_i \right) \right] ,$$

$$(9.7.7) \quad \frac{\partial \log L}{\partial \sigma} = 0 = \frac{1}{\sigma}$$

$$\times \left\{ - n + \sum_{i=1}^{n} \left[ \frac{(\log t_i - \quad)^2}{\sigma^2} + r_i Z_i \xi_i \right] \right\} .$$

where

$$Z_i \triangleq \frac{\frac{1}{\sqrt{2\pi}} e^{-\frac{1}{2}\xi_i^2}}{1 - \int_{-\infty}^{\xi_i} \frac{1}{\sqrt{2\pi}} e^{-(t^2/2)} \, dt}$$

and $\xi_i \triangleq (\log t_i - \mu)/\sigma$ .

Equations (9.7.6) and (9.7.7) must be solved by iterative (approximate) procedures for the estomates $\hat{\mu}$ and $\hat{\sigma}$. As in the previous case (Type I Censoring), Newton's method can be used. Later, the method of obtaining values of $\mu_0$ and $\sigma_0$ to start the iteration will be shown.

Let

$$\hat{\mu} \triangleq \mu_0 + h \quad \text{and} \quad \hat{\sigma} \triangleq \sigma_0 + k$$

where h and k care corrections determined by the iterative process, and satisfy the Equations as in (9.6.15) and (9.6.16). Then we have two linear equations which can be solved for h and k. The process is repeated, using the new values $\mu_1 \triangleq \mu_0 + h_1$ and $\sigma_1 \triangleq \sigma_0 + k_1$ as the approximate solutions. The iteration process is repeated until the desired accuracy is achieved.

In this case $(\partial^2 \log L/(\partial\sigma^2)$, $(\partial^2 \log L)/(\partial\mu\, \partial\sigma)$ and $(\partial^2 \log L/(\partial\mu^2)$ are the same as the case for Type I censoring, except $t_i$ replaces $T_i$. Thus:

(9.7.8) $$\frac{\partial^2 \log L}{\partial\mu^2} = \frac{1}{\sigma^2}\left[-n + \sum_{i=1}^{n} r_i Z_i(\xi_i - Z_i)\right]$$

(9.7.9) $$\frac{\partial^2 \log L}{\partial\mu\ \partial\sigma} = \frac{1}{\sigma^2} \times \left\{\sum_{i=1}^{n}\left[-\frac{2(\log t_i - \mu)}{\sigma} + r_i(Z_i\xi_i^2 - Z_i^2\xi_i - Z_i)\right]\right\}$$

(9.7.10) $$\frac{\partial^2 \log L}{\partial\sigma^2} = \frac{1}{\sigma^2} \times \left\{n + \sum_{i=1}^{n}\left[-\frac{3}{\sigma^2}(\log t_i - \mu)^2 + r_i(Z_i\xi_i^3 - 2\xi_i Z_i - Z_i^2\xi_i^2)\right]\right\}$$

The initial values of $\mu_0$ and $\sigma_0$ can be obtained by the method of probits, in a manner similar to that used for Type I Censoring. In this case, $f_i$ is always 1, thus:

$$(9.7.11)\quad \begin{cases} P_1^* \triangleq \dfrac{1}{N} \\[2ex] P_i^* \triangleq \dfrac{1}{N - \Sigma_1^{i-1} \dfrac{r_j}{1 - F_j^*}}, \quad i = 2,3,\ldots,n \end{cases}$$

and

$$(9.7.12)\quad F_1^* \triangleq P_1^*, \quad F_i^* \triangleq F_{i-1}^*, \qquad i = 2,3,\ldots,n \;.$$

Then, $\xi_i^*$ is obtained by using a table of the standard normal cumulative distribution:

$$(9.7.13)\qquad F_i^* \triangleq \int_{-\infty}^{\xi_i^*} \frac{1}{\sqrt{2\pi}}\, e^{-(u^2/2)}\, du \;.$$

Using the standard probit transformation, $y_i^* = 5 + \xi_i^*$, a straight line can be fitted through the $n-1$ pair of values $(\log\, T_i, y_i^*)$, $1 \le i \le n-1$. The straight line obtained will be of the form

$$y = 5 + \xi = 5 + \frac{\log T - \mu}{\sigma} \;.$$

The value of $\log T$ where $y = 5$, is an approximation $\mu_0$ of $\mu$, and the slope of the line is an approximate value $\sigma_0$ of $\sigma$.

By Theorem 15, $(\hat{\mu},\hat{\sigma})$ are asymptotically normally distributed, with mean $(\mu,\sigma)$ and covariance $\Sigma$, where $\Sigma$ is as in Equation (9.6.31). However, it is very difficult, if not impossible, to obtain in closed form the expressions:

$$-E\left(\frac{\partial^2 \log L}{\partial\mu^2}\right), \quad -E\left(\frac{\partial^2 \log L}{\partial\mu\, \partial\sigma}\right), \quad -E\left(\frac{\partial^2 \log L}{\partial\sigma^2}\right),$$

since this involves evaluating integrals of the type

$$K \triangleq \int_0^\infty g(Z_i)\, f(x)dx \ ;$$

$$g(Z_i) = g\left(\frac{e^{-\frac{1}{2}\xi_i^2}}{1 - \int_{-\infty}^{\xi_i} \frac{1}{\sqrt{2\pi}}\, e^{-\frac{1}{2}t^2}\, dt}\right) .$$

Thus, in practice, the final values of $(\partial^2 \log L)/(\partial\sigma^2)$, $(\partial^2 \log L)/(\partial\mu^2)$ and $(\partial^2 \log L)/(\partial\mu\, \partial\sigma)$, as calculated by (9.6.15) and (9.6.16) will be approximately equal to their expected values and may be used to approximate $\Sigma$.

## 9.8 Estimation of Component Reliability

A best asymptotically normal estimate of the reliability of a component is given by:

$$(9.8.1)\quad \hat{R}(T,\theta_1,\ldots,\theta_\ell) = 1 - \int_0^T f(t,\hat{\theta}_1,\ldots,\hat{\theta}_\ell)dt \quad .$$

For the log-normal distribution this becomes:

$$(9.8.2)\quad \hat{R}(T,\mu,\sigma) = 1 - \int_0^T \frac{1}{\sqrt{2\pi}\hat{\sigma}} e^{-\frac{1}{2}\left(\frac{\log t-\hat{\mu}}{\hat{\sigma}}\right)^2} \frac{1}{t}\,dt \quad .$$

This estimate of the reliability of the component can be used for computing the lower confidence limit of the true reliability of the component, in the case of large sample size. Applying Theorem 16, $\hat{R}(T,\mu,\sigma)$ is asymptotically normally distributed about the "true" reliability $R(T,\mu,\sigma)$ with

$$(9.8.3)\quad \mathrm{Var}\,[\hat{R}(T,\mu,\sigma)]$$

$$= \sum_{i=1}^{2}\sum_{j=1}^{2} \left(\frac{\partial\hat{R}}{\partial\hat{\theta}_i}\right)\left(\frac{\partial\hat{R}}{\partial\hat{\theta}_j}\right)\sigma^{ij}(\hat{\theta}_i,\hat{\theta}_j) \quad ,$$

where $\hat{\theta}_1 = \hat{\mu}$, $\hat{\theta}_2 = \hat{\sigma}$ and $\sigma^{ij}(\hat{\theta}_i,\hat{\theta}_j)$ is the covariance of $\theta_i$ and $\theta_j$. Thus, for the lognormal distribution, the integral

$$(9.8.4)\quad \int_0^T \frac{1}{\sqrt{2\pi}\hat{\sigma}} e^{-\frac{1}{2}\left(\frac{\log t-\hat{\mu}}{\hat{\sigma}}\right)^2} \frac{1}{t}\,dt =$$

$$= \int_{-\infty}^{\left(\frac{\log T - \hat{\mu}}{\hat{\sigma}}\right)} \frac{1}{\sqrt{2\pi}} e^{-(u^2/2)} dt$$

with the substitution, $u \overset{\Delta}{=} (\text{Log } t - \hat{\mu})/\hat{\sigma}$, and

$$(9.8.5) \quad \hat{R}(T,\mu,\sigma) = 1 - \int_{-\infty}^{\left(\frac{\log T - \hat{\mu}}{\hat{\sigma}}\right)} \frac{1}{\sqrt{2\pi}} e^{-(t^2/2)} dt$$

and

$$(9.8.6) \quad \frac{\partial \hat{R}}{\partial \hat{\mu}} = \frac{1}{\sqrt{2\pi}} e^{-\frac{1}{2}\left(\frac{\log T - \hat{\mu}}{\hat{\sigma}}\right)} \frac{1}{\sigma} = \frac{\partial \hat{R}}{\partial \hat{\theta}_1}$$

$$(9.8.7) \quad \frac{\partial \hat{R}}{\partial \hat{\sigma}} = \frac{1}{\sqrt{2\pi}} e^{-\frac{1}{2}\left(\frac{\log T - \hat{\mu}}{\hat{\sigma}}\right)^2} \frac{1}{\sigma^2} (\log T - \hat{\mu}) = \frac{\partial \hat{R}}{\partial \hat{\theta}_2} ;$$

so

$$(9.8.8) \quad \text{Var } \hat{R}(T,\mu,\sigma)$$

$$= \sum_{i=1}^{2} \sum_{j=1}^{2} \left( \frac{\partial \hat{R}}{\partial \hat{\theta}_i} \right) \left( \frac{\partial \hat{R}}{\partial \hat{\theta}_j} \right) \sigma^{ij}(\hat{\theta}_i, \hat{\theta}_j)$$

For the case of the random sample,

$$\sum_{\hat{\mu},\hat{\sigma}} = \begin{pmatrix} \frac{\hat{\sigma}^2}{N} & 0 \\ 0 & \frac{\hat{\sigma}^2}{2N} \end{pmatrix}$$

and

$$(9.8.10)\quad \text{Var}\ \hat{R}(T,\mu,\sigma) = \left(\frac{\partial \hat{R}}{\partial \hat{\mu}}\right)^2 + \frac{\hat{\sigma}^2}{N} + \left(\frac{\partial R}{\partial \hat{\sigma}}\right)^2 \frac{\hat{\sigma}^2}{2N}$$

$$(9.8.11)\quad \text{Var}\ \hat{R}(T,\mu,\sigma) = \frac{1}{2\pi\hat{\sigma}^2}\, e^{-\left(\frac{\log T-\hat{\mu}}{\hat{\sigma}}\right)^2} \left(\frac{\hat{\sigma}^2}{N}\right),$$

$$+ \frac{1}{2\pi\hat{\sigma}^4}\, e^{-\left(\frac{\log T-\hat{\mu}}{\hat{\sigma}}\right)^2} \left(\frac{\hat{\sigma}^2}{2N}\right),$$

$$(9.8.12)\quad \text{Var}\ \hat{R}(T,\mu,\sigma) = \frac{1}{2\pi N}\, e^{-\left(\frac{\log T-\hat{\mu}}{\hat{\sigma}}\right)^2} \left(1 + \frac{1}{2\hat{\sigma}^2}\right).$$

For a given confidence coefficient, $\alpha$, the $100(1 - \alpha)$ percent lower confidence interval for the "true" reliability of an item $R(T,\mu,\sigma)$ is

$$(9.8.13)\qquad \hat{R}(T,\mu,\sigma) - Z_\alpha \sqrt{\text{Var}\ \hat{R}(T,\mu,\sigma)}\ ,$$

where $Z_\alpha$ is the standard normal deviate, such that $P(Z > Z_\alpha) = \alpha$. Thus

$$(9.8.14)\quad P\left[R(T,\mu,\sigma) \geq \hat{R}(T,\mu,\sigma) - Z_\alpha \sqrt{\text{Var}\ \hat{R}(T,\mu,\sigma)}\right]$$

$$= 1 - \alpha\ .$$

For the case of the Type I Censored Sample we have:

(9.8.15)

$$\sum_{\hat{\mu},\hat{\sigma}} = \begin{bmatrix} \dfrac{\hat{\sigma}^2}{n}\left(\dfrac{2+\frac{C}{n}}{2+\frac{C}{n}-\frac{2D}{n}-\frac{DC}{n^2}-\frac{L^2}{n^2}}\right) & \dfrac{\hat{\sigma}^2}{n^2}\left(\dfrac{L}{2+\frac{C}{n}-\frac{2D}{n}-\frac{DC}{n^2}-\frac{L^2}{n^2}}\right) \\ \dfrac{\hat{\sigma}^2}{n^2}\left(\dfrac{L}{2+\frac{C}{n}-\frac{2D}{n}-\frac{DC}{n^2}-\frac{L^2}{n^2}}\right) & \dfrac{\hat{\sigma}^2}{n}\left(\dfrac{1-\frac{D}{n}}{2+\frac{C}{n}-\frac{2D}{n}-\frac{DC}{n^2}-\frac{L^2}{n^2}}\right) \end{bmatrix}.$$

Then

(9.8.16)

$$\text{Var }\hat{R}(T,\mu,\sigma)$$

$$= \frac{\hat{\sigma}^2}{n\left(2+\frac{C}{n}-\frac{2D}{n}-\frac{DC}{n^2}-\frac{L^2}{n^2}\right)}$$

$$\times\left[\left(\frac{\partial R}{\partial\hat{\mu}}\right)^2\left(2+\frac{C}{n}\right)+2\left(\frac{\partial R}{\partial\hat{\mu}}\right)\left(\frac{\partial R}{\partial\hat{\sigma}}\right)\frac{L}{n}+\left(\frac{\partial R}{\partial\hat{\sigma}}\right)^2\left(1-\frac{D}{n}\right)\right]$$

where (9.8.6) and (9.8.7) give $(\partial R/\partial\mu)$ and $(\partial R/\partial\sigma)$. Then for a given $\alpha$ coefficient

(9.8.17) $P\left|R(T,\mu,\sigma) \geq \hat{R}(T,\mu,\sigma) - Z_\alpha\sqrt{\text{Var }\hat{R}(T,\mu,\sigma)}\right| = 1-\alpha.$

with $Z_\alpha$ a standard normal deviate, such that $P(Z > Z_\alpha) = \alpha$.

In the case of the Type II Censored Sample, $\Sigma_{\mu,\sigma}$ must be obtained by the iteration techniques previously developed, then:

(9.8.18)

$$\text{Var } \hat{R}(T,\mu,\sigma) = \left(\frac{\partial\hat{R}}{\partial\hat{\mu}}\right)^2 \text{Var }(\hat{\mu}) + 2\left(\frac{\partial\hat{R}}{\partial\hat{\mu}}\right)\left(\frac{\partial\hat{R}}{\partial\hat{\sigma}}\right)\text{Cov }(\hat{\mu},\hat{\sigma}) + \left(\frac{\partial\hat{R}}{\partial\hat{\sigma}}\right)^2 \text{Var }(\hat{\sigma})$$

and

$$(9.8.19)\quad P\left|R(T,\mu,\sigma) \geq \hat{R}(T,\mu,\sigma) - Z_\alpha \sqrt{\text{Var } \hat{R}(T,\mu,\sigma)}\right| = 1 - \alpha$$

with $Z_\alpha$ a standard normal deviate, such that $P(Z > Z_\alpha) = \alpha$.

## 9.9 Estimation of Component Hazard Rate

A best asymptotically normal estimate of the hazard rate of a component is given in the case of the log-normal by:

$$(9.9.1)\quad \hat{Z}(T,\mu,\sigma) = \frac{g(T,\hat{\mu},\hat{\sigma})}{\hat{R}(T,\hat{\mu},\hat{\sigma})}$$

$$= \frac{\frac{1}{\sqrt{2\pi}\hat{\sigma}} e^{-\frac{1}{2}\left(\frac{\log T-\hat{\mu}}{\hat{\sigma}}\right)^2} \frac{1}{T}}{1 - \int_0^T \frac{1}{\sqrt{2\pi}\hat{\sigma}} e^{-\frac{1}{2}\left(\frac{\operatorname{Log} T-\hat{\mu}}{\hat{\sigma}}\right)^2} \frac{1}{t}\, dt} .$$

In a similar manner to that of Section 9.8, this estimate of the hazard rate involving $\hat{\mu}$ and $\hat{\sigma}$ can be used for computing an upper confidence limit of the "true" hazard rate of a component, in the case of large sample size.

Applying Theorem 16, $\hat{Z}(t,\mu,\sigma)$ is asymptotically normally distributed about the "true" hazard rate $Z(T,\mu,\sigma)$ with

$$(9.9.2)\quad \operatorname{Var}(\hat{Z}(T,\mu,\sigma)$$

$$= \sum_{i=1}^{2} \sum_{j=1}^{2} \left(\frac{\partial \hat{Z}}{\partial \hat{\theta}_i}\right)\left(\frac{\partial \hat{Z}}{\partial \hat{\theta}_j}\right) \sigma^{ij}(\hat{\theta}_i,\hat{\theta}_j)$$

where $\hat{\theta}_1 = \hat{\mu}$, $\hat{\theta}_2 = \hat{\sigma}$ and $\sigma^{ij}(\hat{\theta}_i,\hat{\theta}_j)$ is the covariance of $\hat{\theta}_i$ and $\hat{\theta}_j$.

Thus, for the log-normal distribution, the integral

is as in Section 9.8, Equation (9.8.4), with the substitution

$$u = \frac{\log t - \hat{\mu}}{\hat{\sigma}} .$$

Then

$$(9.9.3) \quad \hat{Z}(T,\mu,\sigma) = \frac{\frac{1}{\sqrt{2\pi}\hat{\sigma}} e^{-\frac{1}{2}\left(\frac{\log T-\hat{\mu}}{\hat{\sigma}}\right)^2} \frac{1}{T}}{1 - \int_{-\infty}^{\left(\frac{\log T-\hat{\mu}}{\hat{\sigma}}\right)} \frac{1}{\sqrt{2\pi}} e^{-\frac{1}{2}u^2} dt}$$

$$(9.9.4) \quad \frac{\partial\hat{Z}}{\partial\hat{\mu}} = \frac{\frac{1}{\sqrt{2\pi}\hat{\sigma}} e^{-\frac{1}{2}\left(\frac{\log T-\hat{\mu}}{\hat{\sigma}}\right)^2} \frac{1}{T}\left(-\frac{2}{2}\right)\left(\frac{\log T-\hat{\mu}}{\hat{\sigma}}\right)\left(-\frac{1}{\hat{\sigma}}\right)}{1 - \int_{-\infty}^{\left(\frac{\log T-\hat{\mu}}{\hat{\sigma}}\right)} \frac{1}{\sqrt{2\pi}} e^{-\frac{1}{2}u^2} du}$$

$$- \frac{\frac{1}{\sqrt{2\pi}\hat{\sigma}} e^{-\frac{1}{2}\left(\frac{\log T-\hat{\mu}}{\hat{\sigma}}\right)^2} \left|\frac{1}{T} - \frac{1}{\sqrt{2\pi}} e^{-\frac{1}{2}\left(\frac{\log T-\hat{\mu}}{\hat{\sigma}}\right)^2} - \frac{1}{\hat{\sigma}}\right|}{\left(1 - \int_{-\infty}^{\left(\frac{\log T-\hat{\mu}}{\hat{\sigma}}\right)} \frac{1}{\sqrt{2\pi}} e^{-\frac{1}{2}u^2} du\right)^2}$$

$$(9.9.5) \quad \frac{\partial\hat{Z}}{\partial\hat{\mu}} = \frac{\frac{1}{\sqrt{2\pi}\hat{\sigma}^2} e^{-\frac{1}{2}\left(\frac{\log T-\hat{\mu}}{\hat{\sigma}}\right)^2} \frac{1}{T}}{1 - \int_{-\infty}^{\left(\frac{\log T-\hat{\mu}}{\hat{\sigma}}\right)} e^{-\frac{1}{2}u^2} du} \times$$

$$\times \left[ \frac{\log T - \hat{\mu}}{\hat{\sigma}} - \frac{\frac{1}{\sqrt{2\pi}} e^{-\frac{1}{2}\left(\frac{\log T-\hat{\mu}}{\hat{\sigma}}\right)^2}}{1 - \int_{-\infty}^{\left(\frac{\log T-\hat{\mu}}{\hat{\sigma}}\right)} \frac{1}{\sqrt{2\pi}} e^{-\frac{1}{2}u^2} du} \right]$$

(9.9.6)

$$\frac{\partial \hat{Z}}{\partial \hat{\sigma}} = \frac{-\frac{1}{\sqrt{2\pi}\sigma^2} e^{-\frac{1}{2}\left(\frac{\log T-\hat{\mu}}{\hat{\sigma}}\right)^2} \frac{1}{T} + \frac{1}{\sqrt{2\pi}\hat{\sigma}^2} e^{-\frac{1}{2}\left(\frac{\log T-\hat{\mu}}{\hat{\sigma}}\right)^2} \frac{1}{T}\left(\frac{-2}{-2}\right)\left(\frac{1}{\hat{\sigma}^3}\right)\left(\log T - \hat{\mu}\right)}{1 - \int_{-\infty}^{\left(\frac{\log T-\hat{\mu}}{\hat{\sigma}}\right)} \frac{1}{\sqrt{2\pi}} e^{-(u^2/2)} du}$$

$$- \frac{\frac{1}{\sqrt{2\pi}\hat{\sigma}} e^{-\frac{1}{2}\left(\frac{\log T-\hat{\mu}}{\hat{\sigma}}\right)^2} \frac{1}{T}\left[-\frac{1}{\sqrt{2\pi}} e^{-\frac{1}{2}\left(\frac{\log T-\hat{\mu}}{\hat{\sigma}}\right)^2} - \frac{1}{\hat{\sigma}^2}(\log T - \hat{\mu})\right]}{\left(1 - \int_{-\infty}^{\left(\frac{\log T-\hat{\mu}}{\hat{\sigma}}\right)} \frac{1}{\sqrt{2\pi}} e^{-(u^2/2)} du\right)}$$

(9.9.7)

$$\frac{\partial \hat{Z}}{\partial \hat{\sigma}} = \frac{\frac{1}{\sqrt{2\pi}\hat{\sigma}^2} e^{-\frac{1}{2}\left(\frac{\log T-\hat{\mu}}{\hat{\sigma}}\right)^2} \frac{1}{T}}{1 - \int_{-\infty}^{\left(\frac{\log T-\hat{\mu}}{\hat{\sigma}}\right)} \frac{1}{\sqrt{2\pi}} e^{-(u^2/2)} du}$$

$$\times \left[ -1 + \left(\frac{\log T - \hat{\mu}}{\hat{\sigma}}\right)^2 - \frac{\frac{1}{\sqrt{2\pi}} e^{-\frac{1}{2}\left(\frac{\log T-\hat{\mu}}{\hat{\sigma}}\right)} \left(\frac{\log T - \hat{\mu}}{\hat{\sigma}}\right)}{1 - \int_{-\infty}^{\left(\frac{\log T-\hat{\mu}}{\hat{\sigma}}\right)} \frac{1}{\sqrt{2\pi}} e^{-(u^2/2)} du} \right]$$

and we have Equation (9.9.2).

For the case of random sampling, we have, as for $\Sigma_{\hat{\mu},\hat{\sigma}}$ the same as that for estimating component reliability in Section 9.8, Equation (9.8.9), and

$$(9.9.8) \qquad \operatorname{Var} \hat{Z}(T,\mu,\sigma) = \left(\frac{\partial \hat{Z}}{\partial \hat{\mu}}\right)^2 \frac{\hat{\sigma}^2}{N} + \left(\frac{\partial Z}{\partial \hat{\sigma}}\right)^2 \frac{\hat{\sigma}^2}{2N}$$

(9.9.9)

$$\operatorname{Var} \hat{Z}(T,\mu,\sigma) = \frac{1}{N} \cdot \frac{\dfrac{1}{2\pi\hat{\sigma}^2 T^2}\, e^{-\left(\frac{\log T - \hat{\mu}}{\hat{\sigma}}\right)^2}}{\left[1 - \int_{-\infty}^{\left(\frac{\log T - \hat{\mu}}{\hat{\sigma}}\right)} \dfrac{1}{\sqrt{2\pi}}\, e^{-(u^2/2)}\, du\right]}$$

$$\times \left\{ \left[ \frac{\log T - \hat{\mu}}{\hat{\sigma}} - \frac{\dfrac{1}{\sqrt{2\pi}}\, e^{-\frac{1}{2}\left(\frac{\log T - \hat{\mu}}{\hat{\sigma}}\right)^2}}{1 - \int_{-\infty}^{\left(\frac{\log T - \hat{\mu}}{\hat{\sigma}}\right)} \dfrac{1}{\sqrt{2\pi}}\, e^{-(u^2/2)}\, du} \right]^2 \right.$$

$$\left. + \frac{1}{2} \left[ -1 + \left(\frac{\log T - \hat{\mu}}{\hat{\sigma}}\right)^2 - \frac{\dfrac{1}{\sqrt{2\pi}}\, e^{-\frac{1}{2}\left(\frac{\log T - \hat{\mu}}{\hat{\sigma}}\right)^2} \left(\dfrac{\log T - \hat{\mu}}{\hat{\sigma}}\right)}{1 - \int_{-\infty}^{\left(\frac{\log T - \hat{\ }}{\hat{\sigma}}\right)} \dfrac{1}{\sqrt{2\pi}}\, e^{-(u^2/2)}\, du} \right]^2 \right\}$$

For a given $\alpha$ confidence coefficient, the $100(1 - \alpha)$ percent upper confidence interval for the "true" hazard rate of an item $Z(T, \ ,\sigma)$ is

$$(9.9.10) \qquad \hat{Z}(T,\mu,\sigma) + h_\alpha \sqrt{\mathrm{Var}\ \hat{Z}(T,\mu,\sigma)} \ ,$$

where $h_\alpha$ is a standard normal deviate such that $P(h > h_\alpha) = \alpha$. Thus,

$$(9.9.11) \quad P\left|Z(T,\mu,\sigma) \le \hat{Z}(T,\mu,\sigma) + h_\alpha \sqrt{\mathrm{Var}\ \hat{Z}(T,\mu,\sigma)}\right| = 1 - \alpha.$$

For the Type I Censored Sample, as previously calculated, the Var of $\hat{Z}(T,\mu,\sigma)$ becomes

(9.9.12)

$$\mathrm{Var}\ \hat{Z}(T,\mu,\sigma) = \frac{\hat{\sigma}^2}{2n + \frac{C}{n} - \frac{2D}{n} - \frac{DC}{n^2} - \frac{L^2}{n^2}}$$

$$\times \left[\left(\frac{\partial\hat{Z}}{\partial\hat{\mu}}\right)^2\left(2 + \frac{C}{n}\right) + 2\left(\frac{\partial\hat{Z}}{\partial\hat{\mu}}\right)\left(\frac{\partial\hat{Z}}{\partial\hat{\sigma}}\right)\frac{L}{n} + \left(\frac{\partial\hat{Z}}{\partial\hat{\sigma}}\right)^2\left(1 - \frac{D}{n}\right)\right]$$

where $(\partial\hat{Z}/\partial\hat{\mu})$ and $(\partial\hat{Z}/\partial\hat{\sigma})$ are given by Equations (9.9.5) and (9.9.7), respectively. Then, for a given $\alpha$ confidence coefficient, we have (9.9.11) where $h_\alpha$ is a standard normal deviate such that $P(h > h_\alpha) = \alpha$.

For the case of Type II Censored Samples, the covariance matrix $\Sigma_{\hat{\mu},\hat{\sigma}}$ must be obtained by the iteration techniques previously developed. Then,

(9.9.13)

$$\text{Var } \hat{Z}(T,\mu,\sigma) = \left(\frac{\partial\hat{Z}}{\partial\hat{\mu}}\right)^2 \text{Var }(\hat{\mu}) + 2\left(\frac{\partial\hat{Z}}{\partial\hat{\mu}}\right)\left(\frac{\partial\hat{Z}}{\partial\hat{\sigma}}\right)\text{Cov }(\hat{\mu},\hat{\sigma}) + \left(\frac{\partial\hat{Z}}{\partial\hat{\sigma}}\right)^2 \text{Var }(\hat{\sigma})$$

and we have (9.9.11) where $h_\alpha$ is a standard normal deviate such that $P(h > h_\alpha) = \alpha$.

# CHAPTER 10. A SIMPLE TWO-PARAMETER WEIBULL MODEL FOR THE INTER-EVENT DISTRIBUTION

Of all the possible candidates for effects, the Weibull distribution, depending on a scale parameter and a shape parameter, receives wide application in a variety of fields, i.e., electronics, engineering and biometrics in the field of human mortality. The reason for the latter is that mortality, under this model, is proportional to the $\beta^{th}$ power of longevity and when $\beta > 1$, the mortality increases with age, as it should be in the case of all mammals, including human beings. Also, interestingly, when $\beta < 1$, the mortality decreases and the model can be used to account for the high infant mortality occurring during the first few days or months of life, settling down to some constant level, the duration of which represents our useful life. We, therefore, have studied in depth (comparing with the work of every other researcher on this distribution) in this chapter, the statistical properties of this distribution. The work is presented in such a way that the reader who wants to use this approach can do so with minimal effort on his part.

## 10.1 The Two-Parameter Weibull Model

We propose an estimator of $1/\beta$, where $\beta$ is the shape parameter of the Weibull distribution that uses the $\ell^{th}$ and $m^{th}$ order statistics of a sample of N failure times. The statistic is unbiased. The exact variance for a given sample size N, N up to 26, is tabulated. The optimum $\ell$ and m are determined. The efficiencies of the optimal estimates, as compared with the Cramer-Rao bound are computed and it is discovered that the efficiency approaches 70 percent for large samples. This result is consistent with the asymptotic result Dubey [56] obtained, using the large-sample properties of quantiles. In fact, is this chapter we discover that the size of the so-called large sample is about 20. The distribution function of the estimator is obtained and applied to testing hypothesis and to obtaining the power of the tests. Several numerical examples are given; a computer program being included. The variance and the cumulative distribution function of the estimator, for small sample sizes, are computed.

Dubey [56] proposed a biased estimator, based on two-order statistics, for the shape parameter. He found the variance of the estimator for large sample sizes to be $0.92\ \beta^2/n$. Menon [139] found the Cramer-Rao bound to be

$0.61/n\beta^2$ for an unbiased estimator of $1/\beta$ when the scale parameter, $\alpha$, is unknown. Mann [135] obtained an estimator of $1/\beta$ as a sum of weighted order statistics, using the results of Lieblein [127] to calculate the weights. Maximum likelihood estimators of $\beta$ have been studied by Harter and Moore [99] for both complete and censored samples of order statistics. Cohen [31] obtained the maximum likelihood estimator of $\beta$ for complete random samples and Weibull [213]. estimated the shape and scale parameters by least-square methods. Menon [139] proposed a consistent estimator of $1/\beta$, using a complete random sample, with an asymptotic efficiency of 55 percent. The estimator of $1/\beta$ developed herein is easy to use, can be applied to censored data, is unbiased for small samples, and appears to be asymptotically 70 percent efficient.

## 10.2 The Estimator

Let the positive random variable, T, have the Weibull distribution (denoted $W(\alpha,\beta)$ ) with shape parameter $\beta$ and scale parameter $\alpha$. The cumulative distribution function is:

$$(10.2.1)\quad F(t) = \begin{cases} 1 - e^{-\alpha t^{\beta}}, & t \geq 0,\ \alpha > 0,\ \beta > 0 \\ 0, & t < 0 \end{cases}.$$

The shape parameter $\beta$ can be expressed as:

$$(10.2.2)\qquad \beta = \frac{\ln \ln \dfrac{1}{(1-\varepsilon)} - \ln \ln \dfrac{1}{(1-\eta)}}{\ln \lambda - \ln \mu}$$

where $F(\lambda) = \varepsilon$ and $F(\mu) = \eta$.

This expression motivates our estimate of $\gamma = 1/\beta$ as:

$$(10.2.3)\qquad \hat{\gamma} = [\ln T_{(m)} - \ln T_{(\ell)}]\, f(N,\ell,m)$$

where $T_{(i)}$, is the $i^{th}$ order statistic and $f(N,\ell,m)$ is an unbiasing factor tabulated in Table 2.

The unbiasing factor is determined so that $E(\hat{\gamma}) = \gamma$. The variance and standard deviation of the estimator are denoted by:

$$G2 = g^2(N,\ell,m) = \text{Var}\ \frac{\hat{\gamma}}{\gamma^2},$$

and

$$g(N,\ell,m) = \text{Std. Dev.}\ \frac{\hat{\gamma}}{\gamma},$$

respectively.

Let

$$Y = (\ln T_{(m)} - \ln T_{(\ell)})\,\frac{\beta}{2} \ .$$

We have for unbiasedness

$$f(N,\ell,m) = \frac{1}{2E(Y)} \ ,$$

and the variance of the estimator is

$$G2 = \frac{E(Y^2)}{E^2(Y)} - 1 \ .$$

Denote the cumulative distribution function of $Y$ by $G(y) = P(Y \le y)$. We derive $E(Y)$ and $E(Y^2)$ as:

$$(10.2.4) \quad E(Y) = 2A \sum_{i=0}^{\ell-1} \sum_{j=0}^{m-\ell-1} C_{ij} \frac{1}{b^2} \frac{1}{4R} \ln \frac{R+1}{R}$$

and

$$(10.2.5) \quad E(Y^2) = 2A \sum_{i=0}^{\ell-1} \sum_{j=0}^{m-\ell-1} C_{ij} \frac{1}{b^2} \frac{1}{8R} \left[ \ln^2 \frac{R+1}{R} + 2g(1+R) \right]$$

where:

$$A = \frac{N!}{(\ell-1)!\,(m-\ell-1)!\,(N-m)!}$$

$$g(x) = \sum_{k=1}^{\infty} \frac{1}{k2^k_X}$$

$$b = m - \ell + i - j$$

$$R = \frac{N + j - m + 1}{b}$$

$$C_{ij} = (-1)^{i+j} \binom{\ell - 1}{i} \binom{m - \ell - 1}{j} ,$$

and $\ell$, m and N are integers with $0 < \ell < m \leq N$.

Lieblein [128] obtained exact formulas for moments of order statistics from the extreme value distribution:

$$G(y) = e^{-e^{-y}}, \qquad -\infty < y < \infty .$$

Let $Y(N - i + 1) = \beta \ln \alpha T(i)$, where $T \sim W(\alpha, \beta)$, then $Y(N - i + 1)$ is an order statistic from $G(y)$. We obtain

$$f(N, N - i + 1, N - j + 1) = \frac{1}{\mu(i) - \mu(j)}$$

and

$$G2 = [\sigma(i,i) + \sigma(i,j)]f^2$$

where

$$\mu(i) = E(Y(i)) \quad \text{and} \quad \sigma(i,j) = E(Y(i) - \mu(i)(Y(j) - \mu(j))$$

are as tabulated by Lieblein [128].

We have obtained concise formulas for $E(Y)$ and $\mathrm{Var}\,(Y)$, as well as the distribution function for $Y$, by direct evaluation.

The estimator $\hat{\gamma}$ can be applied to censored data (i.e., any set of order statistics where the first $\ell - 1$ and/or last $N - m$ may be missing) from a sample of known size, as well as to complete data. The values in Table III can be used when censoring occurs. The results in this table can be applied to censored data because the probability distribution of $T_{(\ell)}$ and $T_{(m)}$ depends only on $\ell$, $m$ and $N$.

The values for $f(N,\ell,m)$ and $g(N,\ell,m)$ are tabulated in Table III. Values for $\ell$ and $m$ that minimize the sample variance are listed in Table 2. We define the function $\varphi(N,\ell,m)$ so that:

$$\text{(10.2.6)} \qquad \mathrm{Var}\,(\gamma) = \gamma^2 \, \frac{\varphi(N,\ell,m)}{N}$$

The efficiency, relative to the Cramér-Rao lower bound, is then given by:

TABLE III

OPTIMUM VALUES

| N | $\ell$ | m | f(N, $\ell$,m) | G | G2 |
|---|---|---|---|---|---|
| 2 | 1 | 2 | 0.7213 | 0.8437 | 0.7119 |
| 3 | 1 | 3 | 0.4809 | 0.6094 | 0.3714 |
| 4 | 1 | 4 | 0.3942 | 0.5111 | 0.2612 |
| 5 | 1 | 5 | 0.3476 | 0.4548 | 0.2068 |
| 6 | 2 | 6 | 0.4872 | 0.4111 | 0.1690 |
| 7 | 2 | 7 | 0.4367 | 0.3714 | 0.1380 |
| 8 | 2 | 8 | 0.4015 | 0.3429 | 0.1176 |
| 9 | 2 | 9 | 0.3754 | 0.3213 | 0.1032 |
| 10 | 2 | 10 | 0.3551 | 0.3042 | 0.0925 |
| 11 | 3 | 11 | 0.4168 | 0.2890 | 0.0835 |
| 12 | 3 | 12 | 0.3958 | 0.2745 | 0.0754 |
| 13 | 3 | 13 | 0.3784 | 0.2625 | 0.0689 |
| 14 | 3 | 14 | 0.3638 | 0.2522 | 0.0636 |
| 15 | 3 | 15 | 0.3514 | 0.2434 | 0.0592 |
| 16 | 3 | 16 | 0.3406 | 0.2358 | 0.0556 |
| 17 | 4 | 17 | 0.3769 | 0.2282 | 0.0521 |
| 18 | 4 | 18 | 0.3658 | 0.2212 | 0.0489 |
| 19 | 4 | 19 | 0.3559 | 0.2150 | 0.0462 |
| 20 | 4 | 20 | 0.3470 | 0.2094 | 0.0439 |
| 21 | 4 | 21 | 0.3391 | 0.2044 | 0.0418 |
| 22 | 4 | 22 | 0.3319 | 0.1998 | 0.0399 |
| 23 | 5 | 23 | 0.3573 | 0.1953 | 0.0381 |
| 24 | 5 | 24 | 0.3499 | 0.1910 | 0.0365 |
| 25 | 5 | 25 | 0.3432 | 0.1871 | 0.0350 |
| 26 | 5 | 26 | 0.3369 | 0.1835 | 0.0337 |

$$\text{(10.2.7)} \qquad \text{Eff}\ (\hat{\gamma}) = \frac{0.61}{\varphi(N,\ell,m)}$$

where we have used the result of Menon [139]. The values of $\varphi$ and Eff are tabulated in Table IV for the values of $\ell$, and $m$ that minimize the variance of the estimator.

## 10.3 Tests of Hypotheses

The distribution of the random variable

$$Y = \frac{\beta}{2}\left(\ln T_{(m)} - \ln T_{(\ell)}\right)$$

depends only on $N$, $\ell$ and $m$, and not on the scale or shape parameter of the Weibull distribution. Hence, it is a useful function to tabulate. The cumulative distribution function of $Y$ will be denoted by $G(y)$, where

$$\text{(10.3.1)}\quad G(y) = P(Y \le y)$$

$$\begin{cases} = A \displaystyle\sum_{i=0}^{\ell-1} \sum_{j=0}^{m-\ell-1} C_{ij} \frac{1}{b^2}\left[\frac{1}{R+e^{-2y}} - \frac{1}{R+1}\right] & \text{for } 0 \le y\ , \\ = \quad 0 & \text{for } y \le 0\ . \end{cases}$$

The cumulative distribution function of the statistic $\gamma$

TABLE IV

EFFICIENCY FOR OPTIMUM $\ell$,m

| N | $\varphi(N, \ell, m)$ | Efficiency in Percent |
|---|---|---|
| 2 | 1.42 | 43 |
| 3 | 1.11 | 55 |
| 4 | 1.04 | 59 |
| 5 | 1.03 | 59 |
| 6 | 1.01 | 60 |
| 7 | 0.97 | 62 |
| 8 | 0.96 | 63 |
| 9 | 0.93 | 65 |
| 10 | 0.93 | 65 |
| 11 | 0.92 | 66 |
| 12 | 0.91 | 67 |
| 13 | 0.90 | 68 |
| 14 | 0.89 | 69 |
| 15 | 0.89 | 69 |
| 16 | 0.89 | 69 |
| 17 | 0.89 | 69 |
| 18 | 0.88 | 70 |
| 19 | 0.88 | 70 |
| 20 | 0.88 | 70 |
| 21 | 0.88 | 70 |
| 22 | 0.88 | 70 |
| 23 | 0.88 | 70 |
| 24 | 0.88 | 70 |
| 25 | 0.88 | 70 |
| 26 | 0.88 | 70 |

can be obtained from this as:

$$(10.3.2)\quad P(\hat{\gamma} \leq z) = \begin{cases} G\left(\dfrac{z}{2\gamma f(N,\ell,m)}\right), & z \geq 0 \\ \\ 0 & , \; z < 0 \end{cases} .$$

This follows, since $\hat{\gamma} = Y2\gamma f(N,\ell,m)$.

We define the test constants, $w_\alpha$, so that $G(w_\alpha) = \alpha$, and we will consider test of the following three hypotheses:

1. $H_0 : \gamma \leq \gamma_0$ vs. $H_1 : \gamma > \gamma_0$ at level $\alpha$ ;
2. $H_0 : \gamma \geq \gamma_0$ vs. $H_1 : \gamma < \gamma_0$ at level $\alpha$ ;
3. $H_0 : \gamma = \gamma_0$ vs. $H_1 : \gamma \neq \gamma_0$ at level $2\alpha$ .

The test for each hypothesis is:

1. Reject $H_0$ if $\hat{\gamma} > C_1$ ;
2. Reject $H_0$ if $\hat{\gamma} < C_2$ ;
3. Reject $H_0$ if $\hat{\gamma} < C_3$ or $C_4 < \hat{\gamma}$ ;

where

$$C_1 = w_{0.95}\, 2\gamma_0 f(N,\ell,m), \qquad C_2 = w_{0.05}\, 2\gamma_0 f(N,\ell,m)$$

and

$$C_3 \;=\; w_3 \; 2\gamma_0 f(N,\ell,m), \quad C_4 = w_4 \; 2\gamma f(N,\ell,m)$$

where

$$(10.3.3) \qquad \int_{w_3}^{w_4} g(y)dy \;=\; 1 - \alpha$$

for $w_3\, g(w_3) = w_4\, g(w_4)$ for unbiased two-sided tests.

The power functions for these tests are (letting $f_n = f(N,\ell,m)$:

1. $H_0 : \gamma \le \gamma_0$ vs. $H_1 : \gamma > \gamma_0$.

Reject $H_0$ if $\gamma > C_1$ where $C_1 = w_{1-\alpha}\, 2\gamma_0 f_n$. The power function is

$$\beta(\gamma) = P\left(\hat{\gamma} > C_1 | \gamma\right) = P\left(\gamma \;>\; \frac{C_1}{2\gamma f_n}\right)\left(\gamma \;>\; \frac{\gamma_0}{\gamma}\, w_{1-\alpha}\right) .$$

Hence

$$(10.3.4) \qquad \beta(\gamma) \;=\; 1 - G\left(\frac{\gamma_0}{\gamma}\, w_{1-\alpha}\right) .$$

2. $H_0 : \gamma \ge \gamma_0$ vs. $H_1 : \gamma < \gamma_0$.

Reject $H_0$ if $\gamma < C_2$ with $C_2 = w_\alpha\, 2\gamma_0 f_n$. The power function is

$$(10.3.5) \qquad \beta(\gamma) = P(\hat{\gamma} < C_2 | \gamma) = G\left(\frac{\gamma_0}{\gamma} w_\alpha\right) .$$

3. $H_0 : \gamma = \gamma_0$ vs. $H_1 : \gamma \neq \gamma_0$.

Reject $H_0$ if $\hat{\gamma} < C_3$ or $C_4 < \hat{\gamma}$. The power function is

$$(10.3.6) \qquad \beta(\gamma) = P(\hat{\gamma} < C_3 | \gamma) + P(\hat{\gamma} > C_4 | \gamma)$$

$$= G\left(w_3 \frac{\gamma_0}{\gamma}\right) + 1 - G\left(w_4 \frac{\gamma_0}{\gamma}\right) ,$$

where $C_4 = w_4 \, 2\gamma_0 f_n$ and $C_3 = w_3 \, 2\gamma_0 f_n$; or

$$(10.3.7) \qquad \beta(\gamma) = 1 - \int_{\frac{\gamma_0}{\gamma} w_3}^{\frac{\gamma_0}{\gamma} w_4} g(y)dy .$$

We have

$$(10.3.8) \; \beta'(\gamma) = - w_4 \frac{\gamma_0}{\gamma} g\left(w_4 \frac{\gamma_0}{\gamma}\right) + w_3 \frac{\gamma_0}{\gamma} g\left(w_3 \frac{\gamma_0}{\gamma}\right) .$$

The unbiased confidence set for $\gamma$ is $(C_3, C_4)$ at confidence $1 - \alpha$.

## 10.4 Computer Program

The computer program used to compute Table III may be found on the following pages. It was written in FORTRAN and was run under the WATFOR compiler on the SDC-TS/DMS time-share service. Double precision was necessary to obtain results for N greater than 10. The number of summands used in computing Spence's function is determined, in line 4720, to give accurate results to at least the $20^{th}$ place. Accuracy in computing Spence's function is important at the minimum variance point for N larger than 15.

The computations herein have been compared with those obtained by using Lieblein's [128] and Mann's [135] tables of first moments and covariances of the order statistics from the extreme value distribution for N = 5, 6, 10, 15 and 20. Our values for $f(N,\ell,m)$ agree to the $9^{th}$ decimal place for N = 5, 6 and 20, and to the $8^{th}$ decimal place for N = 10 and 15. The worst disparity in the value of variance occurs between Mann's value and outs, for N = 10, where a difference occurs in the $5^{th}$ decimal place. We disagree in the $6^{th}$ decimal place with Leiblein's values, when N = 5, with the $8^{th}$ decimal place for N = 6, and in the $7^{th}$ decimal place for N = 15.

**Computer Program**

```
$JOB WEIBULL
       IMPLICIT REAL*8(A-H,O-Z)
       DO 10 N=2,15
       WRITE(6,120)
       WRITE(6,130)
       N1=N-1
       DO 10 L=1,N1
       L1=L+1
       DO 10 M=L1,N
       EY=0.0
       EY2=0.0
       M1=M-L
       DO 15 I1=1,L
       DO 15 J1=1,M1
       I=I1-1
       J=J1-1
       A=N+J-M+1
       B=M-L+I-J
       R=A/B
       BC=(-1.0D0**(I+J))*BIN(I,L-1)*BIN(J,M-L-1)/(B*B)
       VAL1=(1.0D0/(4.0D0*R))*DLOG((R+1.0D0)/R)
       EY=EY+BC*VAL1
       Y=VAL2(R)
       EY2=EY2+BC*Y
15     CONTINUE
       A2=2.0D0*BIN(L-1,N)*BIN(1,N-L+1)*BIN(M-L-1,N-L)
      + *BIN(1,N-M+1)
       EY=A2*EY
       EY2=A2*EY2
       FN=1.0D0/(2.0D0*EY)
       G=(EY2/(EY*EY)-1.0D0)
       G2=0.0
       IF (G .LE. 0.0) GO TO 10
       G2=DSQRT(G)
10     WRITE(6,100) N,L,M,FN,G2,G
100    FORMAT(3I6,F10.4,5X,F10.4,5X,F10.4)
120    FORMAT(1H1,14X,9HTABLE ONE)
130    FORMAT(5X,1HN,5X,1HL,5X,1HM,2X,8HF(N,L,M),
      + 9X,8HG(N,L,M),9X,2HG2)
       STOP
       END
```

```
          FUNCTION BIN(M,N)
          IMPLICIT REAL*8(A-H,O-Z)
          BIN=1.0D0
          IF (M) 20,30,1
 1        B=N-M
          DO 10 I=1,M
          AI=I
 10       BIN=BIN*(B+AI)/AI
          GO TO 30
 20       BIN=0.0
 30       RETURN
          END
          FUNCTION VAL2(R)
          IMPLICIT REAL*8(A-H,O-Z)
          TEMP=(DLOG((1.0D0+R)/R))**2
          SUM=0.0
          T=DLOG10(1.0D0+R)
          M=IDINT(2.0D1/T)
          DO 10 K=1,M
          X=K*K
 10       SUM=SUM+1.0D0/(X*(1.0D0+R)**K)
          VAL2=(TEMP+2.0D0*SUM)/(8.0D0*R)
          RETURN
          END
 $ENTRY
```

**Bias coefficient, standard deviation and variance of the estimator using sample of size N and the L-th and M-th order statistic.**

TABLE ONE

| N | L | M | F(N,L,M) | G(N,L,M) | G2 |
|---|---|---|---|---|---|
| 2 | 1 | 2 | 0.7213 | 0.8437 | 0.7119 |

TABLE ONE

| N | L | M | F(N,L,M) | G(N,L,M) | G2 |
|---|---|---|---|---|---|
| 3 | 1 | 2 | 0.8221 | 0.9046 | 0.8184 |
| 3 | 1 | 3 | 0.4809 | 0.6094 | 0.3714 |
| 3 | 2 | 3 | 1.1587 | 0.8228 | 0.6770 |

TABLE ONE

| N | L | M | F(N,L,M) | G(N,L,M) | G2 |
|---|---|---|---|---|---|
| 4 | 1 | 2 | 0.8690 | 0.9311 | 0.8670 |
| 4 | 1 | 3 | 0.5384 | 0.6539 | 0.4275 |
| 4 | 1 | 4 | 0.3942 | 0.5111 | 0.2612 |
| 4 | 2 | 3 | 1.4150 | 0.8870 | 0.7867 |
| 4 | 2 | 4 | 0.7213 | 0.5761 | 0.3319 |
| 4 | 3 | 4 | 1.4715 | 0.8199 | 0.6722 |

TABLE ONE

| N | L | M | F(N,L,M) | G(N,L,M) | G2 |
|---|---|---|---|---|---|
| 5 | 1 | 2 | 0.8963 | 0.9461 | 0.8950 |
| 5 | 1 | 3 | 0.5678 | 0.6758 | 0.4567 |
| 5 | 1 | 4 | 0.4360 | 0.5470 | 0.2992 |
| 5 | 1 | 5 | 0.3476 | 0.4548 | 0.2068 |
| 5 | 2 | 3 | 1.5495 | 0.9163 | 0.8396 |
| 5 | 2 | 4 | 0.8490 | 0.6199 | 0.3842 |
| 5 | 2 | 5 | 0.5678 | 0.4713 | 0.2221 |
| 5 | 3 | 4 | 1.8781 | 0.8828 | 0.7794 |
| 5 | 3 | 5 | 0.8963 | 0.5695 | 0.3243 |
| 5 | 4 | 5 | 1.7145 | 0.8210 | 0.6740 |

TABLE ONE

| N | L | M | F(N,L,M) | G(N,L,M) | G2 |
|---|---|---|---|---|---|
| 6 | 1 | 2 | 0.9141 | 0.9557 | 0.9133 |
| 6 | 1 | 3 | 0.5861 | 0.6892 | 0.4749 |
| 6 | 1 | 4 | 0.4586 | 0.5661 | 0.3205 |
| 6 | 1 | 5 | 0.3812 | 0.4853 | 0.2355 |
| 6 | 1 | 6 | 0.3178 | 0.4175 | 0.1743 |
| 6 | 2 | 3 | 1.6331 | 0.9334 | 0.8712 |
| 6 | 2 | 4 | 0.9203 | 0.6426 | 0.4129 |
| 6 | 2 | 5 | 0.6538 | 0.5053 | 0.2553 |
| 6 | 2 | 6 | 0.4872 | 0.4111 | 0.1690 |
| 6 | 3 | 4 | 2.1082 | 0.9120 | 0.8318 |
| 6 | 3 | 5 | 1.0902 | 0.6112 | 0.3735 |
| 6 | 3 | 6 | 0.6944 | 0.4620 | 0.2134 |
| 6 | 4 | 5 | 2.2577 | 0.8824 | 0.7786 |
| 6 | 4 | 6 | 1.0355 | 0.5689 | 0.3236 |
| 6 | 5 | 6 | 1.9129 | 0.8232 | 0.6777 |

TABLE ONE

| N | L | M | F(N,L,M) | G(N,L,M) | G2 |
|---|---|---|---|---|---|
| 7 | 1 | 2 | 0.9207 | 0.9624 | 0.9261 |
| 7 | 1 | 3 | 0.5986 | 0.6982 | 0.4874 |
| 7 | 1 | 4 | 0.4732 | 0.5783 | 0.3344 |
| 7 | 1 | 5 | 0.3999 | 0.5023 | 0.2523 |
| 7 | 1 | 6 | 0.3462 | 0.4443 | 0.1974 |
| 7 | 1 | 7 | 0.2968 | 0.3907 | 0.1526 |
| 7 | 2 | 3 | 1.6904 | 0.9446 | 0.8922 |
| 7 | 2 | 4 | 0.9668 | 0.6568 | 0.4313 |
| 7 | 2 | 5 | 0.7034 | 0.5243 | 0.2749 |
| 7 | 2 | 6 | 0.5527 | 0.4392 | 0.1929 |
| 7 | 2 | 7 | 0.4367 | 0.3714 | 0.1380 |
| 7 | 3 | 4 | 2.2584 | 0.9293 | 0.8635 |
| 7 | 3 | 5 | 1.2047 | 0.6333 | 0.4011 |
| 7 | 3 | 6 | 0.8212 | 0.4937 | 0.2438 |
| 7 | 3 | 7 | 0.5888 | 0.4000 | 0.1600 |
| 7 | 4 | 5 | 2.5820 | 0.9110 | 0.8299 |
| 7 | 4 | 6 | 1.2903 | 0.6087 | 0.3705 |
| 7 | 4 | 7 | 0.7964 | 0.4599 | 0.2116 |
| 7 | 5 | 6 | 2.5792 | 0.8833 | 0.7801 |
| 7 | 5 | 7 | 1.1516 | 0.5701 | 0.3250 |
| 7 | 6 | 7 | 2.0805 | 0.8257 | 0.6817 |
| TABLE ONE | | | | | |
| N | L | M | F(N,L,M) | G(N,L,M) | G2 |
| 8 | 1 | 2 | 0.9361 | 0.9673 | 0.9356 |
| 8 | 1 | 3 | 0.6077 | 0.7046 | 0.4965 |
| 8 | 1 | 4 | 0.4834 | 0.5868 | 0.3444 |
| 8 | 1 | 5 | 0.4123 | 0.5135 | 0.2637 |
| 8 | 1 | 6 | 0.3624 | 0.4597 | 0.2113 |
| 8 | 1 | 7 | 0.3216 | 0.4146 | 0.1719 |
| 8 | 1 | 8 | 0.2810 | 0.3702 | 0.1370 |
| 8 | 2 | 3 | 1.7321 | 0.9526 | 0.9074 |
| 8 | 2 | 4 | 0.9998 | 0.6665 | 0.4443 |
| 8 | 2 | 5 | 0.7368 | 0.5368 | 0.2882 |
| 8 | 2 | 6 | 0.5913 | 0.4557 | 0.2077 |
| 8 | 2 | 7 | 0.4899 | 0.3954 | 0.1563 |
| 8 | 2 | 8 | 0.4015 | 0.3429 | 0.1176 |
| 8 | 3 | 4 | 2.3047 | 0.9407 | 0.8850 |
| 8 | 3 | 5 | 1.2823 | 0.6474 | 0.4191 |
| 8 | 3 | 6 | 0.8977 | 0.5121 | 0.2622 |
| 8 | 3 | 7 | 0.6831 | 0.4257 | 0.1812 |
| 8 | 3 | 8 | 0.5227 | 0.3588 | 0.1288 |
| 8 | 4 | 5 | 2.8014 | 0.9280 | 0.8612 |
| 8 | 4 | 6 | 1.4471 | 0.6301 | 0.3970 |
| 8 | 4 | 7 | 0.9606 | 0.4897 | 0.2398 |
| 8 | 4 | 8 | 0.6710 | 0.3967 | 0.1574 |
| 8 | 5 | 6 | 2.9932 | 0.9112 | 0.8303 |
| 8 | 5 | 7 | 1.4620 | 0.6084 | 0.3701 |
| 8 | 5 | 8 | 0.8824 | 0.4603 | 0.2119 |
| 8 | 6 | 7 | 2.8579 | 0.8846 | 0.7825 |
| 8 | 6 | 8 | 1.2512 | 0.5720 | 0.3272 |
| 8 | 7 | 8 | 2.2255 | 0.8281 | 0.6857 |

TABLE ONE

| N | L | M | F(N,L,M) | G(N,L,M) | G2 |
|---|---|---|---|---|---|
| 9 | 1 | 2 | 0.9434 | 0.9711 | 0.9430 |
| 9 | 1 | 3 | 0.6146 | 0.7096 | 0.5035 |
| 9 | 1 | 4 | 0.4911 | 0.5931 | 0.3518 |
| 9 | 1 | 5 | 0.4212 | 0.5216 | 0.2720 |
| 9 | 1 | 6 | 0.3733 | 0.4701 | 0.2209 |
| 9 | 1 | 7 | 0.3359 | 0.4287 | 0.1838 |
| 9 | 1 | 8 | 0.3031 | 0.3919 | 0.1536 |
| 9 | 1 | 9 | 0.2685 | 0.3539 | 0.1253 |
| 9 | 2 | 3 | 1.7639 | 0.9585 | 0.9187 |
| 9 | 2 | 4 | 1.0245 | 0.6737 | 0.4539 |
| 9 | 2 | 5 | 0.7611 | 0.5457 | 0.2978 |
| 9 | 2 | 6 | 0.6178 | 0.4670 | 0.2181 |
| 9 | 2 | 7 | 0.5218 | 0.4101 | 0.1682 |
| 9 | 2 | 8 | 0.4467 | 0.3639 | 0.1324 |
| 9 | 2 | 9 | 0.3754 | 0.3213 | 0.1032 |
| 9 | 3 | 4 | 2.4440 | 0.9490 | 0.9005 |
| 9 | 3 | 5 | 1.3388 | 0.6572 | 0.4319 |
| 9 | 3 | 6 | 0.9508 | 0.5243 | 0.2749 |
| 9 | 3 | 7 | 0.7409 | 0.4414 | 0.1948 |
| 9 | 3 | 8 | 0.5981 | 0.3805 | 0.1447 |
| 9 | 3 | 9 | 0.4769 | 0.3292 | 0.1084 |
| 9 | 4 | 5 | 2.9607 | 0.9394 | 0.8824 |
| 9 | 4 | 6 | 1.5563 | 0.6438 | 0.4145 |
| 9 | 4 | 7 | 1.0633 | 0.5073 | 0.2573 |
| 9 | 4 | 8 | 0.7920 | 0.4205 | 0.1768 |
| 9 | 4 | 9 | 0.5925 | 0.3547 | 0.1258 |
| 9 | 5 | 6 | 3.2811 | 0.9278 | 0.8609 |
| 9 | 5 | 7 | 1.6591 | 0.6291 | 0.3957 |
| 9 | 5 | 8 | 1.0812 | 0.4885 | 0.2386 |
| 9 | 5 | 9 | 0.7408 | 0.3963 | 0.1571 |
| 9 | 6 | 7 | 3.3563 | 0.9119 | 0.8316 |
| 9 | 6 | 8 | 1.6125 | 0.6089 | 0.3708 |
| 9 | 6 | 9 | 0.9568 | 0.4616 | 0.2131 |
| 9 | 7 | 8 | 3.1038 | 0.8860 | 0.7850 |
| 9 | 7 | 9 | 1.3384 | 0.5740 | 0.3295 |
| 9 | 8 | 9 | 2.3532 | 0.8303 | 0.6894 |

TABLE ONE

| N | L | M | F(N,L,M) | G(N,L,M) | G2 |
|---|---|---|---|---|---|
| 10 | 1 | 2 | 0.9491 | 0.9741 | 0.9488 |
| 10 | 1 | 3 | 0.6201 | 0.7134 | 0.5090 |
| 10 | 1 | 4 | 0.4971 | 0.5980 | 0.3576 |
| 10 | 1 | 5 | 0.4280 | 0.5276 | 0.2784 |
| 10 | 1 | 6 | 0.3813 | 0.4776 | 0.2281 |
| 10 | 1 | 7 | 0.3458 | 0.4384 | 0.1922 |
| 10 | 1 | 8 | 0.3161 | 0.4049 | 0.1640 |
| 10 | 1 | 9 | 0.2887 | 0.3738 | 0.1397 |
| 10 | 1 | 10 | 0.2584 | 0.3406 | 0.1160 |
| 10 | 2 | 3 | 1.7889 | 0.9631 | 0.9276 |
| 10 | 2 | 4 | 1.0437 | 0.6792 | 0.4613 |
| 10 | 2 | 5 | 0.7797 | 0.5524 | 0.3052 |
| 10 | 2 | 6 | 0.6375 | 0.4752 | 0.2258 |
| 10 | 2 | 7 | 0.5440 | 0.4203 | 0.1766 |
| 10 | 2 | 8 | 0.4740 | 0.3771 | 0.1422 |
| 10 | 2 | 9 | 0.4148 | 0.3400 | 0.1156 |
| 10 | 2 | 10 | 0.3551 | 0.3042 | 0.0925 |
| 10 | 3 | 4 | 2.5056 | 0.9552 | 0.9123 |
| 10 | 3 | 5 | 1.3820 | 0.6644 | 0.4414 |
| 10 | 3 | 6 | 0.9904 | 0.5331 | 0.2842 |
| 10 | 3 | 7 | 0.7817 | 0.4523 | 0.2046 |
| 10 | 3 | 8 | 0.6448 | 0.3943 | 0.1555 |
| 10 | 3 | 9 | 0.5400 | 0.3479 | 0.1210 |
| 10 | 3 | 10 | 0.4431 | 0.3068 | 0.0941 |
| 10 | 4 | 5 | 3.0820 | 0.9476 | 0.8979 |
| 10 | 4 | 6 | 1.6376 | 0.6535 | 0.4270 |
| 10 | 4 | 7 | 1.1362 | 0.5191 | 0.2695 |
| 10 | 4 | 8 | 0.8682 | 0.4355 | 0.1896 |
| 10 | 4 | 9 | 0.6884 | 0.3744 | 0.1402 |
| 10 | 4 | 10 | 0.5382 | 0.3243 | 0.1052 |
| 10 | 5 | 6 | 3.4945 | 0.9390 | 0.8818 |
| 10 | 5 | 7 | 1.7997 | 0.6424 | 0.4127 |
| 10 | 5 | 8 | 1.2087 | 0.5053 | 0.2554 |
| 10 | 5 | 9 | 0.8864 | 0.4185 | 0.1751 |
| 10 | 5 | 10 | 0.6521 | 0.3536 | 0.1250 |
| 10 | 6 | 7 | 3.7107 | 0.9282 | 0.8616 |
| 10 | 6 | 8 | 1.8480 | 0.6290 | 0.3957 |
| 10 | 6 | 9 | 1.1876 | 0.4884 | 0.2385 |
| 10 | 6 | 10 | 0.8017 | 0.3971 | 0.1577 |
| 10 | 7 | 8 | 3.6813 | 0.9128 | 0.8333 |
| 10 | 7 | 9 | 1.7467 | 0.6098 | 0.3719 |
| 10 | 7 | 10 | 1.0227 | 0.4632 | 0.2146 |
| 10 | 8 | 9 | 3.3237 | 0.8875 | 0.7876 |
| 10 | 8 | 10 | 1.4161 | 0.5760 | 0.3318 |
| 10 | 9 | 10 | 2.4672 | 0.8324 | 0.6929 |

TABLE ONE

| N | L | M | F(N,L,M) | G(N,L,M) | G2 |
|---|---|---|---|---|---|
| 11 | 1 | 11 | 0.2500 | 0.3294 | 0.1085 |
| 11 | 2 | 11 | 0.3388 | 0.2902 | 0.0842 |
| 11 | 3 | 11 | 0.4168 | 0.2890 | 0.0835 |
| 11 | 4 | 11 | 0.4981 | 0.3012 | 0.0907 |
| 11 | 5 | 11 | 0.5906 | 0.3227 | 0.1041 |
| 11 | 6 | 11 | 0.7043 | 0.3539 | 0.1252 |
| 11 | 7 | 11 | 0.8559 | 0.3983 | 0.1587 |
| 11 | 8 | 11 | 1.0817 | 0.4650 | 0.2162 |
| 11 | 9 | 11 | 1.4860 | 0.5780 | 0.3341 |
| 11 | 10 | 11 | 2.5702 | 0.8344 | 0.6962 |

TABLE ONE

| N | L | M | F(N,L,M) | G(N,L,M) | G2 |
|---|---|---|---|---|---|
| 12 | 1 | 12 | 0.2428 | 0.3199 | 0.1023 |
| 12 | 2 | 12 | 0.3253 | 0.2786 | 0.0776 |
| 12 | 3 | 12 | 0.3958 | 0.2745 | 0.0754 |
| 12 | 4 | 12 | 0.4670 | 0.2830 | 0.0801 |
| 12 | 5 | 12 | 0.5452 | 0.2991 | 0.0895 |
| 12 | 6 | 12 | 0.6367 | 0.3226 | 0.1040 |
| 12 | 7 | 12 | 0.7509 | 0.3548 | 0.1259 |
| 12 | 8 | 12 | 0.9046 | 0.3998 | 0.1599 |
| 12 | 9 | 12 | 1.1351 | 0.4668 | 0.2179 |
| 12 | 10 | 12 | 1.5496 | 0.5799 | 0.3362 |
| 12 | 11 | 12 | 2.6641 | 0.8362 | 0.6992 |

TABLE ONE

| N | L | M | F(N,L,M) | G(N,L,M) | G2 |
|---|---|---|---|---|---|
| 13 | 1 | 13 | 0.2366 | 0.3116 | 0.0971 |
| 13 | 2 | 13 | 0.3139 | 0.2688 | 0.0722 |
| 13 | 3 | 13 | 0.3784 | 0.2625 | 0.0689 |
| 13 | 4 | 13 | 0.4421 | 0.2681 | 0.0719 |
| 13 | 5 | 13 | 0.5100 | 0.2804 | 0.0786 |
| 13 | 6 | 13 | 0.5867 | 0.2986 | 0.0892 |
| 13 | 7 | 13 | 0.6780 | 0.3232 | 0.1044 |
| 13 | 8 | 13 | 0.7931 | 0.3560 | 0.1267 |
| 13 | 9 | 13 | 0.9490 | 0.4014 | 0.1611 |
| 13 | 10 | 13 | 1.1840 | 0.4685 | 0.2195 |
| 13 | 11 | 13 | 1.6030 | 0.5816 | 0.3383 |
| 13 | 12 | 13 | 2.7504 | 0.8379 | 0.7020 |

TABLE ONE

| N | L | M | F(N,L,M) | G(N,L,M) | G2 |
|---|---|---|---|---|---|
| 14 | 1 | 14 | 0.2312 | 0.3044 | 0.0927 |
| 14 | 2 | 14 | 0.3041 | 0.2603 | 0.0677 |
| 14 | 3 | 14 | 0.3638 | 0.2522 | 0.0636 |
| 14 | 4 | 14 | 0.4216 | 0.2557 | 0.0654 |
| 14 | 5 | 14 | 0.4818 | 0.2652 | 0.0703 |
| 14 | 6 | 14 | 0.5480 | 0.2796 | 0.0782 |
| 14 | 7 | 14 | 0.6240 | 0.2990 | 0.0894 |
| 14 | 8 | 14 | 0.7155 | 0.3241 | 0.1051 |
| 14 | 9 | 14 | 0.8316 | 0.3574 | 0.1277 |
| 14 | 10 | 14 | 0.9898 | 0.4030 | 0.1624 |
| 14 | 11 | 14 | 1.2291 | 0.4702 | 0.2210 |
| 14 | 12 | 14 | 1.6618 | 0.5833 | 0.3402 |
| 14 | 13 | 14 | 2.8302 | 0.8394 | 0.7046 |

TABLE ONE

| N | L | M | F(N,L,M) | G(N,L,M) | G2 |
|---|---|---|---|---|---|
| 15 | 1 | 15 | 0.2263 | 0.2980 | 0.0888 |
| 15 | 2 | 15 | 0.2956 | 0.2528 | 0.0639 |
| 15 | 3 | 15 | 0.3514 | 0.2434 | 0.0592 |
| 15 | 4 | 15 | 0.4044 | 0.2452 | 0.0601 |
| 15 | 5 | 15 | 0.4586 | 0.2525 | 0.0638 |
| 15 | 6 | 15 | 0.5169 | 0.2641 | 0.0697 |
| 15 | 7 | 15 | 0.5821 | 0.2797 | 0.0782 |
| 15 | 8 | 15 | 0.6579 | 0.2997 | 0.0898 |
| 15 | 9 | 15 | 0.7498 | 0.3253 | 0.1058 |
| 15 | 10 | 15 | 0.8671 | 0.3588 | 0.1287 |
| 15 | 11 | 15 | 1.0275 | 0.4045 | 0.1636 |
| 15 | 12 | 15 | 1.2708 | 0.4717 | 0.2225 |
| 15 | 13 | 15 | 1.7119 | 0.5848 | 0.3420 |
| 15 | 14 | 15 | 2.9044 | 0.8409 | 0.7071 |

TABLE ONE

| N | L | M | F(N,L,M) | G(N,L,M) | G2 |
|---|---|---|---|---|---|
| 16 | 1 | 16 | 0.2220 | 0.2922 | 0.0854 |
| 16 | 2 | 16 | 0.2881 | 0.2463 | 0.0606 |
| 16 | 3 | 16 | 0.3406 | 0.2358 | 0.0556 |
| 16 | 4 | 16 | 0.3897 | 0.2361 | 0.0557 |
| 16 | 5 | 16 | 0.4391 | 0.2417 | 0.0584 |
| 16 | 6 | 16 | 0.4914 | 0.2512 | 0.0631 |
| 16 | 7 | 16 | 0.5485 | 0.2640 | 0.0697 |
| 16 | 8 | 16 | 0.6132 | 0.2802 | 0.0785 |
| 16 | 9 | 16 | 0.6890 | 0.3007 | 0.0904 |
| 16 | 10 | 16 | 0.7815 | 0.3265 | 0.1066 |
| 16 | 11 | 16 | 0.9000 | 0.3602 | 0.1297 |
| 16 | 12 | 16 | 1.0626 | 0.4060 | 0.1648 |
| 16 | 13 | 16 | 1.3098 | 0.4732 | 0.2239 |
| 16 | 14 | 16 | 1.7586 | 0.5862 | 0.3437 |
| 16 | 15 | 16 | 2.9737 | 0.8422 | 0.7093 |

TABLE ONE

| N | L | M | F(N,L,M) | G(N,L,M) | G2 |
|---|---|---|---|---|---|
| 17 | 1 | 17 | 0.2132 | 0.2870 | 0.0824 |
| 17 | 2 | 17 | 0.2815 | 0.2404 | 0.0578 |
| 17 | 3 | 17 | 0.3311 | 0.2290 | 0.0525 |
| 17 | 4 | 17 | 0.3769 | 0.2282 | 0.0521 |
| 17 | 5 | 17 | 0.4225 | 0.2324 | 0.0540 |
| 17 | 6 | 17 | 0.4699 | 0.2402 | 0.0577 |
| 17 | 7 | 17 | 0.5209 | 0.2508 | 0.0629 |
| 17 | 8 | 17 | 0.5774 | 0.2643 | 0.0699 |
| 17 | 9 | 17 | 0.6419 | 0.2811 | 0.0790 |
| 17 | 10 | 17 | 0.7179 | 0.3018 | 0.0911 |
| 17 | 11 | 17 | 0.8109 | 0.3278 | 0.1075 |
| 17 | 12 | 17 | 0.9307 | 0.3616 | 0.1307 |
| 17 | 13 | 17 | 1.0953 | 0.4074 | 0.1660 |
| 17 | 14 | 17 | 1.3462 | 0.4746 | 0.2253 |
| 17 | 15 | 17 | 1.8024 | 0.5876 | 0.3453 |
| 17 | 16 | 17 | 3.0387 | 0.8435 | 0.7115 |

TABLE ONE

| N | L | M | F(N,L,M) | G(N,L,M) | G2 |
|---|---|---|---|---|---|
| 18 | 1 | 18 | 0.2147 | 0.2823 | 0.0797 |
| 18 | 2 | 18 | 0.2755 | 0.2352 | 0.0553 |
| 18 | 3 | 18 | 0.3226 | 0.2230 | 0.0497 |
| 18 | 4 | 18 | 0.3658 | 0.2212 | 0.0489 |
| 18 | 5 | 18 | 0.4081 | 0.2243 | 0.0503 |
| 18 | 6 | 18 | 0.4516 | 0.2307 | 0.0532 |
| 18 | 7 | 18 | 0.4977 | 0.2396 | 0.0574 |
| 18 | 8 | 18 | 0.5479 | 0.2510 | 0.0630 |
| 18 | 9 | 18 | 0.6040 | 0.2650 | 0.0702 |
| 18 | 10 | 18 | 0.6684 | 0.2820 | 0.0795 |
| 18 | 11 | 18 | 0.7447 | 0.3029 | 0.0918 |
| 18 | 12 | 18 | 0.8385 | 0.3291 | 0.1083 |
| 18 | 13 | 18 | 0.9594 | 0.3629 | 0.1317 |
| 18 | 14 | 18 | 1.1261 | 0.4088 | 0.1671 |
| 18 | 15 | 18 | 1.3805 | 0.4760 | 0.2266 |
| 18 | 16 | 18 | 1.8436 | 0.5889 | 0.3468 |
| 18 | 17 | 18 | 3.1000 | 0.8447 | 0.7135 |

TABLE ONE

| N | L | M | F(N,L,M) | G(N,L,M) | G2 |
|---|---|---|---|---|---|
| 19 | 1 | 19 | 0.2114 | 0.2780 | 0.0773 |
| 19 | 2 | 19 | 0.2701 | 0.2304 | 0.0531 |
| 19 | 3 | 19 | 0.3151 | 0.2176 | 0.0474 |
| 19 | 4 | 19 | 0.3559 | 0.2150 | 0.0462 |
| 19 | 5 | 19 | 0.3955 | 0.2172 | 0.0472 |
| 19 | 6 | 19 | 0.4358 | 0.2224 | 0.0495 |
| 19 | 7 | 19 | 0.4779 | 0.2300 | 0.0529 |
| 19 | 8 | 19 | 0.5231 | 0.2397 | 0.0574 |
| 19 | 9 | 19 | 0.5728 | 0.2515 | 0.0633 |
| 19 | 10 | 19 | 0.6287 | 0.2658 | 0.0707 |
| 19 | 11 | 19 | 0.6932 | 0.2831 | 0.0801 |
| 19 | 12 | 19 | 0.7698 | 0.3041 | 0.0925 |
| 19 | 13 | 19 | 0.8643 | 0.3304 | 0.1091 |
| 19 | 14 | 19 | 0.9864 | 0.3642 | 0.1327 |
| 19 | 15 | 19 | 1.1551 | 0.4101 | 0.1682 |
| 19 | 16 | 19 | 1.4128 | 0.4773 | 0.2278 |
| 19 | 17 | 19 | 1.8826 | 0.5901 | 0.3482 |
| 19 | 18 | 19 | 3.1579 | 0.8458 | 0.7154 |

TABLE ONE

| N | L | M | F(N,L,M) | G(N,L,M) | G2 |
|---|---|---|---|---|---|
| 20 | 1 | 20 | 0.2085 | 0.2740 | 0.0751 |
| 20 | 2 | 20 | 0.2652 | 0.2261 | 0.0511 |
| 20 | 3 | 20 | 0.3083 | 0.2127 | 0.0452 |
| 20 | 4 | 20 | 0.3470 | 0.2094 | 0.0439 |
| 20 | 5 | 20 | 0.3844 | 0.2108 | 0.0444 |
| 20 | 6 | 20 | 0.4219 | 0.2151 | 0.0463 |
| 20 | 7 | 20 | 0.4607 | 0.2216 | 0.0491 |
| 20 | 8 | 20 | 0.5019 | 0.2299 | 0.0529 |
| 20 | 9 | 20 | 0.5466 | 0.2401 | 0.0576 |
| 20 | 10 | 20 | 0.5959 | 0.2523 | 0.0636 |
| 20 | 11 | 20 | 0.6517 | 0.2668 | 0.0712 |
| 20 | 12 | 20 | 0.7164 | 0.2842 | 0.0807 |
| 20 | 13 | 20 | 0.7934 | 0.3053 | 0.0932 |
| 20 | 14 | 20 | 0.8887 | 0.3316 | 0.1100 |
| 20 | 15 | 20 | 1.0120 | 0.3655 | 0.1336 |
| 20 | 16 | 20 | 1.1825 | 0.4113 | 0.1692 |
| 20 | 17 | 20 | 1.4434 | 0.4785 | 0.2289 |
| 20 | 18 | 20 | 1.9195 | 0.5912 | 0.3496 |
| 20 | 19 | 20 | 3.2128 | 0.8468 | 0.7171 |

TABLE ONE

| N | L | M | F(N,L,M) | G(N,L,M) | G2 |
|---|---|---|---|---|---|
| 21 | 1 | 21 | 0.2058 | 0.2704 | 0.0731 |
| 21 | 2 | 21 | 0.2608 | 0.2221 | 0.0493 |
| 21 | 3 | 21 | 0.3022 | 0.2083 | 0.0434 |
| 21 | 4 | 21 | 0.3391 | 0.2044 | 0.0418 |
| 21 | 5 | 21 | 0.3744 | 0.2051 | 0.0421 |
| 21 | 6 | 21 | 0.4096 | 0.2086 | 0.0435 |
| 21 | 7 | 21 | 0.4457 | 0.2141 | 0.0459 |
| 21 | 8 | 21 | 0.4836 | 0.2213 | 0.0490 |
| 21 | 9 | 21 | 0.5242 | 0.2302 | 0.0530 |
| 21 | 10 | 21 | 0.5684 | 0.2406 | 0.0579 |
| 21 | 11 | 21 | 0.6176 | 0.2532 | 0.0641 |
| 21 | 12 | 21 | 0.6734 | 0.2677 | 0.0716 |
| 21 | 13 | 21 | 0.7382 | 0.2853 | 0.0814 |
| 21 | 14 | 21 | 0.8157 | 0.3065 | 0.0939 |
| 21 | 15 | 21 | 0.9117 | 0.3328 | 0.1107 |
| 21 | 16 | 21 | 1.0361 | 0.3667 | 0.1345 |
| 21 | 17 | 21 | 1.2085 | 0.4125 | 0.1702 |
| 21 | 18 | 21 | 1.4725 | 0.4796 | 0.2300 |
| 21 | 19 | 21 | 1.9545 | 0.5923 | 0.3508 |
| 21 | 20 | 21 | 3.2649 | 0.8478 | 0.7188 |

TABLE ONE

| N | L | M | F(N,L,M) | G(N,L,M) | G2 |
|---|---|---|---|---|---|
| 22 | 1 | 22 | 0.2033 | 0.2670 | 0.0713 |
| 22 | 2 | 22 | 0.2567 | 0.2185 | 0.0477 |
| 22 | 3 | 22 | 0.2966 | 0.2042 | 0.0417 |
| 22 | 4 | 22 | 0.3319 | 0.1998 | 0.0399 |
| 22 | 5 | 22 | 0.3654 | 0.2000 | 0.0400 |
| 22 | 6 | 22 | 0.3986 | 0.2028 | 0.0411 |
| 22 | 7 | 22 | 0.4324 | 0.2075 | 0.0431 |
| 22 | 8 | 22 | 0.4675 | 0.2138 | 0.0457 |
| 22 | 9 | 22 | 0.5048 | 0.2215 | 0.0490 |
| 22 | 10 | 22 | 0.5449 | 0.2309 | 0.0533 |

TABLE V

UNBIASED ESTIMATOR OF $1/\beta$

| Sample Size | Estimator | Efficiency in |
|---|---|---|
| 2 | $0.721(T_2 - T_1)$ | 43 |
| 3 | $0.481(T_3 - T_1)$ | 55 |
| 4 | $0.394(T_4 - T_1)$ | 59 |
| 5 | $0.348(T_5 - T_1)$ | 59 |
| 6 | $0.487(T_6 - T_2)$ | 60 |
| 7 | $0.437(T_7 - T_2)$ | 62 |
| 8 | $0.402(T_8 - T_2)$ | 63 |
| 9 | $0.375(T_9 - T_2)$ | 65 |
| 10 | $0.355(T_{10} - T_2)$ | 65 |
| 11 | $0.417(T_{11} - T_3)$ | 66 |
| 12 | $0.396(T_{12} - T_3)$ | 67 |
| 13 | $0.378(T_{13} - T_3)$ | 68 |
| 14 | $0.365(T_{14} - T_3)$ | 69 |
| 15 | $0.351(T_{15} - T_3)$ | 69 |
| 16 | $0.341(T_{16} - T_3)$ | 69 |
| 17 | $0.377(T_{17} - T_4)$ | 69 |
| 18 | $0.366(T_{18} - T_4)$ | 70 |
| 19 | $0.356(T_{19} - T_4)$ | 70 |
| 20 | $0.347(T_{20} - T_4)$ | 70 |
| 21 | $0.340(T_{21} - T_4)$ | 70 |
| 22 | $0.332(T_{22} - T_4)$ | 70 |
| 23 | $0.357(T_{23} - T_5)$ | 70 |
| 24 | $0.350(T_{24} - T_5)$ | 70 |
| 25 | $0.343(T_{25} - T_5)$ | 70 |
| 26 | $0.337(T_{26} - T_5)$ | 70 |

$T_m = \ln T_{(m)}$ is the natural logarithm of the m-th order statistic from a Weibull distribution.

## 10.5 Numerical Examples

Example 1. We use as data, 24 failure times given by Mann [135] with $T_{(24)} = 153.20$ and $T_{(5)} = 27.50$, to obtain $\hat{\gamma} = 0.3499(5.031 - 3.314) = 0.60$. Mann obtained the value 0.569, using a linear combination of all 24 failure times.

Example 2. We use as data 20 numbers given by Menon [139] with $T_{20} = \ln T_{20} = 4.054$ and $T_4 = 1.686$, to obtain $\hat{\gamma} = 1.99$. The numbers are from a Weibull distribution with $\gamma = 2.00$. Menon obtained the value 1.76, using all the data points. Cohen [32] used a maximum likelihood estimator on these data to obtain $1/\gamma = 0.506$.

Example 3. We use as data, 20 numbers of cycles-to-failure, given by Wirsching and Yao [215] with $T_{(20)} = 112 \cdot 10^3$ and $T_{(4)} = 48 \cdot 10^3$ to obtain $\hat{\gamma} = 0.295$. The maximum likelihood estimator of $\beta$ was obtained as 3.49, by Wirsching and Yao.

Example 4. The following ten numbers are a random sample from a Weibull distribution with $\gamma = 0.5$: 55, 65, 139, 61, 34, 103, 143, 55, 85 and 5. We obtain $\hat{\gamma} = 0.3551 \ln 143/34 = 0.51$.

## 10.6 Derivation of Density and Moments of Y

The joint probability element of $x = T_{(\ell)}$ and $y = T_{(m)}$ is:

$$(10.6.1)\quad g(x,y)dx\,dy = \frac{N!}{(\ell-1)!\,(m-\ell-1)!\,(N-m)!}$$

$$\cdot\, F(x)^{\ell-1}(F(y)-F(x))^{m-\ell-1}(1-F(y))^{N-m}$$

$$\cdot\, f(x)\,f(y)dx\,dy \quad .$$

Put $x = e^{\xi}$, $y > x > 0$ and $y = e^{\eta}$, $\eta > \xi > -\infty$. We obtain

$$(10.6.2)\quad h(\xi,\eta) = \frac{N!}{(\ell-1)!\,(m-\ell-1)!\,(N-m)!}$$

$$\cdot\, F^{\ell-1}(e^{\xi})(F(e^{\eta}) - F(e^{\xi}))^{m-\ell-1}$$

$$\cdot\, (1-F(e^{\eta}))^{N-m}\, f(e^{\xi})\, f(e^{\eta})e^{\xi}e^{\eta}\, d\xi\, d\eta \quad .$$

Let $x = \eta - \xi$ and $y = \eta + \xi$, where

$$\xi = \frac{y-x}{2}, \qquad x > 0 \quad ,$$

$$\eta = \frac{y+x}{2}, \qquad y > -\infty \quad .$$

We obtain:

$$(10.6.3)\quad P(x,y)dx\,dy = \frac{1}{2}\frac{N!}{(\ell-1)!\,(m-\ell-1)!\,(N-m)!}$$

$$\cdot\, F^{\ell-1}[e^{(y-x)/2}]\{F[e^{(y+x)/2}] - F[e^{(y-x)/2}]\}^{m-\ell-1}$$

$$\cdot\, \{1 - F[e^{(y+x)/2}]\}^{N-m}\, f[e^{(y-x)/2}]\, f[e^{(y+x)/2}]$$

$$\cdot\, e^{y}\, dx\, dy \quad .$$

Let $R(x) = 1 - F(x)$ be the reliability function. For the distribution of

$$X = \ln T_{(m)} - \ln T_{(\ell)}$$

we have

$$(10.6.4)\qquad P(X)dx = \frac{1}{2}\frac{N!\,dx}{(\ell-1)!\,(m-\ell-1)!\,(N-m)!}$$

$$\cdot \int_{-\infty}^{\infty} I(x,y)dy \quad ,$$

where

$$(10.6.5)\qquad I(x,y) = \{1 - R[e^{(y-x)/2}]\}^{\ell-1}$$

$$\cdot\, \{R[e^{(y-x)/2}] - R[e^{(y+x)/2}]\}^{m-\ell-1} \, .$$

$$\cdot\ R^{N-m}[e^{(y+x)/2}]\ f[e^{(y-x)/2}]\ f[e^{(y+x)/2}]e^{y}\quad .$$

Expanding, we obtain:

$$(10.6.6)\ I(x,y) = \sum_{i=0}^{\ell-1} \sum_{j=0}^{m-\ell-1} (-1)^{i+j}\, R^{i}\left(e^{\frac{y-x}{2}}\right) R^{j}\left(e^{\frac{y+x}{2}}\right)$$

$$\cdot\ R^{m-\ell-1-j}\left(e^{\frac{y-x}{2}}\right) R^{N-m}\left(e^{\frac{y+x}{2}}\right)$$

$$\cdot \binom{\ell-1}{i}\binom{m-\ell-1}{j} f\left(e^{\frac{y-x}{2}}\right) f\left(e^{\frac{y+x}{2}}\right) e^{y}\quad .$$

Collecting factors, we have:

$$(10.6.7)\quad I(x,y) = \sum_{i=0}^{\ell-1} \sum_{j=0}^{m-\ell-1} (-1)^{i+j}\binom{\ell-1}{i}\binom{m-\ell-1}{j}$$

$$\cdot\ R^{m-\ell-1+i-j}\left(e^{\frac{y-x}{2}}\right) R^{N+j-m}\left(e^{\frac{y+x}{2}}\right)$$

$$\cdot\ f\left(e^{\frac{y-x}{2}}\right) f\left(e^{\frac{y+x}{2}}\right) e^{y}\quad .$$

Thus

$$(10.6.8)\ P(x)dx = \frac{N!\ dx}{2(\ell-1)!\ (m-\ell-1)!\ (N-m)!}\quad \cdot$$

$$\cdot \sum_{i=0}^{\ell-1} \sum_{j=0}^{m-\ell-1} (-1)^{i+j} \binom{\ell-1}{i} \binom{m-\ell-1}{j} \int_{-\infty}^{\infty} R^{N+j-m}\left(e^{\frac{y+x}{2}}\right)$$

$$\cdot R^{m-\ell-1+i-j}\left(e^{\frac{y-x}{2}}\right) f\left(e^{\frac{y-x}{2}}\right) f\left(e^{\frac{y+x}{2}}\right) e^{y}\, dy \quad .$$

Put $e^{y/2} = r$ with $\frac{1}{2} e^{y/2}\, dy = \frac{1}{2} r\, dy = dr$. We obtain:

$$(10.6.9)\quad P(x)dx = \frac{N!\quad dx}{(\ell-1)!\ (m-\ell-1)!\ (N-m)!}$$

$$\cdot \sum_{i=0}^{\ell-1} \sum_{j=0}^{m-\ell-1} (-1)^{i+j} \binom{\ell-1}{i} \binom{m-\ell-1}{j}$$

$$\cdot \int_{-\infty}^{\infty} R^{N+j-m}\left(re^{x/2}\right) R^{m-\ell-1+i-j}\left(re^{-x/2}\right)$$

$$\cdot f\left(re^{x/2}\right) f\left(re^{-x/2}\right) r\, dr$$

for $x \geq 0$.

The Weibull distribution has:

$$R(t) = 1 - F(t) = e^{-\alpha t^{\beta}}$$

with

$$f(t) = \alpha\beta t^{\beta-1} e^{-\alpha t^{\beta}} \quad .$$

In this case we have:

$$(10.6.10)\qquad R^{N+j-m}\left(re^{x/2}\right) = e^{-\left(\alpha r^{\beta} e^{\frac{x\beta}{2}}\right)(N+j-m)}$$

$$(10.6.11)\qquad R^{m-\ell-1+i\ell j}\left(re^{-x/2}\right) = e^{-\left(\alpha r^{\beta} e^{\frac{-x\beta}{2}}\right)(m-\ell-1+i-j)} ,$$

and

$$(10.6.12)\qquad f(re^{x/2}) = \alpha\beta r^{\beta-1} e^{\frac{x(\beta-1)}{2}} e^{-\alpha r^{\beta} e^{\frac{x\beta}{2}}} ,$$

$$(10.6.13)\qquad f(re^{-x/2}) = \alpha\beta r^{\beta-1} e^{\frac{-x(\beta-1)}{2}} e^{-\alpha r^{\beta} e^{\frac{-x\beta}{2}}} .$$

Put $\alpha r^{\beta} = t$ with $\alpha\beta r^{\beta-1}\, dr = dt$. Thus, for the Weibull:

$$(10.6.14)\qquad P(x)dx = \frac{N!\ dx}{(\ell-1)!\ (m-\ell-1)!\ (N-m)!} \cdot \sum_{i=0}^{\ell-1} \sum_{j=0}^{m-\ell-1} (-1)^{i+j} \binom{\ell-1}{i} \binom{m-\ell-1}{j} \beta \cdot \frac{1}{\left[\left(N+j-m+1\right)e^{\frac{x\beta}{2}} + \left(m-\ell+i-j\right)e^{\frac{-x\beta}{2}}\right]^2} .$$

Put

$$(10.6.15) \qquad Y = \frac{\beta x}{2} = \frac{\beta}{2}\,[\ln T_{(m)} - \ln T_{(\ell)}] \ .$$

Then

$$(10.6.16) \quad g(y)dy = \frac{N! \quad 2dy}{(\ell - 1)!\ (m - \ell - 1)!\ (N - m)!}$$

$$\cdot \sum_{i=0}^{\ell-1} \sum_{j=0}^{m-\ell-1} (-1)^{i+j} \binom{\ell-1}{j} \binom{m-\ell-1}{j}$$

$$\cdot \frac{1}{[(N + j - m + 1)e^{y} + (m - \ell + i - j)e^{-y}]^2} \ ,$$

$y \geq 0$. Hence,

$$(10.6.17) \quad E(Y^k) = \frac{2N!}{(\ell - 1)!\ (m - \ell - 1)!\ (N - m)!}$$

$$\cdot \sum_{i=0}^{\ell-1} \sum_{j=0}^{m-\ell-1} (-1)^{i+j} \binom{\ell-1}{i} \binom{m-\ell-1}{j} I \ ,$$

where

$$(10.6.18) \quad I = \int_{-\infty}^{\infty} \frac{y^k}{[(N + j - m + 1)e^{y} + (m - \ell + i - j)e^{-y}]^2}\, dy \ .$$

Let $a = N + j - m + 1$ and $b = m - \ell + i - j$. Then we have:

$$(10.6.19)\quad I = \int_{-\infty}^{\infty} \frac{y^k}{[ae^y + be^{-y}]^2}\,dy = \int_0^1 \frac{[\ln(\frac{1}{t})]^k}{[\frac{a}{t} + bt]^2}\,\frac{dt}{t}$$

$$= \int_0^1 \frac{t[\ln(\frac{1}{t})]^k}{[a + bt^2]^2}\,dt \;.$$

The integral $I$ is evaluated for $k = 1$ and $k = 2$ in the next section.

## 10.7 Evaluation of Integrals

We have the two integrals

$$(10.7.1)\qquad J = \int_0^1 \frac{-t\ln t}{(\rho + t^2)^2}\,dt$$

and

$$(10.7.2)\qquad I = \int_0^1 \frac{t\ln^2 t}{(\rho + t^2)^2}\,dt$$

in the expressions for $E(Y)$ and $E(Y^2)$.

Using substitutions and integration by parts we obtain for $J$:

(10.7.3)

$$J = -\frac{1}{4}\int_\rho^{\rho+1} \frac{\ln x + \ln(1 - \frac{\rho}{x})}{x^2}\,dx = \frac{1}{4}\,\frac{1}{\rho}\,\ln\left(\frac{1+\rho}{\rho}\right)$$

and for I:

$$(10.7.4)\quad I = \int_0^1 \frac{t \ln^2 t}{(\rho + t^2)^2}\, dt = \int_0^1 \frac{\ln^2 t}{\left(\frac{\rho}{t^2} + 1\right)^2} \frac{dt}{t^3}$$

$$= \frac{1}{8\rho} \int_{1+\rho}^{\infty} \frac{(\ln (y - 1) - \ln \rho)^2}{y^2}\, dy$$

$$= \frac{1}{8\rho} \int_{1+\rho}^{\infty} \frac{\ln^2 (y - 1) - 2 \ln \rho \ln (y - 1) + \ln^2 \rho}{y^2} dy$$

$$= \frac{1}{8\rho} [A - 2 \ln \rho\, B + \ln^2 \rho\, C]$$

$$= \frac{1}{8\rho} [A - 2b\, B + b^2\, C]$$

$$= \frac{1}{8\rho} \left[ \ln^2 \frac{1 + \rho}{\rho} + 2 \sum_{K=1}^{\infty} \frac{1}{K^2 (1 + \rho)^K} \right]$$

where $a = \ln (1 + \rho)$ and $b = \ln \rho$.

Let

$$(10.7.5)\qquad \sum_{K=1}^{\infty} \frac{1}{K^2 (1 + \rho)^K} = f\left( \frac{\rho}{1 + \rho} \right),$$

where $f(x)$ is Spence's function.

We now proceed to evaluate the term $A$:

$$(10.7.6) \quad A = \int_{1+\rho}^{\infty} \frac{\ln^2 (y-1)}{y^2}\, dy = \int_{\rho}^{\infty} \frac{\ln^2 x}{(x+1)^2}\, dx$$

$$= - \frac{\ln^2 x}{1+x}\Bigg|_{\rho}^{\infty} + \int_{\rho}^{\infty} \frac{}{(1+x)x}\, dx \quad .$$

Let $x = y - 1$ and $v = \ln^2 x$, and

$$du = \frac{1}{(1+x)^2}, \qquad u = \frac{1}{1+x}, \qquad dv = \frac{2 \ln x}{x}.$$

Then

$$(10.7.7)\ A = \frac{\ln^2 \rho}{1+\rho} \lim_{A' \to \infty} \int_{\rho}^{A'} 2\left(\frac{\ln x}{x} - \frac{\ln x}{1+x}\right) dx$$

$$= \frac{\ln^2}{1+\rho} \lim_{A' \to \infty} 2 \ln^2 x \Bigg|_{\rho}^{A'} - \lim_{A' \to \infty} 2 \int_{\rho}^{A'} \frac{\ln x}{1+x}\, dx$$

$$= \lim_{A' \to \infty} \left[ \frac{\ln^2 \rho}{1+\rho} - \ln^2 \rho + \ln^2 A - 2 \int_{1+\rho}^{A'+1} \frac{\ln(y-1)}{y}\, dy \right]$$

$$= \lim_{A' \to \infty} \int_{1+\rho}^{A'+1} \frac{\ln^2 \rho}{1+\rho} - \ln^2 \rho + \ln^2 A' - 2 \int_{1+\rho}^{A'+1} \frac{\ln y}{y}$$

$$- 2 \int_{1+\rho}^{A'+1} \frac{\ln\left(1 - \frac{1}{y}\right)}{y}\, dy =$$

$$= \frac{\ln^2 \rho}{1+\rho} - \ln^2 \rho + \ln^2 (1+\rho)$$

$$+ \lim_{A' \to \infty} (\ln^2 A' - \ln^2 (A' + 1))$$

$$- 2\int_{1+\rho}^{\infty} \frac{\ln\left(1 - \frac{1}{y}\right)}{y}\, dy \; .$$

Now

$$(10.7.8) \qquad \int_{1+\rho}^{\infty} \sum_{k=1}^{\infty} \frac{1}{ky^{k+1}} = \sum_{k=1}^{\infty} \frac{1}{k^2 y^k} \Bigg|_{1+\rho}^{\infty}$$

$$= - \sum_{k=1}^{\infty} \frac{1}{k^2 (1+\rho)^k}$$

$$= - g(1+\rho) \; ,$$

and

$$(10.7.9) \qquad \lim (\ln^2 A - \ln^2 (A+1))$$

$$= \lim \; \ln A' \ln\left(1 + \frac{1}{A'}\right)\Bigg| \; = \; 0 \; .$$

Let $a = \ln (1+\rho)$, $b = \ln \rho$. We have

$$(10.7.10) \qquad A = \frac{b^2}{1+\rho} - b^2 + a^2 + 2g(1+\rho) \; .$$

Next, we evaluate the term B. We have

$$(10.7.11) \qquad B = \int_{1+\rho}^{\infty} \frac{\ln (y-1)}{y^2}\, dy$$

$$= \int_{1+\rho}^{\infty} \frac{\ln y}{y^2}\, dy + \int_{1+\rho}^{\infty} \frac{1}{y^2} \ln\left(1 - \frac{1}{y}\right) dy \ .$$

Now

$$(10.7.12) \qquad \int_{1+e}^{\infty} \frac{\ln y}{y^2}\, dy = -\frac{\ln y}{y}\Bigg|_{1+e}^{\infty} + \int_{1+e}^{\infty} \frac{dy}{y^2}$$

$$= \frac{\ln (1+\rho)}{1+e} + \frac{1}{1+e} = \frac{a+1}{1+\rho} \ ,$$

$$(10.7.13) \qquad \int_{1+e}^{\infty} \frac{1}{y^2} \ln\left(1 - \frac{1}{y}\right) dy = \int_{\frac{\rho}{1+e}}^{1} \ln x \quad dx$$

$$= x \ln x \ - \ x \Bigg|_{\frac{\rho}{1+e}}^{1}$$

$$= -1 - \left(\frac{e}{1+e} \ln \frac{e}{1+e} - \frac{e}{1+e}\right) \ .$$

We now have:

$$(10.7.14) \qquad B = -1 + \frac{a + 1 + \rho - \rho b + \rho a}{1 + e}$$

$$= -1 + a + \frac{1 + \rho(1 - b)}{1 + \rho}$$

and

$$(10.7.15) \qquad C = \int_{1+e}^{\infty} \frac{dy}{y^2} = -\frac{1}{y}\Bigg|_{1+\rho}^{\infty} = \frac{1}{1 + e} \; .$$

We may now complete our evaluation of I. From the Equation (10.7.4) we have:

(10.7.16)

$$I = \frac{1}{8\rho}\left[A - 2bB + B^2C\right]$$

$$= \frac{1}{8\rho}\left[\frac{b^2}{1+\rho} - b^2 + a^2 + 2g(1+\rho) + 2b - 2ab - 2b\,\frac{1+\rho(1-b)}{1+\rho} + \frac{b^2}{1+\rho}\right]$$

$$= \frac{1}{8\rho}\left[\frac{2b^2 - 2b - 2\rho b(1-b)}{1+\rho} + 2(a^2 - b^2 + b - ab) + 2g(1+\rho)\right]$$

$$= \frac{1}{8\rho}\left[a^2 - 2ab + 2g(1 + \rho) + b^2\right]$$

$$= \frac{1}{8\rho}\left[(a - b)^2 + 2g(1 + \rho)\right] \; .$$

Now

$$(10.7.17) \qquad g(1+\rho) = \sum_{k=1}^{\infty} \frac{1}{k^2(1+\rho)^k} = f \quad \frac{\rho}{1+\rho}$$

where

$$(10.7.18) \qquad f(x) = -\int_1^x \frac{\ln t}{t-1}\, dt$$

$$= \sum_{k=1}^{\infty} (-1)^k \; \frac{(x-1)^k}{k^2}$$

is Spence's Integral.

## 10.8 Summary

The best estimates of $1/\beta$ using two-order statistics are summarized in Table .

In the following table, our optimal two-order statistic estimator is compared with the various unbiased estimators of $\gamma = 1/\beta$ (where $\beta$ is the Weibull shape parameter) for efficiency relative to the Cramer-Rao lower bound. Notice, that all the estimators except ours are biased on all the order statistics.

TABLE VI

COMPARISON OF OPTIMAL TWO-ORDER STATISTIC ESTIMATORS

| N | Menon | Our Two Order Statistic | Unbiased MLE | MVLUE |
|---|---|---|---|---|
| 5 | 36 | 59 | 38 | 73 |
| 6 | 43 | 60 | 47 | 77 |
| 8 | 52 | 63 | 62 | 83 |
| 10 | 58 | 65 | 70 | 85 |
| 14 | 60 | 69 | 79 | 89 |
| 18 | 60 | 70 | 83 | 91 |
| 25 | 61 | 70 | 87 | 93 |

Data for Menon's estimator and the unbiased maximum likelihood estimator (MLE) were obtained from Thoman, et. al. [215]. The efficiency of the minimum variance, linear unbiased estimator (MVLUE) considered in the last column of the above table was obtained by unbiasing Mann's [135] biased estimator, which was obtained by deliberately "optimally" biasing the formula for the original MVLUE estimator, in order to achieve minimum expected square deviation from the true value.

It is evident from the above table of relative efficiencies, that our statistic is uniformly better than Menon's, which uses all the order statistics. For sample sizes less than 10, our statistic is more efficient than either Menon's or the MLE statistic. It appears that the asymptotic efficiency of our statistic is 70 percent, which is attained when the sample size reaches 18. This result will be validated by obtaining the asymptotic cumulative distribution function.

Finally, our statistic is simple to compute. The exact distribution is obtained and it can be tabulated.

We propose to investigate the relative efficiencies of two other procedures for estimating $\gamma$. One of them is the application of the classical least-squares procedure, rather than the minimum variance procedure, to estimate the regression coefficient $\gamma = 1/\beta$ in the setup, $T_{(i)} = \alpha + \gamma\mu(i)$, $i = 1,2,\ldots,N$, where $T_{(i)}$ is the $i^{th}$ order statistic from the extreme value distribution. The other procedure is based on plotting the points $P_i = (X_i, Y_i)$ where $X_i = \ln T_{(i)}$ and $Y_i = \ln \ln \frac{N+1}{N+1-1}$, $i = 1,2,\ldots,N$ and studying the efficiency of the least squares estimator in this case.

## 10.9 Distributions With a Given Quantile

In this section, the properties of distributions with a specified or given quantile are studied. It is shown that these dsitributions have to satisfy certain inequalities. The case in which the distribution is IHR is examined. The general results are further specialized to the case of a Weibull distribution.

Let $X$ be a random variable in $R_1$ with an absolutely continuous distribution function

$$F(x) = \int_{-\infty}^{x} f(x)dx \quad . \tag{10.9.1}$$

We can write

$$F(x) = 1 - e^{-\int_{-\infty}^{x} z(t)dt} \tag{10.9.2}$$

where

$$z(t)dt = \frac{f(t)dt}{1 - F(t)} \quad , \tag{10.9.3}$$

is the conditional probability that the event "$\mathcal{E}$" happened between $t$ and $t + dt$, given that it did not happen before time $t$.

Let $\tau_\varepsilon$ be the $\varepsilon$ quantile of the distribution given by (10.9.2). Hence,

$$F(\tau_\varepsilon) = \varepsilon . \tag{10.9.4}$$

Combining (10.9.2) and (10.9.4), we have

$$\varepsilon = 1 - e^{-\int_{-\infty}^{\tau_\varepsilon} z(x)dx} . \tag{10.9.5}$$

Now

$$F(t) = 1 - e^{-[\int_{-\infty}^{\tau_\varepsilon} z(x)dx + \int_{\tau_\varepsilon}^{\tau} z(x)dx]} , \tag{10.9.6}$$

so that

$$F(t) = 1 - (1-\varepsilon)e^{-\int_{\tau_\varepsilon}^{t} z(x)dx} . \tag{10.9.7}$$

Thus, (10.9.7) is the representation of an absolutely continuous distribution function with $\tau_\varepsilon$ for its $\varepsilon$ quantile.

From now on, without loss of generality, we will assume that the range of the distribution function is the positive real half-line.

We will now consider the case in which $F(t)$, given by (10.9.7). We have, for $t > \tau_\varepsilon$ and $z(t)$ increasing:

$$(10.9.8) \qquad z(\tau_\varepsilon)(t - \tau_\varepsilon) \leq \int_{\tau_\varepsilon}^{t} z(x)dx \leq z(t)(t - \tau_\varepsilon) .$$

From (10.9.8), it follows that

$$(10.9.9) \qquad 1 - (1-\varepsilon)e^{-z(\tau_\varepsilon)(t-\tau_\varepsilon)} \leq F(t) \leq 1 - (1-\varepsilon)e^{-z(t)(t-\tau_\varepsilon)} .$$

For $t < \tau_\varepsilon$, we have, from (10.9.7)

$$F(t) = 1 - (1-\varepsilon)e^{-\int_t^{\tau_\varepsilon} z(x)dx} .$$

Now

$$z(t)(\tau_\varepsilon - t) \leq \int_t^{\tau_\varepsilon} z(x)dx \leq z(\tau_\varepsilon)(\tau_\varepsilon - t) .$$

Hence,

$$(10, 9 .10) \qquad 1 - (1-\varepsilon)e^{z(t)(\tau_\varepsilon - t)}$$

$$\geq F(t) \geq 1 - (1-\varepsilon)e^{z(\tau_\varepsilon)(\tau_\varepsilon - t)} .$$

Combining (19.9.9) and (10.9 .11), we have proven:

THEOREM 17: <u>If</u> $F(t)$ <u>is IHR, then for</u> $t > 0$

$$(10.9 .11) \qquad \left[1 - (1-\varepsilon)e^{z(\tau_\varepsilon)(\tau_\varepsilon - t)}\right]^+$$

$$\leq F(t) \leq \left[1 - (1-\varepsilon)e^{z(t)(\tau_\varepsilon - t)}\right] .$$

We will now obtain the equivalent of (10.9.7) for the Weibull distribution. From now on, we will drop the subscript $\varepsilon$ and simply denote by $\tau$, the $\varepsilon$-quantile of $F(t)$. We define $f^+ = \max(0,f)$.

For the Weibull distribution with

$$(10. 9 .12) \qquad F(t) = 1 - e^{-\alpha t^\beta} .$$

The hazard rate $z(t)$ for the Weibull distribution is given by

$$z(t) = \alpha\beta t^{\beta-1} \tag{10.9.13}$$

and

$$F(t) = 1 - e^{-\alpha\tau^{\beta}} = \varepsilon \ . \tag{10.9.14}$$

Combining (10.9.12), (10.9.13) and (10.9.14), we discover that the Weibull distribution which has $\tau$ for its $\varepsilon$-quantile is for $\beta > 0$, $t > 0$

$$F(t) = 1 - (1 - \varepsilon)^{\left(\frac{t}{\tau}\right)^{\beta}} \ . \tag{10.9.15}$$

Notice that the scale parameter $\alpha$ does not appear in (10.9.15), which depends only on the shape parameter $\beta$.

In the next section we will study the sampling properties of the $\varepsilon$-quantile, in a random sample from (10.9.15).

## 10.10 Properties of the $\varepsilon$-Quantile in a Random Sample From (10.9.15)

The distribution which has $\tau$ for the $\varepsilon$-quantile is given by

$$F(t) = 1 - (1 - \varepsilon)e^{-\int_{\tau}^{t} z(x)dx} \ . \tag{10.10.1}$$

Now, let $T_1, T_2, \cdots, T_N$ be a random sample of size $N$ from the distribution (10.10.1).

Let t be the $\varepsilon$-quantile of the empirical distribution function

$$(10.10.2) \quad F_N(t) = \frac{1}{n} [\text{No. of observations among the } T_i\text{'s less than or equal to } t] .$$

Let $\mu = [N\varepsilon]$ be the largest integer contained in $N\varepsilon$. Then, the probability density function of t is given by

$$(10.10.3) \quad g(t)dt = \binom{N}{\mu}(N - \mu)[F(t)]^{\mu}[1 - F(t)]^{N-\mu-1} f(t)dt \quad .$$

Substituting for F(t), given by (10.9.15) in (10.10.3) and writing, for $0 < \eta < 1$,

$$(10.10.4) \qquad \eta = 1 - \varepsilon \quad ,$$

we obtain

$$(10.10.5) \quad g(t)dt = \beta \ln \left(\frac{1}{\eta}\right)\binom{N}{\mu}(N - \mu)\left[1 - \eta\left(\frac{t}{\tau}\right)\right]^{\mu} \cdot \eta^{(N-\mu)}\left(\frac{t}{\tau}\right)^{\beta} \tau^{-\beta} t^{\beta} - 1 \quad ,$$

which is the sampling distribution of the $\varepsilon$-quantile $t_\varepsilon$ from a Weibull distribution with shape parameter $\beta$ and $\tau$ for the $\varepsilon$-quantile.

We will not obtain the expected value of $t_\varepsilon$ and, thereby, an expression for the bias in $t_\varepsilon$ as an estimate of $\tau$, the true $\varepsilon$-quantile in the population. The density function (10.10.5) can be written as

$$(10.10.6)\quad g(t)dt = C \sum_{i=0}^{\mu} (-1)^i \binom{\mu}{i} \eta^{\frac{t}{\tau}^{\beta}} t^{\beta-1}\, dt$$

where

$$(10.10.7)\qquad C = \beta \ln\left(\frac{1}{\eta}\right)\binom{N}{\mu}(N - \mu)\tau^{-\beta} .$$

Taking the expectation of $t_\varepsilon$, we have

$$(10.10.8)\quad E(t_\varepsilon) = C \sum_{i=0}^{\mu} (-1)^i \binom{\mu}{i} \int_0^\infty t^\beta \eta^{(N-\mu+i)\left(\frac{t}{\tau}\right)^\beta}\, dt .$$

Now, substituting

$$x = \ln\left(\frac{1}{\eta}\right)(\eta + i - \mu)\left(\frac{t}{\tau}\right)^\beta ,$$

we obtain

$$(10.10.9)\qquad \int_0^\infty t^\beta \eta^{(N-\mu+i)\left(\frac{t}{\tau}\right)^\beta}\, dt =$$

$$= \frac{\beta^{-1}\,\tau^{\beta+1}\,\Gamma\left(1+\frac{1}{\beta}\right)}{(\eta+i-\mu)^{1+(1/\beta)}\left(\ln\left(\frac{1}{\eta}\right)\right)^{1+(1/\beta)}}$$

Combining (10.10.7), (10.10.8) and (10.10.9) we obtain

(10.10.10)

$$E(t_\varepsilon) = \frac{\tau\left[\binom{N}{\mu}(N-\mu)\,\Gamma\left(1+\frac{1}{\beta}\right)\sum_{i=0}^{\mu}(-1)^i\binom{\mu}{i}(N+i-\mu)^{-\left(1+\frac{1}{\beta}\right)}\right]}{\left[\ln\left(\frac{1}{\eta}\right)\right]^{1/\beta}}$$

Thus, the bias in $t_\varepsilon$ for estimating $\tau$ is given by

(10.10.11) $B = E(t_\varepsilon) - \tau$

$$= \frac{\tau}{\left[\ln\left(\frac{1}{\eta}\right)\right]^{1/\beta}}\left[\binom{N}{\mu}(N-\mu)\Gamma\left(1+\frac{1}{\beta}\right)\sum_{i=0}^{\mu}(-1)^i \cdot (N+i-\mu)^{-\left(1+\frac{1}{\beta}\right)} - \left[\ln\left(\frac{1}{\eta}\right)\right]^{1/\beta}\right].$$

Since the sample quantile is consistent for estimating the population quantile, we obtain

(10.10.12)

$$\lim_{N\to\infty}\binom{N}{\mu}(N-\mu)\,\Gamma\left(1+\frac{1}{\beta}\right)\sum_{i=0}^{\mu}(-1)^i\binom{\mu}{i}(N+i-\mu)^{-\left(1+\frac{1}{\beta}\right)} =$$

$$= \left[\ln\left(\frac{1}{\eta}\right)\right]^{1/\beta}$$

Let us put $\varepsilon = 1/2$ and $N = 2m+1$ in the above. In this case

$$\mu = [N\varepsilon] = m ,$$

and $t_\varepsilon$ is the median, equal to the $(m+1)^{st}$ order statistic $T_{(m+1)}$.

The bias in the sample median of the Weibull distribution, as an estimate of the population median is, therefore, given by

(10.10.13)

$$B = \frac{\tau_{1/2}}{[\ln 2]^{1/\beta}} \left[ \binom{2m+1}{m} (m+1)\, \Gamma\left(1 + \frac{1}{\beta}\right) \cdot \sum_{i=1}^{m} (-1)^i \binom{m}{i} (m+i+1)^{-\left(1+\frac{1}{\beta}\right)} - [\ln 2]^{1/\beta} \right].$$

We, therefore, obtain the interesting formula, for any integer $m$ and any real number $\beta > 0$

(10.10.14) $$\lim_{m \to \infty} \frac{(2m+1)!}{(m!)^2} \sum_{i=1}^{m} (-1)^i \binom{m}{i} (m+i+1)^{-\left(1+\frac{1}{\beta}\right)} =$$

$$= \frac{(\ln 2)^{1/\beta}}{\Gamma\left(1 + \frac{1}{\beta}\right)} .$$

We can also express (10.10.14) in its integral representation as

$$\text{(10.10.15)} \quad \lim_{m \to \infty} \frac{(2m+1)!}{(m!)^2} \int_0^\infty x^{1/\beta} (1 - e^{-x})^m e^{-(m+1)x} dx$$

$$= (\ln 2)^{1/\beta} .$$

As a particular case of (10.10.14) and (10.10.15), for $\beta = 1$, we have the following representations for $\ln 2$ which are otherwise very difficult to prove

$$\ln 2 = \lim_{m \to \infty} \frac{(2m+1)!}{(m!)^2} \sum_{i=0}^{m} (-1)^i \binom{m}{i} \frac{1}{(m+i+1)^2}$$

$$= \lim_{m \to \infty} \frac{(2m+1)!}{(m!)^2} \int_0^\infty x(1 - e^{-x})^m e^{-(m+1)x} dx .$$

In general we obtain, for the $k^{th}$ moment of the $\varepsilon$-quantile $t_\varepsilon$ of the Weibull distribution, the following:

$$\text{(10.10.16)} \qquad \mu'_k = E(\tau_\varepsilon^k) =$$

$$= \Gamma\left(1 + \frac{k}{\beta}\right)\tau^k \left[\ln \frac{1}{\eta}\right]^{-(k/\beta)} \binom{N}{\mu}(N - \mu)$$

$$\cdot \sum_{i=0}^{\mu} (-1)^i \binom{\mu}{i} \left[\frac{1}{(N + i + \mu)}\right]^{1+(k/\beta)} .$$

Let

$$S_{N,\varepsilon,\beta}(k) = \sum_{i=0}^{\mu} \frac{(-1)^i \binom{N}{\mu}(N - \mu)\binom{\mu}{i}}{(N + i + \mu)^{1+(k/\beta)}} \tag{10.10.17}$$

$$= \frac{\mu_k' \left[\ln\left(\frac{1}{\eta}\right)\right]^{k/\beta}}{\tau^k \, \Gamma\left(1 + \frac{k}{\beta}\right)} .$$

Clearly

$$S_{N,\varepsilon,\beta}(0) = 1 .$$

Then

$$\lim_{\beta \to \infty} S_{N,\varepsilon,\beta} = \frac{\mu_k'}{\tau^k} . \tag{10.10.18}$$

## 10.11 A Large Sample Confidence Band for $\beta$ With a Given Quantile

By applying a well known result (see Cramér [45]), we obtain that $t_\varepsilon$, the $\varepsilon$-quantile in a random sample from a Weibull distribution with a given $\varepsilon$-quantile $\tau_\varepsilon$, is asymptotically normally distributed with mean $\tau_\varepsilon$ and standard deviation

$$(10.11.1) \qquad \sigma = \frac{1}{\sqrt{N}} \frac{\tau_\varepsilon}{\beta} C(\varepsilon)$$

where

$$(10.11.2) \qquad C(\varepsilon) = \sqrt{\frac{\varepsilon}{1-\varepsilon}} \frac{1}{\ln\left(\frac{1}{1-\varepsilon}\right)} .$$

Thus,

$$(10.11.3) \qquad \sqrt{N} \frac{(t_\varepsilon - \tau_\varepsilon)\beta}{\tau_\varepsilon C(\varepsilon)} \xrightarrow[N \to \infty]{D} N(0,1),$$

which leads to the $\alpha$ percent large sample confidence interval for $\beta$, given by

$$(10.11.4) \qquad \frac{-K_\alpha\, C(\varepsilon)}{\sqrt{N}\left(\dfrac{t_\varepsilon}{\tau_\varepsilon} - 1\right)} < \beta < \frac{K_\alpha\, C(\varepsilon)}{\left(\sqrt{N}\,\dfrac{t_\varepsilon}{\tau_\varepsilon} - 1\right)}$$

where $K_\alpha$ is the $\alpha$ percent value of a normal distribution with zero mean and unit variance.

## 10.12 Properties of Distributions With a General Class of Hazard Rates

Barlow, Proschan and Hunter [11] obtained results concerning distribution functions with increasing hazard rates. We obtain these results for a class of distribution that includes increasing hazard rate and increasing hazard rate average distributions. In addition, distributions with decreasing mean residual lifetimes are considered and restrictions imposed that result in the theorems, stated below, for this class of function.

In determining the connection between the reliability function and mean residual lifetime function, we consider a positive-valued random variable, T, and the reliability function, (ref) with $R(t) = 1 - F(t)$. The cumulative distribution function (cdf), $F(t) = P(T \leq t)$, is assumed to be absolutely continuous with $F(t) = \int_0^t f(x)dx$. We assume that $f(x)$ is concentrated on the positive axis $(f(t) > 0, t > 0)$ and $f'(t)$ exists. The expected value of $T$, $E(T)$, is denoted by $\mu$. The hazard rate (HR),

$$Z(t) = -\frac{d}{dt} \log R(t) \tag{10.12.1}$$

and the mean residual lifetime (MRL) is

$$V(t) = \frac{1}{R(t)} \int_t^{\infty} R(x)dx \tag{10.12.2}$$

for $R(t) > 0$ and $V(t) = 0$ when $R(t) = 0$ are useful functions in reliability theory. We define the hazard rate average as

$$A(t) = \frac{1}{t} \int_0^t Z(x)dx \tag{10.12.3}$$

with $t > 0$ and $A(t) = Z(0)$ for $t = 0$. We list below some connections between these functions.

THEOREM 18: The differential equation connecting $V(t)$ and $Z(t)$ is:

$$V'(t) + 1 = Z(t)\, V(t) \quad .$$

THEOREM 19: The following properties of (10.12.3) are true:

1. $V(t) \geq 0$ ;

2. *If* $\mu < \infty$, *then* $V(0) = \mu$ ;

3. $V(\infty) = \lim_{t \to \infty} - \frac{f(t)}{f'(t)}$ *only if* $\lim \frac{f(t)}{f'(t)} = A$

   (*or* $\pm \infty$) ;

4. $V'(t) \geq -1$ ;

5. $V(t)$ *is constant if and only if* $R(t)$ *is an exponential ref.*

6. $Z(t) \geq 0$ ;

7. $\int_0^\infty Z(t)dt = \infty$ ;

8. $A(t) = -\frac{\log R(t)}{t}$ ; *and*

9. $\int_0^\infty \frac{dt}{V(t)} = \infty$ .

*Proof*:

$$\int_0^\infty \frac{dt}{V(t)} = -\log\left( \int_t^\infty R(x)dx \right) \Big|_0^\infty = \infty \ . \qquad (10.12.4)$$

THEOREM 20 : *Let* $Z(t)$, $V(t)$ *and* $A(t)$ *be obtained from* $R(t)$. *If*

$$\lim_{t \to \infty} Z(t) = Z(\infty)$$

<u>exists, then</u>

$$Z(\infty) = \frac{1}{V(\infty)} \quad \underline{\text{and}} \quad A(\infty) = Z(\infty) .$$

<u>Proof</u>: We have

$$(10.12.5) \qquad Z(\infty) = \lim_{t \to \infty} \frac{f(t)}{R(t)} = \lim_{t \to \infty} \frac{f'(t)}{f(t)} = \frac{1}{V(\infty)}$$

and

$$(10.12.6) \qquad A(\infty) = \lim_{t \to \infty} - \frac{\log R(t)}{t} = \lim_{t \to \infty} \frac{f(t)}{R(t)} = Z(\infty).$$

The next theorem shows that an ref is uniquely determined by a function with the properties of a mean residual lifetime function.

THEOREM 21: <u>If</u> $V(t)$ <u>has a first derivative,</u> $V(t) > 0$, $V(0) < \infty$ <u>and</u> $V'(t) \geq 1$,

$$(10.12.7) \qquad \begin{cases} \displaystyle\int_0^\infty \frac{v'(x) + 1}{v(x)}\, dx = \infty \\ \displaystyle\int_0^\infty \frac{dx}{V(x)} = \infty \end{cases} ,$$

<u>then there exists a unique</u> <u>ref,</u> $R(t)$ <u>such that</u>:

(10.12.8) $$V(t) = \frac{1}{R(t)} \int_t^\infty R(x)dx \quad .$$

<u>Furthermore, the ref is given by</u>:

(10.12.9) $$R(t) = \frac{V(0)}{V(t)} e^{-\int_0^t \frac{dx}{V(x)}} \quad .$$

<u>Proof</u>: From (10.9.2) we have $R(t) \geq 0$, $R(0) = 1$, $R(t)$ continuous, and $R(\infty) = 0$. Differentiating (10.9.2) we have:

$$R'(t) = \frac{V'(t) + 1}{V(t)} R(t)$$

and hence, $R(t)$ is non-increasing.

From (10.9.2) , we have:

$$\frac{d}{dt} V(t) R(t) = - R(t)$$

and hence,

(10.12.10) $$V(t) R(t) = - \int_0^t R(x)dx + V(0) \quad .$$

Now

(10.12.11) $$\int_0^\infty R(t)dt = \int_0^\infty \frac{V(0)}{V(t)} e^{\int_0^t \frac{dx}{V(x)}} dt =$$

$$= - V(0)e^{\int_0^t \frac{dx}{V(x)}} \Big|_0^{\infty} = V(0)$$

Since

$$\int_0^{\infty} \frac{dx}{v(x)} = \infty ,$$

we have

$$V(t)\ R(t) = \int_t^{\infty} R(x)dx \tag{10.12.12}$$

since $V(0) < \infty$.

Let $R_1(t)$ and $R_2(t)$ both satisfy the Equation (10.12.8). Then $R_1(t) = K\ R_2(t)$, where $K$ is a constant, since both are solutions of

$$\frac{d}{dt} \log R(t) = - \frac{V'\text{[illegible]}) + 1}{\text{[illegible]}t)}$$

and since $R_1(0) = K\ R_2(0)$ and $K = 1$. [illegible]e, $R_1(t) = R_2(t)$.

The condition

$$\int_0^{\infty} \frac{V'(x) + 1}{V(x)} dx = \infty$$

can be removed if we assume that $\lim V'(t)$ exists or is infinite for large $t$. If the limit exists we have

$V'(t) \geq 0$ for large $t$, otherwise $V(t)$ would eventually go negative. If follows that

$$\int_0^\infty \frac{dx}{v(x)} = \infty \quad \text{implies} \quad \int_0^\infty \frac{V'(x)+1}{V(x)} = \infty \ .$$

The divergence of $\int_0^\infty dx/(V(x))$ is needed, as can be seen by considering $V_1(t) = e^{t^2}$ and

$$V_2(t) = e^{t^2}\left(1 - e^{\frac{\sqrt{\pi}}{2}\text{ref}(t)}\ e^{-\frac{\sqrt{\pi}}{2}}\right)$$

Both generate

$$R(t) = e^{-\left(t^2 + \frac{\sqrt{\pi}}{2}\text{ref}(t)\right)}$$

by Equation (10.12.9). Only $V_2(t)$ satisfies $V(t) = 1/(R(t)\int_t^\infty R(x)dx$ and $\int_0^\infty dx/(V(x) = \infty$.

A useful computation formula is

$$V(t) = \frac{\int_t^\infty x\ f(x)dx}{R(t)} - t \ . \tag{10.12.10}$$

Some examples are listed below.

Example 1. $V(t) = 1$, $0 < t \leq 1$; $V(t) = t$, $1 < t$. We obtain $f(t) = e^{-t}$, $0 < t \leq 1$; $f(t) = 2/t^3$, $1 < t$.

<u>Example</u> 2. $V(t) = 1 + t$ and $f(t) = 2/((1 + t)^3)$.

<u>Example</u> 3. $V(t) = e^{-t^2}$. $Z(t) = - 2t + e^{t^2}$.

<u>Example</u> 4. $R(t) = e^{-4\sqrt{t}}$, $f(t) = \frac{2e^{-4\sqrt{t}}}{\sqrt{t}}$. $Z(t) = \frac{2}{\sqrt{t}}$, $V(t) = \frac{\sqrt{t}}{2} + \frac{1}{8}$.

<u>Example</u> 5. $R(t) = e^{-t^2}$, $f(t) = 2t\ e^{-t^2}$. $Z(t) = 2t$ and $V(t) = e^{t^2}(1 - \mathrm{ref}(t))\frac{\sqrt{\pi}}{2}$.

<u>Example</u> 6. $R(t) = e^{-e^t - 1}$, $f(t) = e^{(t-1-e^t)}$. $Z(t) = e^t$, $V(t) = e^{e^t} E_1(e^t)$ where $E_1(z) = \int_z^\infty \frac{e^{-t}}{t}\,dt$ is the exponential integral, $V(0) = 0.598$.

<u>Example</u> 7. $R(t) = 1 - \mathrm{erf}\left(\sqrt{\frac{t}{2}}\right)$, $f(t) = \frac{e^{-t/2}}{\sqrt{2\pi t}}$. $Z(t) = \left(e^{-t/2}/\left(\sqrt{2\pi t}\left(1 - \mathrm{erf}\left(\sqrt{\frac{t}{2}}\right)\right)\right)\right)$, and $V(t) = 2/\sqrt{\pi} \cdot \sqrt{t}/2 \cdot \left(e^{-t/2}/\left(1 - \mathrm{erf}\left(\sqrt{\frac{t}{2}}\right)\right)\right)$. $V(0) = 1$ and $V(\infty) = 2$.

<u>Example</u> 8. $R(t) = 3^{-t/2}\left(1 + \frac{t}{2}\right)$ and $f(t) = (t\ e^{-t/2})/4$. $Z(t) = \frac{t}{2(t + 2)}$, $V(t) = \frac{2(t + 4)}{t + 2}$, $V(0) = 4$ and $V(\infty) = 2$.

Now, we consider special classes of functions.

Random variables with increasing hazard rate (IHR) are used in applications. Random variables with decreasing mean residual lifetimes (DMR) and with increasing hazard rate average (IHRA) are generalizations of IHR functions.

THEOREM 22. Let $Z(t)$ and $V(t)$ correspond to $R(t)$. If $Z(t)$ is an increasing hazard rate function, then $V(t)$ is a decreasing mean residual lifetime function.

Proof: We have

$$V(t) = \frac{Z(t)}{f(t)} \int_t^\infty \frac{f(x)}{t(x)}\,dx \tag{10.12.11}$$

$$= \frac{1}{f(t)} \int_t^\infty f(x)\,\frac{Z(t)}{Z(x)}\,dx\,,$$

$$V(t) < \frac{R(t)}{f(t)} = \frac{1}{Z(t)} \tag{10.12.12}$$

and $V'(t) + 1 \leq 1$ implies $V'(t) \leq 0$.

In Example 3, we find an example of a DMR that is not IHR.

THEOREM 23. If $Z(t)$ is IHR, then $A(t)$ is IHRA.

Proof: The identity

$$A'(t) = \frac{1}{2} \int_0^t x\, Z'(x)dx \quad ,$$

obtained by integration-by-parts, proves the theorem.

We give, in a later section another proof of this.

## 10.13 Comparison With the Exponential Reliability Function

The exponential ref, $G(t) = e^{-t/\mu}$, has constant mean residual lifetime $V(t) = \mu$ and is a natural boundary between decreasing and increasing mean residual lifetimes. We will compare the ref corresponding to a very general hazard rate with an exponential ref having the same mean. We show that, for a very general class of hazard rates, which includes increasing hazard rate that cross $1/\mu$, the ref crosses the exponential distribution once and only once, from above.

We find it convenient, in the following proofs to work with the auxiliary functions $K(t)$ and $H(t)$, defined as:

$$K(t) = -\ln R(t) \quad ,$$

$$H(t) = \frac{R(t)}{G(t)}$$

Some properties of these functions are:

1. $K(t) = \int_0^t Z(x)dx > 0$ ;

2. $\int_0^\infty e^{-K(t)} dt = \mu$ ;

3. $K'(t) = Z(t) > 0$ ;

4. $K''(t) = Z'(t)$ ;

5. $A(t) = \frac{K(t)}{t}$ ;

6. If $V'(0) \leq 0$, then $K'(0) < \frac{1}{\mu}$ ;

7. $\ln H(t) = \int_0^t \left( \frac{1}{\mu} - Z(x) \right) dx$ ;

8. $H'(t) = H(t) \left( \frac{1}{\mu} - Z(t) \right)$ ; and

9. $H(0) = 1$ .

THEOREM 24. _Let_ $Z(t)$, $H(t)$ _and_ $A(t)$ _correspond to_ $R(t)$. _Let_ $G(t) = e^{-t/\mu}$ _where_ $\mu = E(T)$. _If_ $Z(t) = 1/\mu$ _for one and only one_ $t$, $Z(0) \leq 1/\mu$ _and_ $Z(\infty) > 1/\mu$, _then there exists one and only one_ $t_0$ _such that_

$$A(t_0) = \frac{1}{\mu} .$$

NOTE: We assume in the following that $\mu < \infty$ and that

$$\lim_{t \to \infty} Z(t) = A \quad (\text{or } \pm\infty) .$$

<u>Proof</u>. Since $A(0) = Z(0) \leq 1/\mu$, $A(\infty) = Z(\infty) > 1/\mu$ and $A(t)$ is continuous, there is at least one $t_0$ such that $A(t_0) = 1/\mu$. At $t_0$ we have

$$R(t_0) = e^{-t_0/\mu}$$

Let $Z(t_1) = 1/\mu$, $t_1 \geq 0$, then $H'(t_1) = 0$ and $H'(t) > 0$ for $t < t_1$ and $H'(t) < 0$ for $t > t_1$. $H(0) = 1$ and $H(t)$ increases from one, until $t_1$. It decreases to one at $t_0$ and continues to decrease. Since there is only one $t_1$, there is only one $t$.

THEOREM 25. <u>If</u>

$$Z(0) \leq \frac{1}{\mu}, \quad Z(\infty) > \frac{1}{\mu} \quad \underline{\text{and}} \quad Z(t) = \frac{1}{\mu}$$

<u>for one and only one</u> $t$, <u>then</u> $R(t)$ <u>crosses</u> $G(t)$ <u>exactly once from above</u>.

<u>Proof</u>. By Theorem 24 we have $A(t_0) = 1/\mu$ and $H(t_0) = 1$. Hence, $R(t_0) = G(t)$. Since

$$H(t) = t\left(\frac{1}{\mu} - A(t)\right) > 0$$

for $t < t_0$, we have $R(t) > G(t)$ for $t < t_0$ and for

$t > t_0$ we obtain $R(t) < G(t)$.

THEOREM 26. *If* $V(t)$ *is* DMR, *then* $Z(0) \leq 1/\mu$ *and* $Z(\infty) > 1/\mu$.

*Proof*. $V(0) = \mu$ and $V(\infty) < \mu$, hence, $Z(\infty) \geq 1/\mu$ by Theorem 22. Also

$$Z(0) = \frac{1 + V'(0)}{V(0)} \leq \frac{1}{\mu} .$$

COROLLARY. *If* $Z(t)$ *is* IHR, *then* $R(t)$ *crosses* $G(t)$ *exactly once from above*.

*Proof*. By Theorem 22 we have $Z(0) \leq 1/\mu$. Since $Z(t)$ is IHR, it crosses $1/\mu$ exactly once.

THEOREM 27. *If* $A(t)$ *is* IHRA *and* $Z(0) \leq 1/\mu$ *and* $Z(\infty) > 1/\mu$, *then*, $R(t)$ *crosses* $G(t)$ *exactly once from above. If* $R(t)$ *crosses* $G(t)$ *exactly once from above, then*, $Z(0) \leq 1/\mu$, $Z(\infty) > 1/\mu$ *and* $A(t) = 1/\mu$ *for exactly one* $t$.

THEOREM 28. *If* $Z(0) \leq 1/\mu$, $Z(\infty) > 1/\mu$ *and* $Z(t)$ *crosses* $1/\mu$ *exactly once at* $t_0$, *and*

$$K(t) \geq K(\mu) + K'(\mu)(t - \mu)$$

*for all* $t$, *then* $t_0 > \mu$.

*Proof*. Since $K(t) \geq K(\mu) + K'(u)(X - \mu)$ we have

$$\int_0^\infty K(t)\, f(t)dt \geq K(\mu) \quad .$$

Now

$$\int_0^\infty \left( \int_0^t \frac{f(s)}{R(s)}\, ds \right) f(t)dt = \int_0^\infty \frac{f(s)}{R(s)} \int_s^\infty f(t)dt$$

$$= 1$$

and $1 \geq K(u)$ or $A(u) \leq 1/\mu$. Since there is only one point where $A(t) = 1/\mu$ and $A(0) \leq 1/\mu$ we have $t_0 > \mu$.

COROLLARY. *If* $Z(t)$ *is* IHR, *then* $t_0 > \mu$.

*Proof*. $K(t)$ is convex, since $K''(t) = Z'(t) > 0$.

THEOREM 29. $[R(t)]^{1/t}$ *decreases as* $t$ *increases, for* $t > \tau$, *if and only if* $A'(t) > 0$ *for* $t > \tau$, *with* $\tau$ *a constant*.

*Proof*. We have

$$\frac{\ln R(t)}{t} = - A(t)$$

and $- A'(t) < 0$. Hence $(\ln R(t))/t$ is decreasing and $[R(t)]^{1/t}$ is decreasing for $t > \tau$. If $[R(t)]^{1/t}$ is decreasing, then $(\ln R(t))/t$ is decreasing and $-A(t)$ is decreasing.

THEOREM 30. <u>If</u> $Z(t)$ <u>is</u> IHR, <u>then</u> $A(t)$ <u>is</u> IHRA.

<u>Proof</u>. We have $K''(t) = Z'(t) > 0$ and $K$ is convex. Hence, $K(t) \geq K(\mu) + K'(\mu)(t - \mu)$, for all $t$ and

$$-\frac{k(t)}{t} \leq \frac{\mu K'(u) - K(u)}{t} - K'(u)$$

is a decreasing function as $t$ increases. Since

$$A(t) = \frac{K(t)}{t},$$

it follows that $A(t)$ increases as $t$ increases.

THEOREM 31. <u>If</u> $A'(t) > 0, \quad t > \tau,$ <u>then all moments of the distribution exist</u>.

<u>Proof</u>. Write

$$\int_0^\infty X^r R(X)dx = M_1 + M_2$$

with

$$M_2 = \int_K^\infty X^r R(X)dx \quad \text{and} \quad M_1 = \int_0^K X^r R(X)\,dx .$$

Then

$$M_2 \leq \int_K^\infty X^r (R(K))^{X/K}\, dx$$

since $R(X)^{1/X} < R(K)^{1/K}$ for $X > K$ by the previous theorem. Use repeated integration-by-parts to obtain

$$M_2 < K^{r+1} \sum_{i=1}^{r+1} \frac{(-1)^i}{\ln i} \frac{R(k)}{R(k)} \left(i - 1\right)! \binom{r}{i-1} .$$

The constant terms are of the form, $X^r\, R(K)^{X/r}$, and go to zero as $X$ goes to infinity.

## 10.14 Bounds on Expected Failure Times

We obtain bounds on the expected failure time of parallel and series systems by using the following theorem:

THEOREM 32. _If_ $Z(0) \leq 1/\mu$, $Z(\infty) > 1/\mu$ _and_ $Z(t)$ _crosses_ $1/\mu$ _exactly once at_ $t_0$, _and_ $\varphi(t)$ _is an increasing function of_ $t$, _then_

$$\int_0^\infty \varphi(t)\, R(t)dt \leq \int_0^\infty \varphi(t)\, G(t)dt .$$

_Proof_. We have

$$\int_0^\infty \varphi(t)\, R(t)dt - \int_0^\infty \varphi(t)\, G(t)dt =$$

$$= \int_0^\infty \varphi(t)(R(t) - G(t))dt + \int_0^\infty \varphi(t_0)(R(t) - G(t)dt$$

$$= \int_0^\infty (\varphi(t) - \varphi(t_0))(R(t) - G(t))dt$$

$$= \int_0^{t_0} (\varphi(t) - \varphi(t_0))(R(t) - G(t))dt$$

$$+ \int_{t_0}^\infty (\varphi(t) - \varphi(t_0))(R(t) - G(t))dt$$

$$\leq 0 ,$$

by Theorem 25.

The mean life of a series system with components having hazard rates of the general class $Z(0) \leq 1/\mu$, $Z(\infty) > 1/\mu$ and $Z(t) = 1/\mu$, one $t$ only, and with means $\mu_i$, $i = 1,2,\ldots,n$, exceeds the mean life of a series system with exponential ref's and means $\mu_i$. The reverse is true for parallel systems. This is the result of the following theorem.

THEOREM 33. <u>Let the ref's,</u> $R_i(t)$, <u>have hazard rate</u> $Z_i(t)$ <u>with</u> $Z_i(0) \leq 1/\mu_i$, $Z_i(\infty) > 1/\mu_i$ <u>and</u> $Z_i(t) = 1/\mu_i$ <u>for only one</u> $t$, <u>with</u> $i = 1,2,\ldots,n$. <u>Let</u> $G_i(t) = e^{-t/\mu_i}$, $i = 1,2,\ldots,n$. <u>The following are true</u>:

$$\int_0^\infty \prod_{i=1}^n R_i(t)dt \geq \int_0^\infty \prod_{i=1}^n G_i(t)dt$$

$$= \frac{1}{\sum_{i=1}^n \frac{1}{\mu_i}}$$

and

$$\int_0^\infty \left[1 - \prod_{i=1}^n R_i(t)\right]dt \leq \int_0^\infty \left[1 - \prod_{i=1}^n G_i(t)\right]dt .$$

Proof. The proof is exactly as in Barlow, Proschan and Hunter [11, p. 33], but using Theorem 32.

## 10.15 Summary and Future Research

Denote the several classes of reliability functions by the following:

1. General Hazard Rates

GHR = $\{R(t)$ : $R(t)$ is a ref with $Z(t)$ and $Z(0) < 1/\mu$, $Z(\infty) > 1/\mu$ and $Z(t) = 1/\mu$, for exactly one $t\}$ .

2. Increasing Hazard Rates

{IHR = $\{R(t)$ : $R(t)$ is a ref with $Z(t)$ and and $Z'(t) \geq 0\}$ .

3. Increasing Hazard Rate Average

$$\text{IHRA} = \{R(t) : R(t) \text{ is a ref with } A(t) \text{ and } A'(t) \geq 0\} .$$

4. Decreasing Mean Residual Lifetime

$$\text{DMR} = \{R(t) : R(t) \text{ is a ref with } V(t) \text{ and } V'(t) < 0 \text{ almost everywhere}\} .$$

We have shown in Theorem 21 that IHR $\subset$ DMR and Example 3 of Section 10.12 shows that DMR $\not\subset$ IMR. In Theorem 29 we proved that IHR $\subset$ IHRA. The example in Section 10.8 shows that IHRA $\not\subset$ GHR. We show in Theorem 25 that DMR and $Z(t) = 1/\mu$ for exactly one $t$ implies GHR. We do not know whether DMR $\subset$ GHR or GHR $\subset$ DMR. It may be possible to have a hazard rate as shown in Figure 11.

FIGURE 11
HAZARD RATE

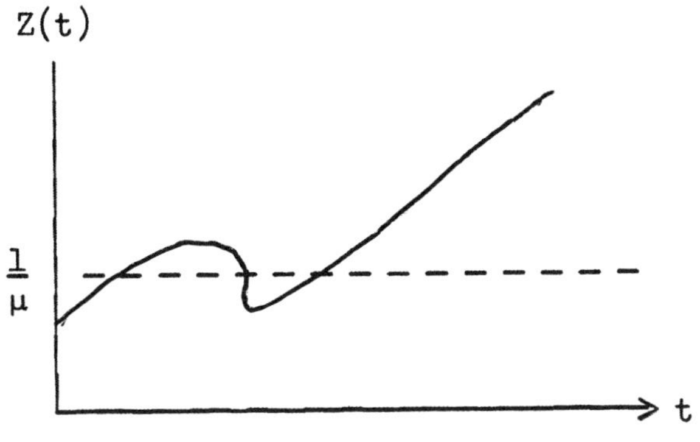

and still have DMR.

The question could be investigated by computer generated graphical output of $V(t)$ in response to a $Z(t)$, specified by using a light pen.

We have shown in Theorem 25 that if $R \in \text{GHR}$, then $R$ crosses $G$ exactly once from above. This fact is the key to the system theorem, Theorem 33. This result would be true for a hazard rate, as shown in Figure 12 if $1/\mu \in A(t)$ for $t > t_0$ where $A(t) = 1/\mu$. The relaxation of the condition $Z(t) = 1/\mu$ for exactly one $t$ depends on the inter-relationship of $\mu$ and $Z(t)$. Since the relation

$$\int_0^\infty e^{-\int_0^t z(x)dx} dt = \mu$$

is complicated, some insight could be obtained by a graphical program that shows $\mu$ on the graph of $Z(t)$ as the user specified $Z(t)$ via a light pen.

We have established the following relationships among the classes of cumulative distribution functions:

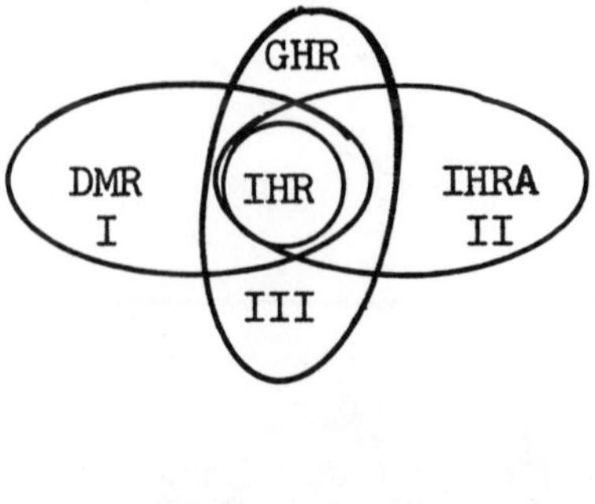

In the above diagram, we do not know if Regions I and III are empty or not.

## 10.16 Example of a Distribution Function Which is IHRA, GHR and DMR, But Not IHR

Barlow and Proschan [11] gave an example of a distribution function which is IHRA but not IHR. In this section we show that the distribution function is also GHR and DMR.

Let the reliability function $R(t) = 1 - F(t)$ be given by:

$$R(t) = e^{-t} g(t) , \tag{10.16.1}$$

where

$$g(t) = \ln (1 + e^{-(k-1)t} - e^{-kt})$$

for $k > 1$ and $t \geq 0$. Let

$$r(t) = \frac{d}{dt} \ln g(t) . \tag{10.16.2}$$

We have:

$$Z(t) = 1 - r(t) \quad , \quad A(t) = 1 - \frac{\ln g(t)}{t} \tag{10.16.3}$$

and

$$(10.16.4) \qquad V(t) = \frac{1}{k+1}\left(1 + \frac{k}{g(t)} + \frac{e^{-(k-1)t}}{k\, g(t)}\right).$$

The mean

$$\mu = \frac{1}{k(k+1)} .$$

We sketch the graphs of these functions using the derivatives:

$$(10.16.5) \quad Z'(t) = -r'(t)$$

$$= e^{-(k-1)t}(2k + k^2 e^{-t} + e^{-tk} - (k^2+1)) ,$$

$$(10.16.6) \qquad A'(t) = \frac{\int_0^t r(x)dx - t\,r(t)}{t^2} ,$$

and

$$(10.16.7) \quad V'(t) = -\frac{1}{(k+1)\,g(t)}$$

$$\cdot\left(k\,r(t) + \frac{k-1}{k} e^{-(k-1)t} + r(t)\frac{e^{-(k-1)t}}{k}\right).$$

We have $Z'(t) > 0$ for $0 < t < tm$, where $-e^{-tm} = (k-1)/k$ and $Z'(t) < 0$ for $tm < t$.

Since $r(x)$ is a decreasing function of $0 < x < tm$, we have that

$$\int_0 t\, r(x)dx > \int_0 t\, r(t)dx = t\, r(t) \quad . \tag{10.16.8}$$

It follows that $A'(t) > 0$ for $0 < t < tm$. Since $A'(t) = (Z(t) - A(t))/t$, and $Z(t) \geq 1$ for $tm < t$ and $A(t) < 1$ for all $t$, we easily have $A'(t) > 0$ for $tm < t$. Hence, $A(t)$ is increasing. Each term in the expression of $V'(t)$ is positive; hence, $V'(t) \leq 0$. These functions are sketched in Figures 12, 13, and 14 on the following page.

## 10.17 Formulation of Realistic Models for Life Distribution and Their Estimation Problems

From the relations

$$F(t) = 1 - e^{-\int_0^t Z(x)dx} \tag{10.17.1}$$

and

$$Z(t) = \frac{f(t)}{1 - F(t)} \quad , \tag{10.17.2}$$

there is a one-to-one relationship between the cumulative distribution function of life length $F(t)$ and the hazard

FIGURE 12. HAZARD RATE

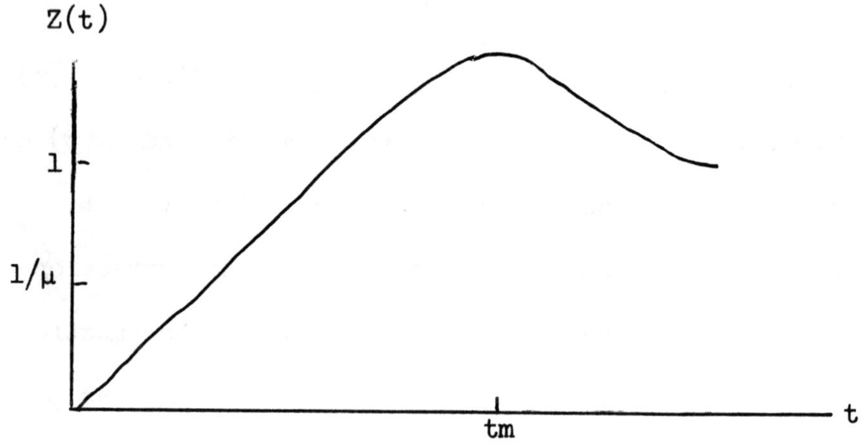


FIGURE 13. HAZARD RATE AVERAGE

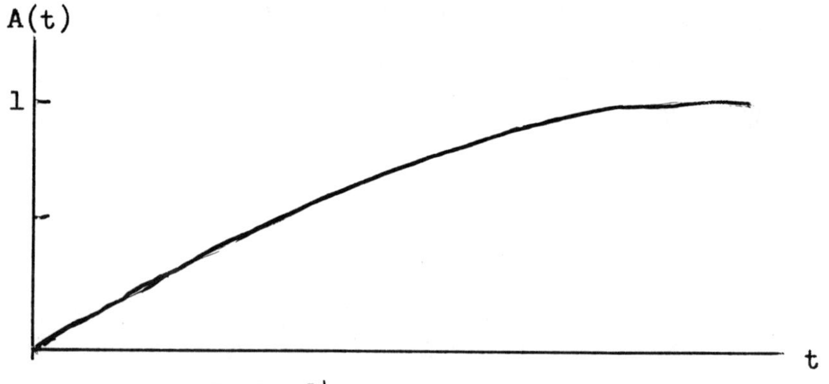


FIGURE 14. MEAN RESIDUAL LIFETIME

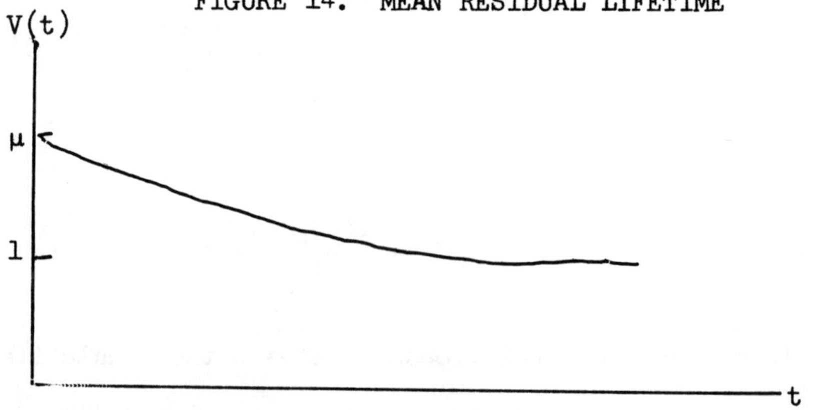


Reference: Barlow, R.E. and Proschan, F. [11].

rate $Z(t)$.

Let us plot a typical curve of the failure rate, against the lifetime $T$, based on a very large sample from a homogeneous component population. The resulting failure rate graph is shown on the following page. At time $T = 0$, we place in operation a very large number of new components of a given kind. This population will initially exhibit a high failure rate if it contains some proportion of sub-standard, weak specimens. As these weak components fail, one by one, the failure rate decreases comparatively rapidly, during the so-called "burn-in" or "debugging" period, and stabilizes to an approximately constant value at the time $\tau_B$, when the weak components have died out. The component population, after having been burned-in or debugged, reaches its lowest failure rate level, which is approximately constant. This period of life is called the "useful life" period, because it is in this period that the components can be utilized to the greatest advantage, and it is in this period that the exponential law is a good approximation. When the components reach the age $\tau_W$, wearout begins to make itself noticeable. From this time on, the failure rate increases rather rapidly until the components all fail.

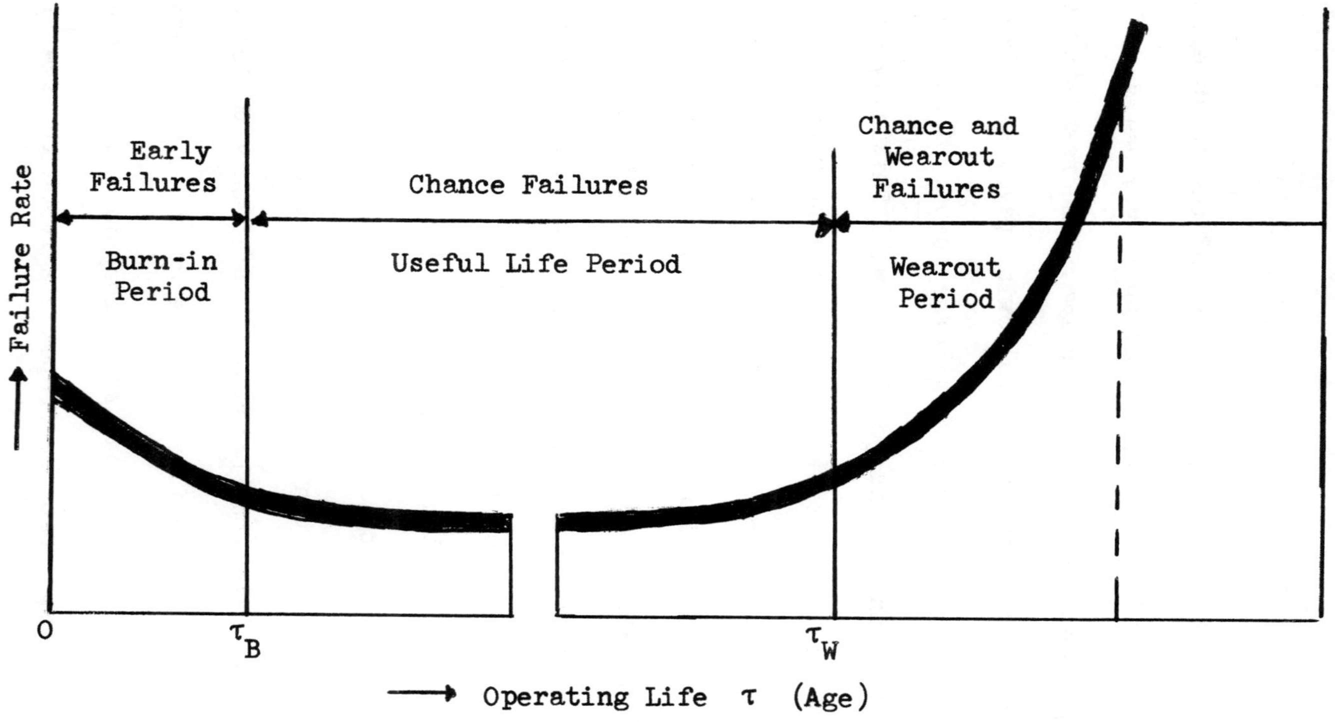


FIGURE 15. COMPONENT FAILURE RATE AS A FUNCTION OF AGE

Bath-Tub Model I for the Failure Rate $Z(t)$:

Consider the model for $Z(t)$ given by

$$Z(t) = \frac{\alpha}{1 + \beta t} + \gamma t^{\delta} , \tag{10.17.3}$$

where the parameters $\alpha$, $\beta$, $\gamma$ and $\delta$ are all real and nonnegative and $t \geq 0$.

When $\gamma = 0$, $Z(t) = \alpha/(1 + \beta t)$, which is a decreasing function of time, corresponding to the burn-in period. Also,

$$\begin{cases} Z(t) = \gamma & \text{when} \quad \alpha = 0,\ \delta = 0 \\ Z(t) = \alpha & \text{when} \quad \gamma = 0,\ \beta = 0 \end{cases} . \tag{10.17.4}$$

Equations (10.17.4) correspond to the useful life period and, finally, $Z(t) = \gamma t^{\delta}$, when $\alpha = 0$, corresponding to the final wearout period.

The distribution function of time-to-failure, corresponding to $Z(t)$ in Equation (10.17.3) is given by:

$$F(t) = 1 - e^{-\int_0^t \left[ \frac{\alpha}{1+\beta x} + \gamma x^{\delta} \right] dx} \tag{10.17.5}$$

which simplifies to

$$(10.17.6)\qquad F(t) = 1 - \frac{1}{(1+\beta t)^{\alpha/\beta}} \exp - \frac{\gamma t^{\delta+1}}{\delta+1}, \quad t \geq 0 .$$

Changing the parameter sequence, for the sake of familiar notation (at least for those of us who have dealt with the Weibull distribution extensively), we will rewrite $F(t)$, given by (10.17.6), as:

$$(10.17.7)\qquad F(t) = 1 \frac{1}{(1+\delta t)^{\delta/\gamma}} e^{-\alpha t^{\beta}}, \qquad \begin{matrix} \beta \geq 1 \\ \alpha, \gamma, \delta > 0 \end{matrix} ,$$

with corresponding probability density $f(t)$, given by

$$(10.17.8)\qquad f(t) = \frac{1}{(1+\delta t)^{\delta/\gamma}} e^{-\alpha t^{\beta}} \left[\alpha\beta t^{\beta-1} + \frac{\delta}{1+\gamma t}\right] ,$$

and the hazard rate $Z(t)$, given by

$$(10.17.9)\qquad Z(t) = \frac{\delta}{1+\gamma t} + \alpha\beta t^{\beta-1} .$$

The graphs of (10.17.9) for different values of $\alpha$, $\beta$, $\gamma$ and $\delta$, are displayed in Figures 16 - 21.

Let $\tau_i$ be the $\varepsilon_i$-quantile of the distribution given by (10.17.7), where

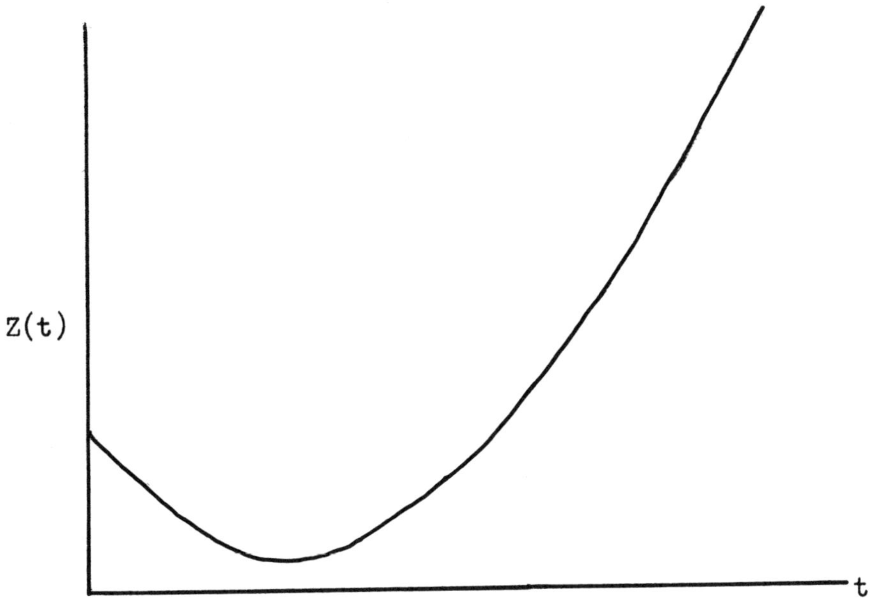


FIGURE 16. $Z(t) = \frac{10}{1 + 0.1t} + 0.36t^{1.5}$

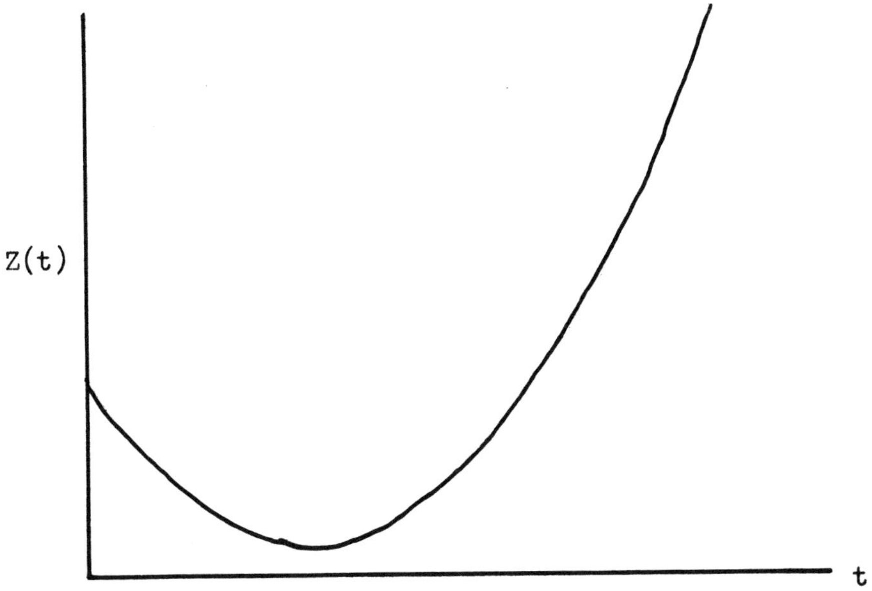


FIGURE 17. $Z(t) = \frac{10}{1 + 0.1t} + 0.09t^{2.5}$

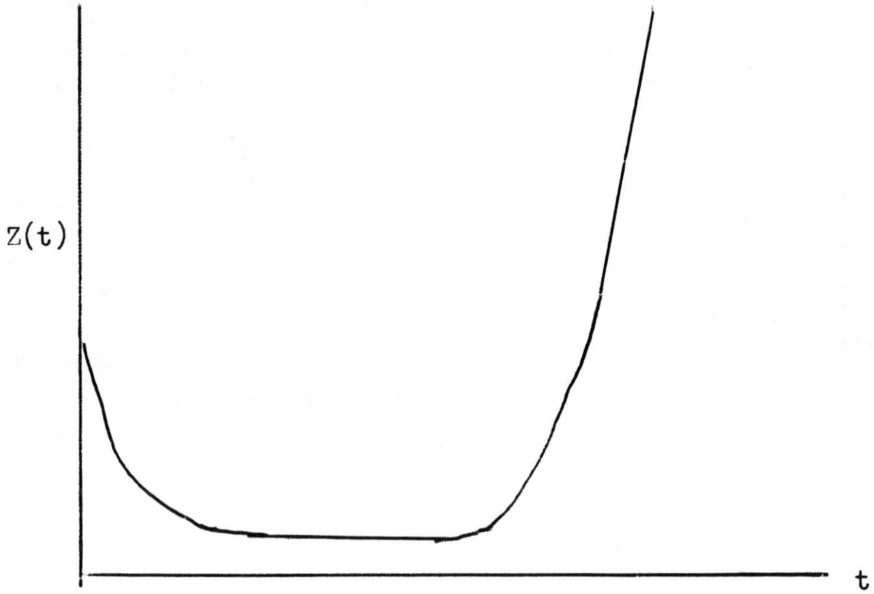


FIGURE 18. $Z(t) = \frac{100}{1 + 10t} + 0.0001t^{10}$

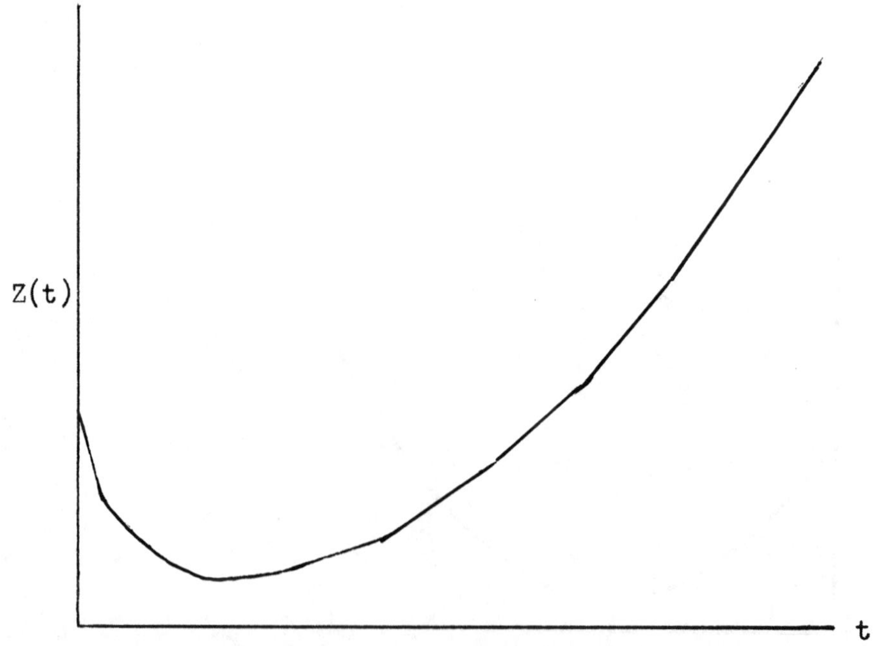


FIGURE 19. $Z(t) = \frac{10}{1 + 10t^2} + 0.3t^{2.5}$

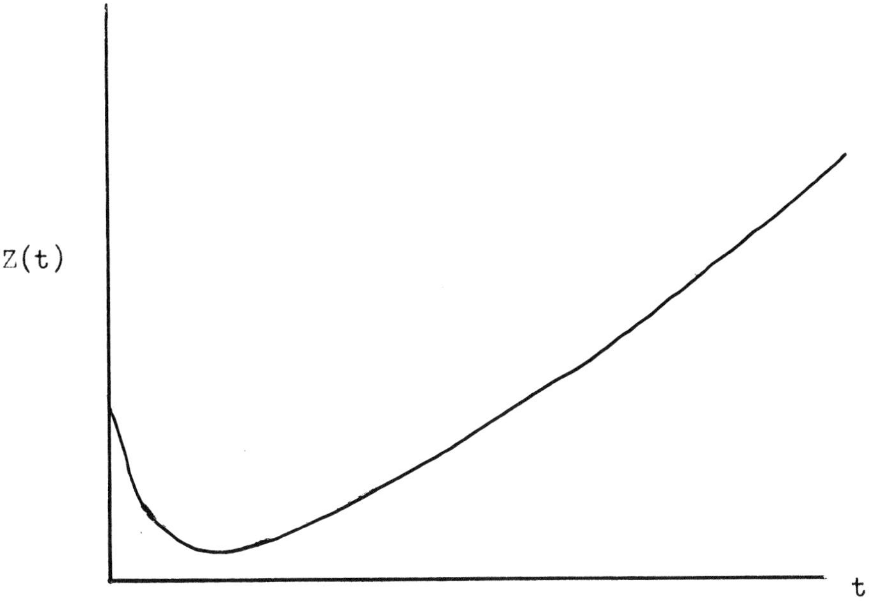


FIGURE 20. $Z(t) = \frac{10}{1 + 10t^2} + 1.22t^{1.5}$

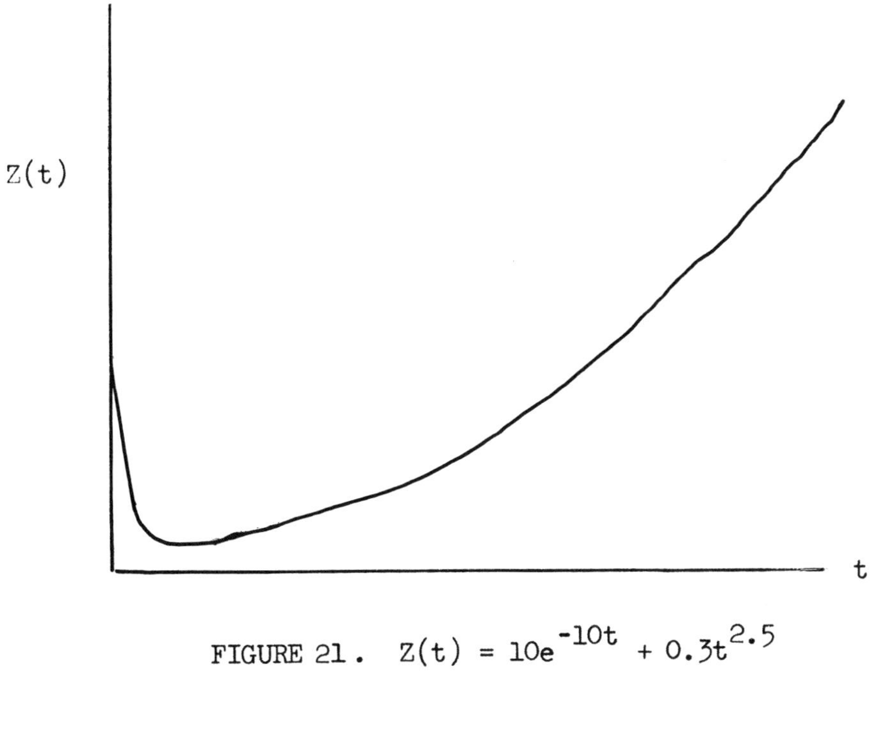


FIGURE 21. $Z(t) = 10e^{-10t} + 0.3t^{2.5}$

$$\varepsilon_i = F(\tau_i) = 1 - R(\tau_i) \quad , \tag{10.17.10}$$

i.e.,

$$R(\tau_i) = 1 - \varepsilon_i \quad .$$

We obtain from (10.17.7), in terms of $\tau_1$, $\tau_2$, $\tau_3$ and $\tau_4$, the following four equations for solving for $\alpha$, $\beta$, $\gamma$ and $\delta$.

$$\ln \frac{1}{R(\tau_i)} = \ln \frac{1}{1 - \varepsilon_i} = \eta_i, \quad \text{say} \quad . \tag{10.17.11}$$

The equations are:

$$\left\{ \begin{aligned} \eta_1 &= \frac{\delta}{\gamma} \ln (1 + \gamma\tau_1) + \alpha\tau_1^\beta \\ \eta_2 &= \frac{\delta}{\gamma} \ln (1 + \gamma\tau_2) + \alpha\tau_2^\beta \\ \eta_3 &= \frac{\delta}{\gamma} \ln (1 + \gamma\tau_3) + \alpha\tau_3^\beta \\ \eta_4 &= \frac{\delta}{\gamma} \ln (1 + \gamma\tau_4) + \alpha\tau_4^\beta \end{aligned} \right. \quad . \tag{10.17.12}$$

Let $T_{(1)} \le T_{(2)} \le \cdots \le T_{(N)}$ be the order statistics of a sample of size $N$ from the distribution (10.17.7). Let

$$\varepsilon_i = \frac{1}{N + 1}, \qquad i = 1,2,\ldots,N \quad .$$

Then, the sample quantile $\tau_i$, corresponding to $\varepsilon_i$, is given by the $i^{th}$ order statistic $T_{(i)}$, because the largest integer contained in $Ni/(N+1)$ is $(i-1)$.

Equations (10.17.12) correspond to the first four order statistic, given by:

$$(10.17.13)\begin{cases} \ln(N+1) - \ln N = \frac{\delta}{\gamma}\ln(1+\gamma T_{(1)}) + \alpha T^{\beta}_{(1)} \\ \ln(N+1) - \ln(N-1) = \frac{\delta}{\gamma}\ln(1+\gamma T_{(2)}) + \alpha T^{\beta}_{(2)} \\ \ln(N+1) - \ln(N-2) = \frac{\delta}{\gamma}\ln(1+\gamma T_{(3)}) + \alpha T^{\beta}_{(3)} \\ \ln(N+1) - \ln(N-3) = \frac{\delta}{\gamma}\ln(1+\gamma T_{(4)}) + \alpha T^{\beta}_{(4)} \end{cases} .$$

We will not discuss, herein, the details of solving (10.17.13) for $\alpha$, $\beta$, $\gamma$ and $\delta$, in terms of the first four order statistics $T_{(1)}$, $T_{(2)}$, $T_{(3)}$ and $T_{(4)}$, or the question of which set of four order statistics is optimum for estimating $\alpha$, $\beta$, $\gamma$ and $\delta$.

## 10.18 Maximum Likelihood and its Equivalent Procedures

Let $T_1, T_2, \ldots, T_N$ be a random sample of size $N$ from the distribution $F(t)$, given by (10.17.7). The likelihood of the observed sample is given by

$$(10.18.1) \qquad L = e^{-\alpha \sum_{i=1}^{N} T_i^{\beta}} \prod_{i=1}^{N} \frac{1}{(1+\gamma T_i)^{\delta/\gamma}}$$

$$\cdot \prod_{i=1}^{N} \left( \alpha \beta T_i^{\beta-1} + \frac{\delta}{1+\gamma T_i} \right)$$

and its natural logarithm by

$$(10.18.2) \ \ln L = -\alpha \sum_{i=1}^{N} T_i + \sum_{i=1}^{N} \ln\left( \alpha \beta T_i^{\beta-1} + \frac{\delta}{1+\gamma T_i} \right)$$

$$- \frac{\delta}{\gamma} \sum_{i=1}^{N} \ln (1+\gamma T_i) \ .$$

Then the likelihood equations are:

$$(10.18.3) \qquad \frac{d \ln L}{d\alpha} = - \sum_{i=1}^{N} T_i^{\beta} + \sum_{i=1}^{N} \frac{\beta T_i}{\left( \alpha \beta T_i^{\beta-1} + \frac{\delta}{1+\gamma T_i} \right)}$$

$$= 0 \ .$$

$$(10.18.4) \ \frac{d \ln L}{d\beta} = -\alpha \sum_{i=1}^{N} T_i^{\beta} \ln T_i + \sum_{i=1}^{N} \frac{\alpha T_i^{\beta-1} + \alpha\beta T_i^{\beta-1} \ln T_i}{\left( \alpha\beta T_i^{\beta-1} + \frac{\delta}{1+\gamma T_i} \right)}$$

$$= 0 \ .$$

$$(10.18.5) \ \frac{d \ln L}{d\gamma} = - \sum_{i=1}^{N} \frac{\delta T_i}{\left( \alpha\beta T_i^{\beta-1} + \frac{\delta}{1+\gamma T_i} (1+\gamma T_i)^2 \right)} \ -$$

$$- \frac{\delta}{\gamma} \sum_{i=1}^{N} \frac{T_i}{1 + \gamma T_i} + \frac{\gamma}{\delta^2} \sum_{i=1}^{N} \ln(1 + \gamma T_i) = 0 .$$

(10.18.6)
$$\frac{d \ln L}{d\delta} = \sum_{i=1}^{N} \frac{1}{\left( \alpha\beta T_i^{\beta-1} + \frac{\delta}{1 + \gamma T_i} \right)\left( 1 + \gamma T_i \right)}$$

$$- \frac{1}{\gamma} \sum_{i=1}^{N} \ln(1 + \gamma T_i) = 0 .$$

Denoting by $Z_N(T_i)$, the hazard rate estimate considered earlier by Murthy [152], we can solve Equation (10.18.6) for $\hat{\gamma}$ as

(10.18.7)
$$\hat{\gamma} = \frac{\sum_{i=1}^{N} \ln(1 + \hat{\gamma} T_i)}{\sum_{i=1}^{N} \frac{1}{Z_N(T_i)(1 + \hat{\gamma} T_i)}}$$

Equation (10.18.7) can be solved iteratively for $\hat{\gamma}$ using classical methods. Similarly, Equation (10.18.3) can be solved for $\hat{\beta}$ as

(10.18.8)
$$\hat{\beta} = \frac{\sum_{i=1}^{N} T_i^{\hat{\beta}}}{\sum_{i=1}^{N} \frac{T_i^{\hat{\beta}}}{Z_N(T_i)}}$$

Having obtained estimators for $\hat{\gamma}$ and $\hat{\beta}$, given by (10.18.7) and (10.18.8), respectively, we will consider the following two equations of the type (10.17.13) corresponding to two specific order statistics $T_{(\ell)}$ and $T_{(m)}$, given by

$$\text{(10.18.9)} \quad \ln (N+1) - \ln (N-\ell+1) = \hat{\delta}\, Y_{1,\ell} + \hat{\alpha}\, Y_{2,\ell}\,,$$

$$\text{(10.18.10)} \quad \ln (N+1) - \ln (N-m+1) = \hat{\delta}\, Y_{1,m} + \hat{\alpha}\, Y_{2,m}\,,$$

where

$$\text{(10.18.11)} \quad \begin{cases} Y_{1,\ell} = \dfrac{\ln (1+\hat{\gamma} T_{(\ell)})}{\hat{\gamma}}\,, \\[2ex] Y_{1,m} = \dfrac{\ln (1+\hat{\gamma} T_{(m)})}{\hat{\gamma}}\,, \\[2ex] Y_{2,\ell} = T_{(\ell)}^{\hat{\beta}}\,, \\[2ex] Y_{2,m} = T_{(m)}^{\hat{\beta}}\,. \end{cases}$$

Solving (10.18.9) and (10.18.10) for $\hat{\alpha}$ and $\hat{\delta}$, we obtain:

$$\text{(10.18.12)} \quad \hat{\alpha} = \frac{Y_{1,n} \ln \dfrac{N+1}{N-\ell+1} - Y_{1,\ell} \ln \dfrac{N+1}{N-m+1}}{Y_{1,m}\, Y_{2,\ell} - Y_{1,\ell}\, Y_{2,m}}\,,$$

$$(10.18.13) \qquad \hat{\delta} = \frac{Y_{2,m} \ln \frac{N+1}{N-\ell+1} - Y_{2,\ell} \ln \frac{N+1}{N-m+1}}{Y_{2,m} Y_{2,\ell} - Y_{2,\ell} Y_{1,m}} \; .$$

The properties of these estimators, as well as those obtained by solving the maximum likelihood equations are not discussed herein.

Bath-Tub Model II

This class of distributions is characterized by the hazard rate:

$$(10.18.14) \qquad Z(t) = \alpha e^{-\beta t} + \gamma t^{\delta} \; .$$

The distribution function, corresponding to the above hazard rate is given by

$$(10.18.15) \qquad F(t) = 1 - e^{-\frac{\alpha}{\beta}(1-e^{-\beta t}) - \gamma \frac{t^{\delta+1}}{\delta+1}} \; .$$

Relabelling the parameters in familiar notation, we can write

$$(10.18.16) \qquad F(t) = 1 - e^{-\gamma(1-e^{-\delta t})-\alpha t^{\beta}}$$

with corresponding hazard rate, given by

$$(10.18.17) \qquad Z(t) = \gamma\delta e^{-\delta t} + \alpha\beta t^{\beta-1} , \qquad \begin{cases} \beta \geq 0 \\ \alpha,\gamma,\delta \geq 0 \end{cases} .$$

The special case of (10.18.16) where $\gamma = 1/\delta^2$, is of special interest to us, as it is a three-parameter family of distributions containing the bath-tub models for the hazard rate. This class of distributions is given by

$$(10.18.18) \qquad F(t) = 1 - e^{-\frac{1}{\delta^2}(1-e^{-\delta t})-\alpha t^{\beta}}$$

with corresponding hazard rate, displayed in Figure 21:

$$(10.18.19) \qquad Z(\tau) = \frac{1}{\gamma\delta} e\delta^{-\gamma t} + \alpha\beta \;{}^{\beta-1} , \qquad \begin{cases} \alpha \geq 0, \ \beta \geq 1 \\ \delta\gamma > 0 \end{cases} .$$

The only known reference on bath-tub type hazard rate curves, with empirical estimation, is found in [84]. In this, the hazard rate curve is given by

$$(10.18.20) \quad Z(\tau) = \frac{\theta_1}{\theta_2 + \tau^2} + \theta_3 \, e^{\frac{\tau^{\theta_4}}{\theta_5}} , \qquad 0 < \tau < \infty .$$

The function (10.18.20), while versatile like our families of hazard rate curves given by (10.17.9) and (10.18.17) unfortunately does not give the distribution function of time-to-failure in a closed form and, consequently, the classical methods of estimation procedures are not readily applicable.

# CHAPTER 11. APPLICATIONS TO BIOLOGICAL AND MEDICAL PROBLEMS

## 11.1 Introduction

The mean and variance of a one-dimensional general point process, and, therefore, of the one-dimensional equilibrium process, were obtained in Chapter 1. Also obtained and tabulated for the purpose of convenience of use, were the higher moments, up to order $8$, of the renewal random variable, which is the number of events that have happened by time $t$, for any $t > 0$. In the first part of this chapter we deal at length with the application of the general theory developed in Chapter 1, in order to obtain expressions for the mean and variance of the number of points or events, such as live births that occur within a given period of a marriage. We also obtain expressions for the mean and variance of still births and miscarriages in a given period of time, or that occur by any specified time, $t > 0$. This chapter essentially summarizes the fundamental work of Edward B. Perrin and Mindel C. Sheps [164].

In recent decades, there has been a considerable amount of interest generated in the analysis of the pregnancies of cohorts of married women. Special emphasis on the pattern of live births, as they occur in time, is one of the factors studied by Henry [104]. In studies of this nature, the usual period of observation has been defined as an arbitrary calendar interval, i.e., as the period from marriage until the occurrence of some event such as the birth of the $n^{th}$ child, dissolution of the marriage, or attainment of an age assumed to be past the reproductive period. The greatest amount of the variables studied have been related to live births, since these data tend to be more readily available and complete than that about conceptions or total pregnancies. Some of the typical data analyzed in the study of reproductive cohorts, for example, are the distribution of intervals between successive live births, the distribution of the number of live births per individual in a defined period of time, and the annual probability of a live birth (i.e., fertility rate).

The consideration of cohorts of married women results in a more concentrated population for study than the usual groups on whom vital statistics are available. Not only is the study group undiluted by women who are not exposed to the risk of conception, but the history of each woman is known and, thus, the investigator may view the process sequentially in time. Individual patterns of reproduction can be studied in detail. However, the interpretation of relations between the different variables and comparison of findings in different cohorts have proven quite difficult, since the data are complicated by the number and interaction of biological parameters on which the observed distributions may depend. In view of this difficulty, there is a considerable need to develop a mathematical model which might further the understanding of the natural phenomena which underlie the reproductive process. In this chapter such a mathematical model will be developed; one in which the phenomenon of human reproduction is viewed as a special form of a stochastic process, i.e., a Markov Renewal Process. Out main concern will be with the exposition of the model and with the results of the theoretical investigations. More complete discussions of the practical applications which result from the above mathematical model may be found in Sheps and Perrin [184], [185].

## 11.2 Previous Work

Several investigations concerned with the formulation of models for the study of human fertility have been reported in the literature. Dandekar [46], for example, derived an expression for the probability of at most x conceptions in n trials, assuming only conceptions that end in live births and the period of physiological sterility associated with these conceptions. By treating the risk of pregnancy as continuous, rather than discrete, in time, he obtained a modified Poisson expression for the distribution of pregnancies. Although the resulting expression does not apparently give a good fit to an observed distribution, Dandekar's formulation has received further application in the work of Brass [24] and Potter [166], [167].

Louis Henry [104],[105] has, by ingenious reasoning, derived interesting relations using some of the same assumptions that are employed in this chapter. His results are, indeed, a special case of those derived herein. Perrin and Sheps [163], Sheps and Perrin [185] and Sheps [183] have developed special cases of the one presented in this paper.

The work of Lotka [131] gave impetus to the development of the theoretical aspects of renewal theory as such, although he did not specifically apply his techniques to the problems of individual fertility which we are considering here, but was, rather, concerned with the theory of populations in the aggregate.

## 11.3 Biological Considerations in the Construction of the Model

This section is concerned with the following biological considerations which are important in the construction of the mathematical model for human reproduction.

### 1. Fecundability

Since there are many factors which determine whether an ovum becomes fertilized and embedded, it is not unreasonable to consider conception in the human female as a chance event. The probability that a nonpregnant married woman will conceive in any one month (fecundability) may depend on a number of factors, some of which are: the occurrence or nonoccurrence of ovulation during that particular cycle, its timing within the cycle if it does occur, the frequency and timing of intercourse as related to ovulation, the use or nonuse of contraceptives, characteristics of the semen, and other individual characteristics of the woman and her spouse, including age and health status, all of which may act through their effects on the preceding factors, or in other ways (Hartman [101]).

### 2. Probability of Fetal Loss

A proportion of all conceptions end in the death of

the fetus and such conceptions are frequently omitted in the type of data routinely collected. The probability that any one conception will end in the death of the fetus may depend on maternal age, rank order of the pregnancy, length of the interval from the end of the last pregnance to the present one, and the health of the mother [183]. This probability may also be affected by individual genetic or other characteristics [184].

3. "Inactive" or Infecundable Periods

A conception is followed by a period during which the woman is essentially sterile and thus not exposed to the risk of pregnancy. The length of this period depends, in general, on the duration of the pregnancy and the interval after birth before ovulation or cohabitation is resumed, whichever comes later, and this period also varies from pregnancy to pregnancy. The mean and variance of the duration of the pregnancy itself are correlated with the outcome, the mean length being shorter in the case of a fetal death than in a live birth, for example, Hartman [101] and Sheps [183].

The onset of ovulation in a female, following termination of pregnancy, or the resumption of cohabitation may be delayed for some time. The factors involved in this delay may depend on the outcome of the pregnancy, on the survival time of a live-born child, on maternal age, and on rank order of the pregnancy, as well as on social customs and physiological factors [101], [183]. For example, when ovulation is first resumed, it is possible that the level of fecundability may be lower than before the pregnancy and that it may then increase over a period, to reach the previous level or some new level. On the other hand, it is also possible that it immediately returns to the prepregnancy level.

## 11.4 The Mathematical Model

Let us consider the reproductive pattern of the married female, known to be nonpregnant and fecundable at the time of marriage. At any time after marriage (and before the occurrence of menopause or secondary sterility) this woman can be assumed to be in one and only one of the following states, with respect to reproductivity; she will be either:

(1) nonpregnant and fecundable,

(2) in the course of a pregnancy,

(3) in the postpartum infecundable period associated with an abortion or early fetal death,

(4) in the postpartum infecundable period associated with a stillbirth (late fetal death), or

(5) in the postpartum infecundable period associated with a live birth.

For simplicity, we will label these five states as follows:

$S_0$ = nonpregnant, fecundable state

$S_1$ = pregnant state

$S_2$ = postpartum sterile period associated with abortion or fetal loss

$S_3$ = postpartum sterile period associated with stillbirth, and

$S_4$ = postpartum sterile period associated with live birth.

It is clear that the reproductive history of a female is characterized completely by the knowledge of the sequence in which these states are visited and the length of time spent in each state, at each visit. For example, the number of live births produced by a woman in time $t$ is given by the number of transitions from $S_1$ to $S_4$ in that time $t$. The total number of pregnancies entered is given by the number of transitions made from $S_0$ to $S_1$, etc.

As described in Section 11.3, biological considerations make it logical to view, as a random variable, the length of time spent in the fecundable, nonpregnant state, $S_0$, after the beginning of marriage or after return from a postpartum sterile state. We shall assume as a first approximation, that a female in state $S_0$ is subject, at intervals of approximately one month, to a given probability, $\rho$, of entering state $S_1$ (i.e., becoming pregnant). Under this assumption, the total number of months spent in state $S_0$, during any single visit to that state, is easily seen to be a random variable with a geometric distribution.

In the same manner, the lengths of stay of a woman in each of the other four states of the model are naturally viewed as random variables. In particular, we can let the duration of stay in the pregnancy state, $S_1$, depend on the outcome of the pregnancy and we designate, $f_i$, as the (conditional) distribution function of the length of stay, in months, in state $S_1$, given that the next state visited is $S_i$, $i = 2,3,4$ and the mean and variance of the length of that stay will be designated as $\nu_i$ and $\xi_i^2$, respectively. Likewise, for $i = 2,3,4$, the distribution function of the duration of time (in months) spent in the postpartum state, $S_i$, is represented by $g_i$ with mean and variance $\mu_{i0}$ and $\sigma_{i0}^2$, respectively. Finally, we let $\Theta$, be the probability that a given pregnancy ends with a transition to state $S_i$, i.e., that the pregnancy ends in fetal death, stillbirth, or a live birth, respectively.

Under these assumptions, the reproductive proces is viewed, rather simply, as a stochastic process in which a woman, beginning in state $S_0$, passes after a period of time into state $S_1$, thence, with given probability, into state $S_2$, $S_3$ or $S_4$, and from one of these states back to state $S_0$ (see Figure 22), to begin the reproductive cycle again. In this process, the length of stay in each state is, as already mentioned, a random variable whose distribution function can depend on the state being occupied as well as on the next state to which the process will move. If the parameters involved are assumed to be constant, with respect to time, as measured from the beginning of the process, it is not difficult to show that this is, indeed, a Markov Renewal Process [184],[185]. Similarly, a less general model in which the postpartum sterile periods are studied, in combination with the three types of pregnancies mentioned above, can be shown to generate a zero-order Markov Renewal Process [170] and, as such, has also been studied by [104] and [185]. In the proofs that follow, however, little use will be made of the machinery of the generalized Markov Renewal Process, since the results for the present model follow more intuitively from simple probability considerations.

It is important to take a critical look at the model generated above in light of the biological considerations mentioned in Section 11.3. First, it should be noted that this model allows for more than one type of pregnancy, i.e., with a given probability that any pregnancy can terminate in either fetal death, stillbirth, or a live birth. It also allows for a variable period of gestation and a variable period of infecundability associated with each pregnancy, the length of these periods depending on the form of the pregnancy termination. In both respects this model is appreciably more general than previous fertility models for which explicit probability solutions have been obtained.

On the other hand, the present model does not allow the probabilities of conception, stillbirth or early fetal loss, or the lengths of the periods of gestation and infecundability to depend on such factors as age or birth order in the individual female. It is commonly held, for example, that the assumption of a constant probability of conception, in the absence of the use of contraceptives, is reasonably valid over a large part, but not all, of a woman's childbearing life. Further probabilities of fetal death are more apt to be a function of time than the probability of conception itself. Hence, the period for which this model can be assumed to hold for each woman, must necessarily be restricted to an interval of , at most, from 10 to 15 years in the middle of the childbearing age.

Monte Carlo simulation procedures offer an obvious means for studying the process under less stringent assumptions of time and age dependence and such studies are now being carried out.

There is a tacit assumption, in this model, of independence between the distributions of durations of stay in each of the fertility states. It should be obvious that this assumption may not always hold, since, for example, premature live births are accompanied by an increased probability of neonatal death and, consequently, a shorter lactation period. Hence, a shorter period of postpartum infecundability might be expected in this case. However, it is doubtful if such dependence seriously affects the applicability of the model considered herein. At any rate, the problem may be dealt with by subdividing $S_4$ into two postpartum states; $S_{4a}$ indicating the state after a premature infant and $S_{4b}$ the state after a full term infant.

The assumption of a constant probability of pregnancy, per cycle, and the resulting geometric distribution of waiting times in the fecundable, nonpregnant state $S_0$, can, of course, be relaxed somewhat without destroying the Markov Renewal Property of the model. The probability of conception may be allowed to vary with the time spent in the nonpregnant, fecundable state $S_0$, as long as the distribution is the same for each visit to $S_0$, without altering the results which follow except for the substitution of the appropriate moments of the new distribution. If desired, the model could also be extended to include a state $S_0'$, indicating a state to which a woman might return after a visit to a postpartum infecundable state, $S_2$, $S_3$ or $S_4$, and in which the monthly probability of conception would be allowed to return gradually to the level originally exhibited in $S_0$, or to some other specified level.

The underlying stochastic model constructed here is, of course, quite general and its usefulness is not restricted to consideration of problems of reproduction alone. One could, for example, define the various states of the process as the successive stages of a single disease, or as different disease entities, etc., through which an individual might pass in a given period of exposure [163]. The stochastic relationships derived below would apply with equal validity to studies of this sort.

## 11.5 Results

We shall confine our attention here to an investigation of the three characteristics previously identified as important in the study of human fertility: (1) the distribution of the intervals between successive pregnancy terminations of the various types, (2) the distribution of the number of miscarriages, stillbirths, or live births per individual, occurring in a given period of time, and (3) the monthly probability of the occurrence of a live birth, i.e., the fertility rate. The results obtained will, of course, be valid for any woman for whom the model can be assumed to hold, regardless of the particular parameter values for the individual involved. Further, the results will have direct interpretation for cohorts of married women for which it is reasonable to assume that little variation in parameter values exists between individuals. Extension of the results to cohorts of women, nonhomogeneous with respect to one or more of the fertility parameters will be omitted here.

### 1. First Passage and Recurrence Times

It is necessary, first, to introduce some additional notation. Let $T_{ij}$, $i,j = 0,1,\ldots,4$ represent the random time in months required by a female for passage from state $i$ to state $j$ in our model, and let $\mu_{ij}$ and $\sigma^2_{ij}$ represent the mean and variance, respectively, of that time. $T_{ij}$ will then be the first passage time from $i$ to $j$ and $T_{ii}$, will be the recurrence time, as defined in classical renewal theory [195]. Further, let $T^*_{ij}$ be the time spent in state $i$, given that $j$ is the next state entered. Note that $T^*_{ij}$ is defined only if direct passage from state $i$ to state $j$ is possible, and, in general, $T^*_{ij}$ need not equal $T_{ij}$ since in the latter process any number of states may be visited before eventual passage to state $j$.

For example, $T_{01}$ is the first passage from $S_0$ to $S_1$, i.e., the time spent by a woman in the fecundable, non-pregnant state until the first, or next, pregnancy. $T_{01}$ is thus defined as a waiting time, and put equal to zero if conception occurs in the first month of marriage, or in the first month after returning to $S_0$. From our assumptions it is easy to see that $T_{01} = T^*_{01}$ and that $T_{01}$ has a geometric distribution with parameter $\rho$. Hence,

$$E(T_{01}) = \mu_{01} = \frac{1 - \rho}{\rho^2}$$

(11.5.1) $$\operatorname{Var}(T_{01}) = \sigma_{01}^2 = \frac{1-\rho}{\rho^2}.$$

Also, under our model, we note that:

$$T_{00} = \begin{cases} T_{01} + T_{12}^* + T_{20} & \text{with probability } \theta_2 \\ T_{01} + T_{13}^* + T_{30} & \text{with probability } \theta_3 \\ T_{01} + T_{14}^* + T_{40} & \text{with probability } \theta_4 \end{cases},$$

Thus, the expected value of $T_{00}$, the recurrence time for the fecundable nonpregnant state, is a weighted mean of the expected time spent in each of the three paths leading to recurrence. In particular, of we let $\eta_i = \nu_i + \mu_{i0}$, with $i = 2,3,4$, we can write

(11.5.2) $$\mu_{00} = E(T_{00}) = E(T_{01}) + \theta_2 E(T_{12}^* + T_{20}) + \theta_3 E(T_{13}^* + T_{30}) + \theta_4 E(T_{14}^* + T_{40})$$
$$= \frac{1-\rho}{\rho} + \sum_{i=2}^{4} \theta_i \eta_i .$$

By similar reasoning

(11.5.3)

$$E(T_{00}^2) = \sum_{i=2}^{4} \theta_i E(T_{0i} + T_{1i}^* + T_{i0})^2 = E(T_{01}^2)$$
$$+ \sum_{i=2}^{4} \theta_i [E(T_{1i}^* + T_{i0})^2 + 2E(T_{01}) E(T_{1i}^* + T_{i0})].$$

It then follows directly, that

$$\mathrm{Var}\ (T_{00}) = E(T_{00}^2) - [E(T_{00})]^2$$

$$= \mathrm{Var}\ (T_{01}) + \sum_{i=2}^{4} \theta_i\ \mathrm{Var}\ (T_{1i}^* + T_{i0})$$

$$+ \sum_{i<1}^{4} \theta_i\theta_j [E(T_{1i}^* + T_{i0}) - E(T_{i1}^* + T_{i0})]^2 \quad .$$

Thus, in the terms of our model, if we let $\lambda_i^2 = \xi_i^2 + \sigma_{i0}^2$, $i = 2,3,4$, we have that

$$\mathrm{Var}\ (T_{00}) = \frac{1 - \rho}{\rho^2} + \sum_{i=2}^{4} \theta_i \lambda_i^2$$

$$+ \sum_{i<1}^{4} \theta_i\theta_j [\eta_i - \eta_j]^2$$

A quantity of special interest is $T_{44}$, the waiting time between successive live births per female. This time can be represented as follows:

$$(11.5.4) \quad T_{44} = T_{40} + T_{01} + T_{11.4}^{(1)}$$

$$+ T_{11.4}^{(2)} + \cdots + T_{11.4}^{(N)} + T_{14}^*$$

where $T_{11.4}^{(k)}$ represents the time spent in the $k^{th}$

recurrence of state 1, accomplished without passage through state 4. The total number of time, N, which the female cycles between pregnancies without the occurrence of a live birth is a random variable and is easily seen to have in this model a geometric distribution with mean and variance

$$\frac{\theta_2 + \theta_3}{\theta_4} \quad \text{and} \quad \frac{\theta_2 + \theta_3}{\theta_4^2} ,$$

respectively. From (11.5.4) then, and by a well known result on random sequences of random variables [ ], we have

$$(11.5.5) \quad E(T_{44}) = \mu_{40} + \frac{1 - \rho}{\nu} + E(N)\ E(T_{11.\bar{4}}) + \nu_4 \ .$$

Now, since

$$T_{11.\bar{4}} = \begin{cases} T^*_{12} + T_{20} + T_{01} & \text{with probability } \theta_2/(\theta_2 + \theta_3) \\ T^*_{12} + T_{30} + T_{01} & \text{with probability } \theta_3/(\theta_2 + \theta_3) \end{cases} ,$$

we can view the distribution function of $T_{11.\bar{4}}$ as a weighted mean of the distribution functions of the time associated with each of these paths and it will follow (as in the derivation of (11.5.2) and (11.5.3) above) that:

$$(11.5.6)\quad E(T_{11.4}) = \frac{\theta_2}{\theta_2+\theta_3}\eta_2 + \frac{\theta_3}{\theta_2+\theta_3}\eta_3 + \frac{1-\rho}{\rho} ,$$

and

$$(11.5.7)\quad \text{Var}\,(T_{11.4}) = \frac{\theta_2}{\theta_2+\theta_3}\lambda_2^2 + \frac{\theta_3}{\theta_2+\theta_3}\lambda_3^2 + \frac{1-\rho}{\rho^2} + \frac{\theta_2\theta_3}{(\theta_2+\theta_3)^2}(\eta_2-\eta_3)^2 .$$

Thus, from (7.5.5) and (7.5.6)

$$(11.5.8)\quad E(T_{44}) = \mu_{44} = \frac{1}{\theta_4}\left(\frac{1-\rho}{\rho} + \sum_{i=2}^{4}\theta_i\eta_i\right)$$

a result similar to one obtained previously by Henry [105].

In an analogous fashion, the average waiting time betwenn miscarriages or stillbirths for an individual are found to be respectively:

$$(11.5.9)\quad \mu_{22} = \frac{1}{\theta_2}\left(\frac{1-\rho}{\rho} + \sum_{i=2}^{4}\theta_i\eta_i\right)$$

and

$$(11.5.10)\quad \mu_{33} = \frac{1}{\theta_3}\left(\frac{1-\rho}{\rho} + \sum_{i=2}^{4}\theta_i\eta_i\right) .$$

It remains to find the variance of $T_{44}$, the waiting time between live births. To do this, we write (11.5.4) as:

(11.5.11)

$$T_{44} - \left[ \mu_{40} + \frac{1-\rho}{\rho} + E(N)\, E(T_{11.\bar{4}}) + \nu_4 \right]$$

$$= \left( T_{40} - \mu_{40} \right) + \left( T_{01} - \frac{1-\rho}{\rho} + T^*_{14} - \nu_4 \right)$$

$$+ \left[ T^{(1)}_{11.\bar{4}} - E(T_{11.\bar{4}}) \right] + \cdots + \left[ T^{(N)}_{11.\bar{4}} - E(T_{11.\bar{4}}) \right]$$

$$+ \left[ N \cdot E(T_{11.\bar{4}}) - E(N) \cdot E(T_{11.\bar{4}}) \right]$$

Squaring both sides and taking expected values, we get (cf. Blackwell and Girshick [21, p. 272) the result:

$$(11.5.12) \quad \sigma^2_{44} = E(T_{44} - \mu_{44})^2$$

$$= E(T_{40} - \mu_{40})^2 + E(T_{01} - \mu_{01})^2 + E(T^*_{14} - \nu_4)^2$$

$$+ E(N)\, E[T_{11.\bar{4}} - E(T_{11.\bar{4}})]^2$$

$$+ [E(T_{11.\bar{4}})]^2\, E[N - E(N)]^2$$

$$= \lambda_4^2 + \sigma^2_{01} + E(N)\, \mathrm{Var}(T_{11.\bar{4}})$$

$$+ [E(T_{11.\bar{4}})]^2\, \mathrm{Var}\,(N) \quad =$$

$$= \lambda_4^2 + \frac{1-\rho}{\rho^2} + \frac{(\theta_2 + \theta_3)}{\theta_4} \text{ Var } (T_{11.\bar{4}})$$

$$+ \frac{(\theta_2 + \theta_3)}{\theta_4^2} [E(T_{11.\bar{4}})]^2 \quad .$$

This can be evaluated, using Equations (11.5.6) and (11.5.7). The analogous expressions for $\sigma_{22}^2$ and $\sigma_{33}^2$ are easily derived.

It is also of interest to determine the expected length and variance of the waiting time, $T_{04}$, between the onset of marriage and the first live birth. This is easily done, since $T_{44} = T_{40} + T_{04}$, and, therefore,

$$(11.5.13) \quad \mu_{04} = E(T_{04}) = \mu_{44} - \mu_{40}$$

$$= \nu_4 + \frac{1}{\theta_4} \quad \theta_2\eta_2 + \theta_3\eta_3 + \frac{1-\rho}{\rho}$$

and

$$(11.5.14) \quad \sigma_{04}^2 = \sigma_{44}^2 - \sigma_{40}^2$$

$$= \xi_4^2 + \frac{1-\rho}{\rho^2} + \frac{(\theta_2 + \theta_3)}{\theta_4} \text{ Var } (T_{11.\bar{4}})$$

$$+ \frac{(\theta_2 + \theta_3)}{\theta_4^2} E(T_{11.\bar{4}}) \quad .$$

The analogous expressions for the first two moments of the waiting times between marriage and the first miscarriage or stillbirth (i.e., of $T_{02}$ and $T_{03}$) are similarly derived. Applications of the above results to the study of intervals to first live birth and between births, have been described by Shepps and Perrin in [185].

## 2. Expected Number and Variance of Live Births, Stillbirths, and Miscarriages in a Given Time Period

In addition to studying the moments of the distributions of time intervals between the various types of pregnancy terminations, it is useful to consider the number of pregnancy terminations of the various kinds which can be expected to occur in a given period of time in a woman's reproductive history. If we let $N_i(t)$ be the random number of times a woman enters $S_i$, $i = 0,1,\ldots,4$, in time interval $t$, the number of live births in time $t$, for example, is given by $N_1(t)$. We would like to be able to compute the expected value and variance of $N_i(t)$ for any set of fertility parameters, and are especially interested in the conditional mean and variance of $N_i(t)$ given that the process starts in $S_0$ (i.e., nonpregnancy), since this is the situation assumed in our model.

The behavior of $N_i(t)$ is, as one would imagine, difficult to characterize for finite values of $t$. However, if we consider the sequence of recurrence times of $S_i$, i.e., $\{T_{ii}^{(1)}, T_{ii}^{(2)}, \ldots,\}$, we note that these random variables form a renewal process [195], and further, if we augment the sequence with the first passage time from $S_j$ to $S_i$, i.e., $\{T_{ji}, T_{ii}^{(1)}, T_{ii}^{(2)}, \ldots,\}$, it is easy to show that we have a general point process. From the cumulants for the general point process (Murthy [149]), it then follows directly that the mean and variance of $N_i(t)$, the number of passages into $S_i$ in time $t$, given that the process starts in $S_j$, are given, approximately, by the following expressions:

$$(11.5.15) \qquad E\left[\frac{N_i(t)}{J_0} = j\right] \simeq \frac{t}{\mu_{ii}} + \frac{\mu_{ii}^{(2)}}{2\mu_{ii}^2} - \frac{\mu_{ji}}{\mu_{ii}}$$

and

$$(11.5.16) \qquad \mathrm{Var}\left[\frac{N_i(t)}{J_0} = j\right] \simeq \frac{\sigma_{ii}^2}{\mu_{ii}}\, t + \frac{5(\mu_{ii}^{(2)})^2}{4\mu_{ii}^4} - \frac{2\mu_{ii}^{(3)}}{3\mu_{ii}^2} - \frac{\mu_{ii}^{(2)}}{2\mu_{ii}^2} - \frac{\mu_{ji}\,\mu_{ii}^{(2)}}{\mu_{ii}^3} + \frac{\sigma_{ji}^2}{\mu_{ii}^2} + \frac{\mu_{ji}}{\mu_{ii}}$$

where $J_0$ designates the initial state of the process, and $\mu_{ji}^{(n)}$ is the $n^{th}$ moment about the origin of $T_{ji}$.

For example, the expected number of live births for

a woman in $t$ months of marriage, assuming that she starts marriage in the fecundable, nonpregnant state, is approximately:

$$E\,[N_4(t) \mid J_0] \simeq \frac{t}{\mu_{44}} + \frac{\mu_{44}^{(2)}}{2\mu_{44}^2} - \frac{\mu_{04}}{\mu_{44}} .$$

Likewise, the expected number of total pregnancies (in a sense, the total fertility) for a woman in $t$ months, under the same assumptions is approximately:

$$E\,[N_1(t) \mid J_0 = 0] - \frac{t}{\mu_{11}} + \frac{\mu_{11}^{(2)}}{2\mu_{11}^2} - \frac{\mu_{01}}{\mu_{11}} .$$

This is easily evaluated from (7.5.2) and (7.5.3), since $\mu_{11} = \mu_{00}$ and $\sigma_{11}^2 = \sigma_{00}^2$.

## 3. Fertility Rate

The fertility rate for a homogeneous cohort of women, or the monthly probability of live birth for an individual woman, obviously depends on the duration of exposure of the women in the cohort, or of the individual since marriage. For example, the probability of a live birth will tend to be higher during the early months of a marriage (after a suitable lag for gestation) than later. Since each woman is assumed to enter marriage in a fecundable, nonpregnant state, she consequently has a greater probability, during the early months, of conceiving. The derivation of an exact expression for the monthly fertility rate, as a function of the duration of marriage, is exceedingly difficult. If we were once again to view the model in the guise of a point process, however, with entrance into $S_4$ (i.e., a live birth) being the act of renewal, we see that:

$$P \text{ [Passage into } S_4 \text{ at } t] = E[N_4(t)] - E[N_4(t) - 1)]$$

i.e., the probability of a live birth occurring at month, $t$, is equal to the expected number of live births in $t$ months, less the number expected in $(t-1)$ months. Since Blackwell's theorem states that: [Smith [195])

$$E(N_4(t+1)] - E(N_4(t)] \longrightarrow \mu_{44}^{-1} \quad \text{as} \quad t \longrightarrow \infty ,$$

it follows, immediately, that the asymptotic fertility rate is equal to $\mu_{44}^{-1}$, i.e., to the inverse of the mean recurrence time for live births. This then affords an approximation to the exact fertility rate for homogeneous cohorts which are under observation a reasonable length of time.

An application of this result to the examination of the expected effects of programs for birth control has been reported in [183], as has an evaluation of the effects of different probabilities of fetal loss on fertility [183].

## 11.6 Further Results

The method of derivation employed earlier does not lend itself easily to finding $\mu_{ij}^{(n)}$, the $n^{th}$ moment of $T_{ij}$ about the origin, when $n > 2$. These moments may be required for various reasons, including the need for $\mu_{ii}^{(3)}$ found in Expression (7.5.16). For this purpose we follow the method of Pyke [169].

With the stated assumptions and the permissible paths illustrated in Figure 22, a matrix of the transition distributions (Pyke's $Q$ matrix) may be formulated as shown. In this matrix, the $i,j^{th}$ element represents the probability that, given that the female is in state $i$, she will pass directly into state $j$, within $t$ units of time after entering state $i$. As before, $t$ is the waiting time.

From the matrix of transition distributions, explicit expressions may be obtained to yield the moments for all passage times in the model. Let $M_{ij}(s)$ be the Laplace-Stieltjes transform of the probability distribution of the first passage times from $S_i$ to $S_j$, and let $F_i$ and $G_i$

| | $S_0$ | $S_1$ | $S_2$ | $S_3$ | $S_4$ |
|---|---|---|---|---|---|
| $S_0$ | 0 | $\rho \sum_{x=0}^{t} (1-\rho)^2$ | 0 | 0 | 0 |
| $S_1$ | 0 | 0 | $\Theta_2 \int_0^t f_2(\mathbf{x})dx$ | $\Theta_3 \int_0^t f_3(\mathbf{x})dx$ | $\Theta_4 \int_0^t f_4(\mathbf{x})dx$ |
| $S_2$ | $\int_0^t g_2(\mathbf{x})dx$ | 0 | 0 | 0 | 0 |
| $S_3$ | $\int_0^t g_3(\mathbf{x})dx$ | 0 | 0 | 0 | 0 |
| $S_4$ | $\int_0^t g_4(\mathbf{x})dx$ | 0 | 0 | 0 | 0 |

FIGURE 22. MATRIX OF TRANSITION DISTRIBUTIONS

be the Laplace-Stieltjes transforms of $f_i(x)$ and $g_i(x)$, respectively. It can then be shown, for example, that

$$M_{00}(s) = M_{11}(s) = \rho \sum_{i=2}^{4} \frac{\Theta_i F_i G_i}{1 - e^{-3}(1 - \rho)} ,$$

$$M_{01}(s) = \frac{\rho}{1 - e^{-1}(1 - \rho)} ,$$

$$M_{04}(s) = \frac{\rho \, \Theta_4 F_4}{1 - e^{-3}(1 - \rho) - \rho(\Theta_2 F_2 G_2 + \Theta_3 F_3 G_3} ,$$

and

$$M_{44}(s) = \frac{\rho \, \Theta_4 F_4 G_4}{1 - e^{-3}(1 - \rho) - \rho(\Theta_2 F_2 G_2 + \Theta_3 F_3 G_3)} .$$

Then, $\mu_{ij}^{(n)} = (-1)^n M_{ij}^{(n)}(0)$, where $M_{ij}^{(n)}(0)$ is the $n^{th}$ derivative of $M_{ij}(s)$ with respect to $s$, evaluated at zero. In particular, if we let $\eta_i^{(r)}$ be the $r^{th}$ moment of the compound distribution $f_i g_i$ and $\beta^{(r)}$ be

$$\rho^{-1} - 1 + \sum_{i=2}^{4} \Theta_i \eta_i^{(r)} ,$$

and letting $(\beta^{(r)} - \Theta_i \eta_i^{(r)})$ be represented by $\omega_i^{(r)}$, we have that $\mu_{44}^{(3)}$, the quantity of interest in Expression (11.5.16), is given by:

$$\mu_{44}^{(3)} = \frac{\beta^{(3)}}{\theta_4} + \frac{3\omega_4 \beta^{(2)}}{\theta_4^2} + \frac{3\omega_4^{(2)} \beta}{\theta_4^2} + \frac{6(\omega_4)^2 \beta}{\theta_4^3} ,$$

where the superscript is omitted for $r = 1$.

By Pyke's methods, we can also obtain the asymptotic probability distribution of the five states of the model from the transition matrix. If we let $P_i$, $i = 0,\ldots,4$, be the asymptotic probability of $S_i$ under our model, we have that:

$$P_0 = \frac{1 - \rho}{1 - \rho\left(1 - \sum_{i=2}^{4} \theta_i \eta_i\right)} ,$$

$$P_1 = \frac{\rho \sum_{i=2}^{4} \theta_i \nu_i}{1 - \rho\left(1 - \sum_{i=2}^{4} \theta_i \eta_i\right)} ,$$

$$P_2 = \frac{\rho\, \theta_2 \mu_{20}}{1 - \rho\left(1 - \sum_{i=2}^{4} \theta_i \eta_i\right)} ,$$

$$P_3 = \frac{\rho\, \theta_3 \mu_{30}}{1 - \rho\left(1 - \sum_{i=2}^{4} \theta_i \eta_i\right)} ,$$

and

$$P_4 = \frac{\rho \theta_i \mu_{40}}{1 - \rho\left(1 - \sum_{i=2}^{4} \theta_i \eta_i\right)} .$$

That is, the probability that a woman will be in state $S_1$ (i.e., will be pregnant) at a given time after a number of months of marriage is, approximately,

$$\rho \sum_i \frac{\theta_i \nu_i}{1 - \rho\left(1 - \sum_{i=2}^{4} \theta_i \eta_i\right)} ,$$

and so forth, for each of the states of the model.

## 11.7 Comparison of Asymptotic and Exact Results for a Special Case

The expressions derived above for the mean and variance of $N_4(t)$, the number of live births per woman in a given time period $t$, and for the monthly fertility rate expected under the model are, of course, only approximately correct for a finite number, $t$, of months since marriage. In order to measure the degree of accuracy of the approximations and the rapidity with which the exact and asymptotic results converge, the exact mean and variance of the number of conceptions leading to a live birth and the exact

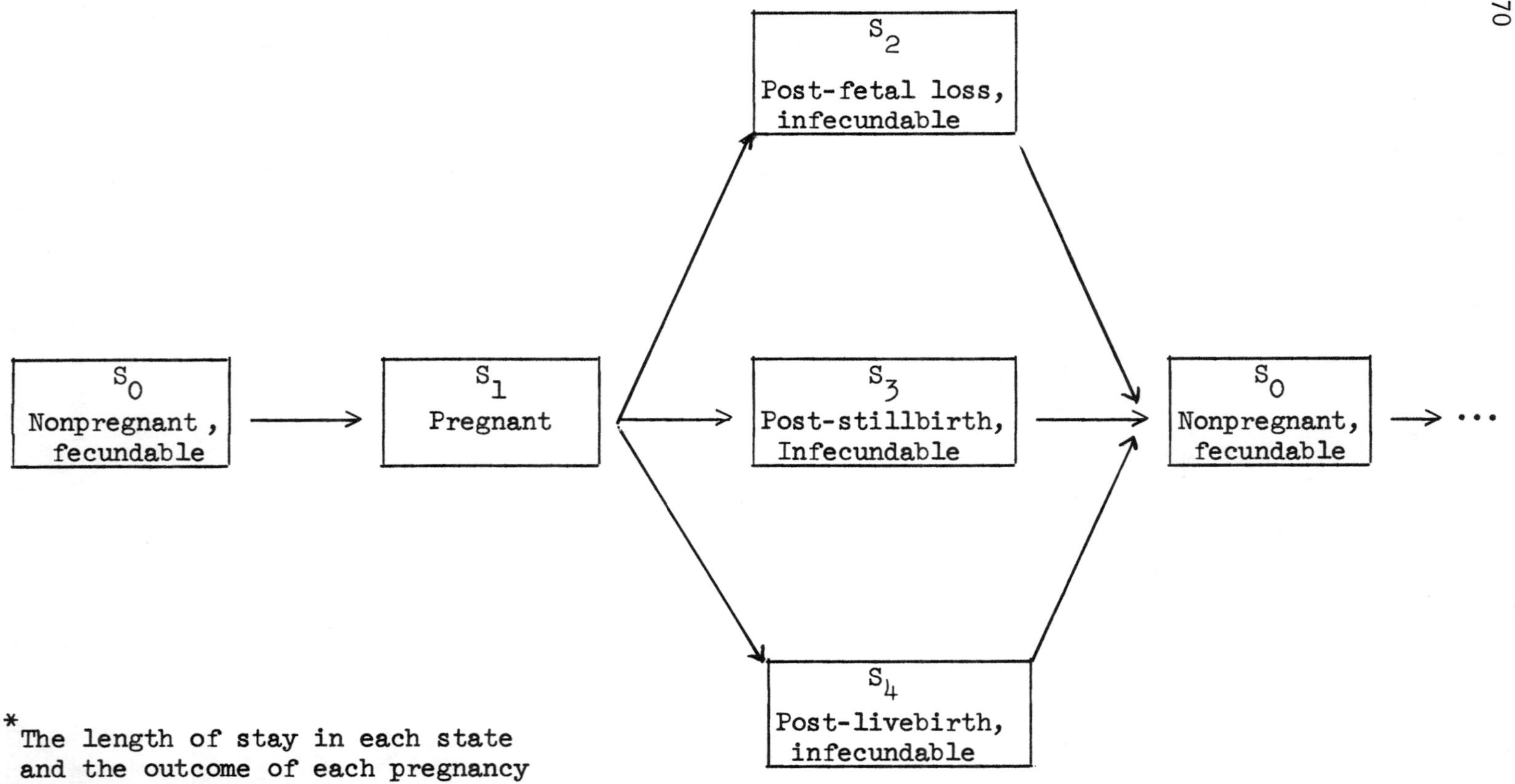


*The length of stay in each state and the outcome of each pregnancy are assumed to be random variables.

DIAGRAM OF

FERTILITY PATTERNS IN THE MARRIED FEMALE*

fertility rate for a range of $t$, from 0 to 180 months, was determined with the aid of an electronic computer for the special case: $\rho = 2$, $\theta_2 = 0$, $\theta_4 = .75$, $\eta_2 = 5$, $\eta_3 = 0$, $\eta_4 = 18$ $\lambda_2^2 = \lambda_3^2 = 0$. That is, a case with only two types of pregnancy outcomes, fetal loss and live birth, and no variance in the length of infecundability associated with each type. The same results would hold also, of course, for the slightly more general case where $\theta_2 + \theta_3 = .25$ and $(\theta_2\eta_2 + \theta_3\eta_3) = 5$.

Figure 23 gives the probability under these assumptions of a conception that will lead to a live birth as a

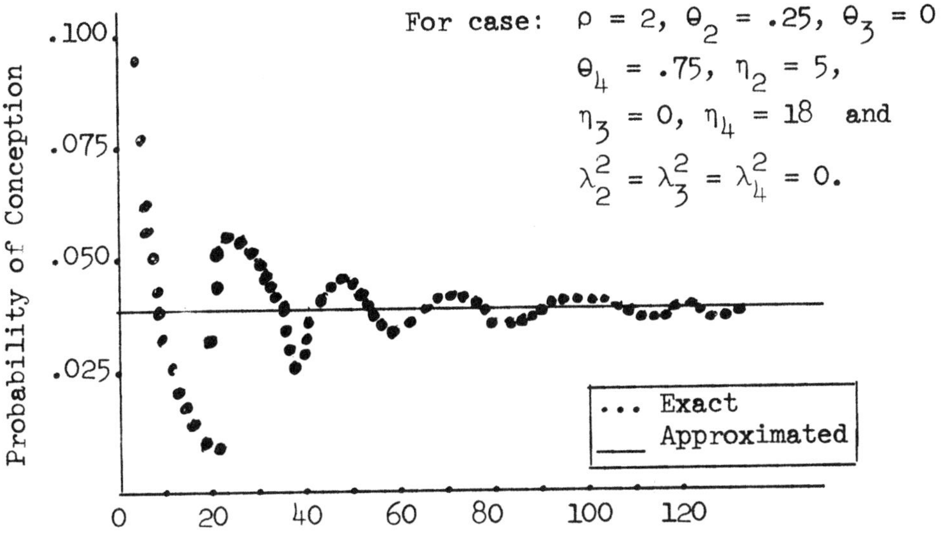


FIGURE 23

PROBABILITY OF A CONCEPTION IN THE NEXT MONTH THAT WILL LEAD TO A LIVE BIRTH AS A FUNCTION OF THE NUMBER OF COMPLETED MONTHS SINCE MARRIAGE

as a function of the number of months since marriage. It can be seen that the exact probability of this type of conception during a given cycle is approximated well by the estimated (i.e., asymptotic) probability, within 60 months (approximately 5 years) of the beginning of marriage.

Figures 24 and 25 give the expected number of conceptions per woman, leading to a live birth, and the variance of this number as a function of the duration of marriage. From (11.5.15) and (11.5.16) of Section 5, one obtains as estimators of the expected number and variance of such conceptions, the expressions $.040t + .230$ and $.004t + .121$,

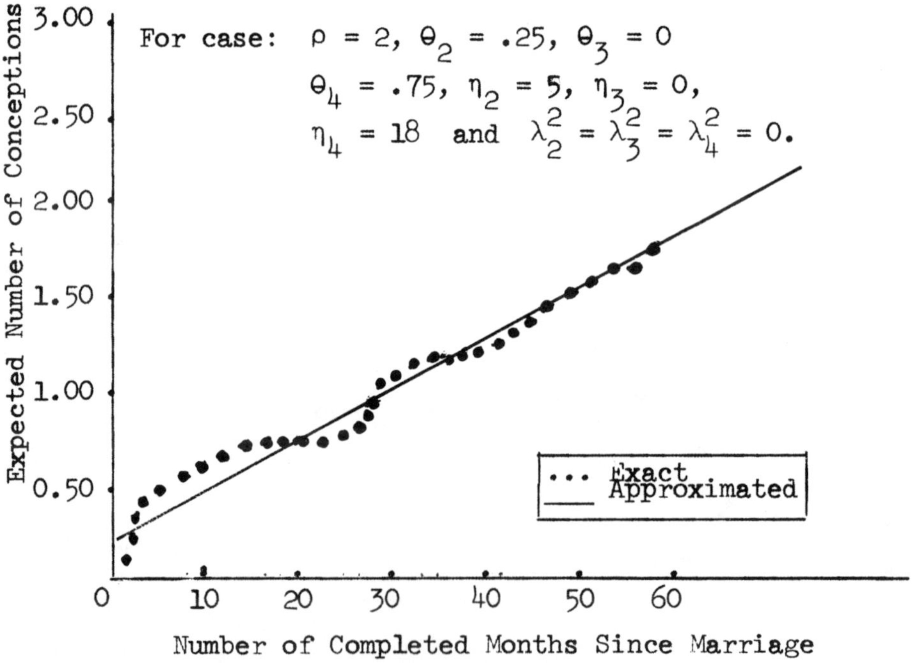


FIGURE 24

EXPECTED NO. OF CONCEPTIONS/WOMAN LEADING TO A LIVE BIRTH AS A FUNCTION OF THE NO. OF COMPLETED MOS. SINCE MARRIAGE

respectively. That these also yield a good approximation to the exact moments, within five years of marriage, is apparent. In fact, as can be seen in Figure 25, the degree and rapidity of the approximation is striking in the case of the expected number of conceptions.

While this is admittedly a very special case under examination, the results do tend to indicate the approximate expressions obtained in Section 5 become quite useful in describing the reproductive cohort or individual, within a relatively short period of observation.

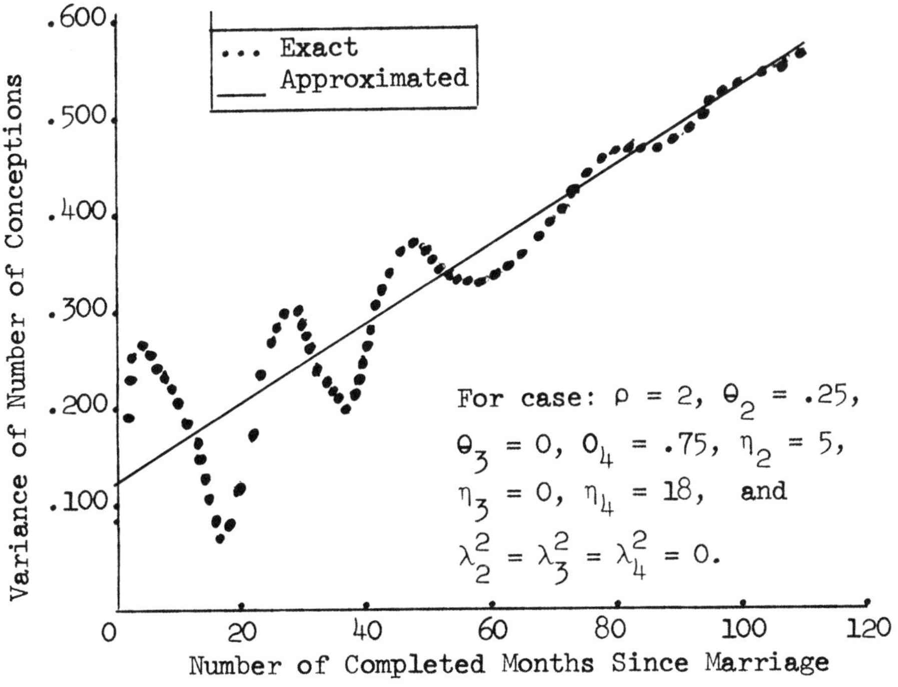


Figure 25

VARIANCE OF THE NUMBER OF CONCEPTIONS PER WOMAN LEADING TO A LIVE BIRTH AS A FUNCTION OF THE NUMBER OF COMPLETED MONTHS SINCE MARRIAGE

## 11.8 Realistic Models for Event (Points) Rate

Observed times to failure can be used to estimate the event rate function (mortality rate, hazard rate, or risk, will be used interchangeable). Nonparametric methods for estimating hazard rates were considered by the author in [152] and by Grenander [89]. However, the most they can do is to throw light on the shape of the underlying hazard rate function and cannot be used for decision making and prediction. Thus, parametric procedures, based on realistic models for the event rate function, are the only suitable approaches for estimation and prediction. It is generally accepted that the most general event rate curve consists of an early decreasing phase, followed by a section of constant failure, corresponding to the useful life period followed by a rapidly increasing failure rate as death approaches.

### Theory

Let the nonnegative random variable $T$ be the time-to-death of the subject under consideration. Let $T$ have a cumulative distribution function (cdf) of

$$F(t) = P(T < t) \tag{11.8.1}$$

and assume that $T$ has mean $\mu$ and variance $\sigma^2$, and that the probability density function is

$$(11.8.2) \qquad f(t)dt = dF(t) \quad .$$

The mortality rate, $\lambda(t)$, is the instantaneous chance of dying at time $t$, given that the subject has survived to time $t$, and may be defined as

$$(11.8.3) \qquad \lambda(t) = \frac{f(t)}{R(t)}, \qquad t \geq 0$$

where

$$(11.8.4) \qquad R(t) = 1 - F(t)$$

is the survivorship function. That $\lambda(t)$ is a mortality rate, can be seen by finding the probability of death in the time interval, $(t, t + \Delta t)$, where $\Delta t$ is a small positive time increment, given survival to time $t$. We have from the definition of conditional probability that

$$(11.8.5) \qquad \frac{P\left(t \leq T < \frac{t + \Delta t}{T} > t\right)}{P(T \geq t)} = \frac{F(t + \Delta t) - F(t)}{R(t)} \quad .$$

By the mean value theorem of calculus, $F(t + \Delta t) - F(t) = f(\xi)\Delta t$ for some $\xi$ between $t$ and $t + \Delta t$, hence

$$(11.8.6) \qquad P\left(t \leq T < \frac{t + \Delta t}{T} \geq t\right) = \frac{f(\xi)}{R(t)}\Delta t, \qquad t \leq \xi \leq t + \Delta t \quad .$$

In the limit, as $\Delta t \to 0$, the conditional probability is $\lambda(t)dt$.

The mortality rate also uniquely defines the survivorship function, as can be seen by writing the difference equation for the probability of death by time $t + \Delta t$, i.e.,

$$F(t + \Delta t) = F(t) + [1 - F(t)]\, \lambda(t)\Delta t \quad . \tag{11.8.7}$$

The right-hand side is the sum of the probabilities of two mutually exclusive events:

(1) death by time $t$ with probability $F(t)$; and

(2) no death until time $t$ and death in the interval, $(t, t + \Delta t)$, with probability

$$[1 - F(t)]\, \lambda(t)\Delta t \quad .$$

Dividing both sides by $\Delta t$ and taking the limit as $\Delta t \to 0$, gives

$$\frac{dF(t)}{dt} = [1 - F(t)]\, \lambda(t) \tag{11.8.8}$$

which can be written as

$$\lambda(t) = -\frac{d}{dt} \ln R(t) \quad . \tag{11.8.9}$$

Solving this differential equation for $R(t)$ and using the initial condition $R(0) = 1$ and $R(\infty) = 0$, we obtain

$$(11.8.10) \qquad R(t) = e^{-\int_0^t \lambda(x)dx} .$$

The integral $\Lambda(t) = \int_0^t \lambda(x)dx$ is also called the accumulated, or cumulative hazard, by time $t$; its derivative $\lambda(t)$ is the event rate.

Another interpretation of the mortality rate is to compute the ratio of expected deaths in the interval $(t, T + \Delta t)$ to the expected number of subjects alive at time $t$. Let $n(t)$ be the expected number of subjects alive at time $t$ from an original population of $N = n(0)$, then

$$(11.8.11) \qquad n(t + \Delta t) = N[R(t + \Delta t) - R(t)] .$$

By dividing both sides by $\Delta t$ and taking the limit as $\Delta t \to 0$, we have

$$(11.8.12) \qquad \frac{dn(t)}{dt} = - Nf(t) = - N \frac{f(t)}{1 - F(t)} [1 - F(t)]$$

$$= - n(t) \lambda(t)$$

or

$$(11.8.13) \qquad \lambda(t) = - \frac{1}{n(t)} \frac{dn(t)}{dt} .$$

This differential equation may be solved for $n(t)$ to produce

$$n(t) = N e^{-\int_0^t \lambda(x)dx} \quad . \tag{11.8.14}$$

The mortality rate is sometimes referred to as a conditional density. However, $\lambda(t)$ is not a density since $\int_0^\infty \lambda(x)dx = \infty$. $\lambda(t)$ is, in fact, $f(t/(T \geq t))$ which is a conditional density only when $x = t$, but it is not a conditional density as $t$ varies.

We are concerned in this section with selecting a mortality function that models a medical follow-up study and that also can be integrated to give a survivorship function in closed form. Murthy and Swartz [157] show that any function, $h(x)$, which is positive and for which

$$\lim_{t \to \infty} \int_0^t h(x)dx \tag{11.8.15}$$

is unbounded, can be used as a mortality rate which will give a unique survivorship function

$$R(t) = e^{-\int_0^t h(x)dx} \quad . \tag{11.8.16}$$

## Realistic Models of the Mortality Rate

In this section we discuss three different models of the mortality rate:

MODEL I: This class of distributions is characterized by the event rate

$$\lambda(t) = \frac{1}{1 + bt} + c\, dt^{d-1}, \quad t \geq 0 \qquad (11.8.17)$$

where the parameters $a,b,c \geq 0$ and $d \geq 1$. Some special cases of this model are when $c = 0$, where we have

$$\lambda(t) = \frac{a}{1 + bt} , \qquad (11.8.18)$$

a decreasing function of time.

The mortality rate reduces to a constant when $a = 0$, $d = 1$ or $b,c = 0$, and we have an exponential distribution. When $b = 0$ and $d = 2$ we have the linear rate used by Kodlin [123] to model death from breast cancer. Finally,

$$\lambda(t) = c\, dt^{d-1} \text{ when } a = 0 , \qquad (11.8.19)$$

corresponds to a two-parameter Weibull distribution. The cumulative distribution function for Model I is

$$F(t) = 1 - \frac{1}{(1 + bx)^{a/b}} e^{-ct^d} \qquad (11.8.20)$$

and the density function is

$$(11.8.21) \qquad f(t) = \left( \frac{a}{1+bt} + c\,dt^{d-1} \right) \times \left( \frac{1}{(1+bt)^{a/b}}\, e^{ct^d} \right) .$$

MODEL II: is a class of distributions which have the event rate

$$(11.8.22) \quad \lambda(t) = ab\, e^{-bt} + c\,dt^{d-1}; \qquad d \geq 1,\ a,b,c > 0 \ .$$

The corresponding cumulative distribution function is

$$(11.8.23) \qquad F(t) = 1 - e^{-a(1-e^{-bt})-ct^d}$$

and the density is

$$(11.8.24) \quad f(t) = (ab\, e^{-bt} + c\,dt^{d-1})\, e^{-a(1-e^{-bt})-ct^d} \ .$$

The special case of Equation (11.8.24) where $a = 1/b^2$ may be of interest, as it is a three-parameter family of distributions having the bath-tub property. This class of distribution is given by

$$(11.8.25) \qquad F(t) = 1 - e^{-\frac{1}{b^2}\left(1-e^{-bt}\right)-ct^d}$$

with density function

$$(11.8.26) \qquad f(t) = \left( \frac{e^{-bt}}{b} + c\, ct^{d-1} \right) \times \left( e^{\frac{1}{b^2}\, 1-e^{-bt}\; -ct^d} \right) .$$

Note that, the two-parameter Weibull model and Kodlin's models are also special cases of this general model.

MODEL III: In this class the event rate is

$$(11.8.27) \quad \lambda(t) = \frac{a}{1 + bt} + cd\, e^{dt}, \quad a,b,c,d \geq 0 .$$

The corresponding cumulative distribution and density functions are, respectively, given by

$$(11.8.28) \qquad F(t) = 1 - \frac{1}{(1 + bt)^{a/b}}\, e^{-c(e^{dt}-1)}$$

and

$$(11.8.29) \quad f(t) = \left( \frac{a}{1 + bt} + cd\, e^{dt} \right) \times \left( \frac{1}{(1 + bt)^{a/b}}\, e^{-c(e^{dt}-1)} \right) .$$

When $a = 0$ and $d > 0$, we have $\lambda(t) = cd\, e^{dt}$, which is a monotonically increasing event rate called the Gompertz rate by Broadbent in [25] in which it was applied to the lifetimes of milkbottles. This rate is also studied by Garg, et. al. [81] and is used to model the mortality of mice in oral contraceptive studies.

## 11.9 Application to Medical Followup Studies

The mortality rates corresponding to many real life situations fall within the domain of our models described in the previous section. From the practical point of view, we distinguish among three categories of mortality rates, namely, BTR, DHR and IHR, depending on the shape. Category BTR is marked by a decreasing risk or mortality function, followed by an increasing one. Category DHR is purely decreasing, while category IHR is increasing. The classical example of a bath-tub event curve is the survival data of humans (as well as other animals). It is characterized by a high infant mortality during the first year of life, with a slowly decreasing risk from ages 1 - 4, and a low mortality rate from ages 5 to around 35, and with increasing risk for older ages.

Figure 15 in Chapter 10 may also be used to depict typical mortality rate as a function of age, where the interval from 0 to $\tau_B$ represents infantile mortality, that from $\tau_B$ to $\tau_W$ the period of useful life and from $\tau_W$ to the broken, dotted line the period of chance and fatigue mortality.

Usually, in statistical analysis of data, a cumulative distribution function is assumed. The random variable under study, in this case it is the time-to-death, can in many situations be described by a mathematical model which also determines the functional form of the distribution function. Zelen [221] has given several such models for death due to specific types of cancer. These models lead him to consider the exponential distribution. Davis [47] showed that the exponential model gave a good fit in the case of thirty nonhuman systems. Unfortunately, the exponential distribution has a constant mortality rate, which may be a reasonable assumption in the case of certain short periods of time. That it is not the case for time periods of over five years in medical followup studies on humans, was shown by Berg and Robbins [17]. In the absence of a mathematical model to guide the selection of a distribution, the concept of the mortality rate has been adopted. Buckland [ ] discusses many examples of event rates that correspond to the Weibull, gamma, normal, lognormal, and extreme value distribution. Boag [22] considered the Weibull, gamma, lognormal and exponential distributions in a study on deaths from cancer, after treatment. He found the best fit to be given by the lognormal distribution, and for a large group, he suggested that the survivorship be modeled by a mixture of $c$ percent completely cured and $1 - c$ percent whose survival times follow a lognormal distribution. It was shown by Gehan [82] that the mortality rate of the lognormal distribution was inappropriate for medical follow-up studies and that in this instance a bath-tub rate was necessary.

The DHR class of distributions characterize situations where there is an initial high risk, but which decreases with time. Over a limited time period, this might describe survival data of patients after transplants or implantations of mechancial devices, besides the usual infantile mortality in a "normal" situation.

The IHR class of distributions fit situations where a very high mortality rate is reduced and the patient is given a longer time to live, but is not "cured." This class may be a useful approximation to the mortality rate over the 100 odd years of human life because the high mortality rate of the final years is several orders of magnitude greater than the initially high infant death rate. Broadbent [25],

Garg, et. al. [81], Kodlin [123] and Grenander [90] consider this type of hazard in their work.

To demonstrate the versatility of the three models proposed in the previous section, with respect to their ability to describe the various mortality rates that one encounters in real life, an interactive graphics program was written so that a person at the console can select one of the models and the parameter values. The corresponding hazard function is displayed on the screen. If desired, increments of the parameters can be typed in, and plots of these curves displayed one after the other, as the parameters increase or decrease. Thus, the characteristics of each model can be fully illustrated. Pictures of some of these plots are shown in Section 11.15 of this chapter in Figures 26, 27 and 28 for Models I, II and III, respectively.

Life Table Model

Assume a homogeneous collection of people. Let the time to death of a person in the group be a positive random variable $T$ with hazard $Z(t)$ of one of our models I, II or III. At a particular time, we have recorded $n$ time-to-deaths, $t_1 \leq \cdots \leq t_n$, of the first $n$ people to die.

One problem is to estimate the parameters in the model. Another is to compare the hazard of one such group with another.

Followup Model

In this model a fixed number of people, $n$, at the same age and all assumed to have similar mortality rates are observed for a fixed length of time, $L$, with their times-to-death recorded as $t_1 \leq t_2 \leq \cdots \leq t_r$, where $r$ is an integer-valued random variable $r \leq n$. (If $r < n$, we refer to the sample as being truncated.) The problem is to estimate the model parameters and to compare the hazard with other groups.

A probabilistic model of the preceding models is obtained by letting a positive random variable, $T$, be the time-to-death of an individual and assuming that the individual times-to-death are independent and identically distributed random variables with common survivorship, $R(t)$. A random sample of size $n$ of the random variable $T$ will be denoted by $t_1, \ldots, t_n$. In the first model, the times are observed in order, and hence, correspond to the order statistics $t_{(1)} \leq t_{(2)} \leq \cdots \leq t_{(n)}$ with distribution of the $t_{(i)}$ being

$$(11.9.1)\quad P(t_{(i)} \leq t) = i \binom{n-1}{i-1} F^{i-1}(t)\, R^{n-i}(t), \quad 0 \leq t$$

and having joint density

$$(11.9.2)\quad g(t_1, \ldots, t_\ell) = \begin{cases} n!\; f(t_1) \quad f(t_\ell), & 0 \leq t_1 \leq t_2 \leq \quad \leq t_\ell \\ 0 & , \text{otherwise} \end{cases} .$$

Even when the sample is censored, information is provided by the nonfailed items, as indicated by the $R^{n-i}(t_1)$ term.

Variation in these models, to consider patients lost from followup and the possibility of contamination by an individual with a markedly different survivorship, will be considered in a following section.

We will now consider several estimates of the event rate at the random points $t_{(i)}$, where $t_{(i)}$ is the $i^{th}$ order statistic. The three models will be fitted, by nonlinear least square technique, to the estimated hazard.

Hazard rate, $\lambda(t)$, defined as

$$(11.9.3)\qquad \lambda(t) = -\frac{1}{R(t)} \frac{dR(t)}{dt} =$$

$$= - \lim_{h \to 0} \frac{R(t + h) - R(t)}{hR(t)} ,$$

suggests the estimator $Z_n(t)$, written as

$$(11.9.4) \qquad Z_n(t_i) = - \frac{\frac{n_{i+h}}{n_i} - \frac{n_i}{n}}{h \frac{n_i}{n}} = \frac{1}{h} \frac{m_i}{n_i}$$

where $n_i = \# \{j:t_j > t_i\}$, is the number of persons alive at time $t_i$, $n_{i+h} = \# \{j:t_j > t_i + h\}$ is the number alive at time $t_i + h$, and $m_i = n_i - n_{i+h}$ is the number who die in the time interval $(t_i, t_{i+h})$. Because the ratio of random variables is involved, it has not been possible to evaluate the expected value of this estimator.

Another estimator is provided by the definition

$$(11.9.5) \qquad \lambda(t) = - \frac{d}{dt} \ln R(t)$$

$$= - \lim_{h \to 0} \frac{\ln R(t + h) - \ln R(t)}{h} .$$

This suggests the estimator, which we call the empirical estimator

$$(11.9.6) \quad Z_n(t_i) = -\frac{\ln n_{i+h} - \ln n_i}{h}$$

$$= -\frac{1}{h} \ln \frac{n_{i+h}}{n_i} \quad \text{for} \quad n_{i+h} > 0 \ .$$

For small $m_i$, this estimate approaches the $Z_n(t_i)$ of the previous paragraph. The following program segment will compute $Z_n(t_i)$ for time-to-death dates, in days, stored in order in array, T(I), with TOT = $n_i$ and SUM = $n_{i+h}$.

```
    DO 100 I=1,N
    TOT=0
    SUM=0
    DO 200 J=I,N
    IF(T(J).GT.T(I) TOT=TOT+1
200 IF(T(J).GT.(T(I)) TOT=TOT+1
    IF(SUM.LE.O.) SUM=1
100 AN(K)=ALOG(TOT/SUM)/H.
```

We compute the expected value of the empirical estimator as

$$(11.9.7) \quad E\,Z_n(t_i) = -\frac{1}{h}\left(E \ln n_{i+h} - E \ln n_i\right) \ .$$

Since $n_i$ has a binomial distribution, then

$$(11.9.8) \qquad P(n_i = k) = \binom{n}{k} R^k(t_i)\, F^{n-k}(t_i) \ ,$$

and we have

$$(11.9.9)\quad E\,Z_n(t_i,h) = -\frac{1}{h}\left[\sum_{k=0}^{n} \ln k\binom{n}{k}(G(t_i+h)-G(t_i))\right]$$

where

$$(11.9.10)\qquad G(t) = R^k(t)\,F^{n-k}(t)\ .$$

The expected value, as $h$ is made arbitrarily small is

$$(11.9.11)\qquad E\,Z_n(t_i) = \lim_{h\to 0} E\,Z_n(t_i,h)$$

$$= -\sum_{k=0}^{n} \ln k\binom{n}{k}\,G'(t_i)\ .$$

Evaluating $G'(t)$, we obtain

$$(11.9.12)\qquad E\,Z_n(t_i) = \frac{f(t_i)}{R(t_i)}\ b(n,t_i,\Theta_1,\ldots,\Theta_P)$$

where $b(\cdot)$ is a bias factor that depends on $n$, $t_i$ and the parameters, $\Theta_1,\ldots,\Theta_P$, of the survival and

$$(11.9.13)\quad b(n,t_i,\Theta_1,\ldots,\Theta_P) = \sum_{k=0}^{n} \ln k\binom{n}{k}\,R^k(t_i)$$

$$\times\ (1-R(t_i))^{n-k}\ (k-nR(t_i))\ .$$

If the time-to-death has an exponential survival, $R(t) = e^{-t/\Theta}$, $t \geq 0$, it was shown by Epstein and Sobel [66] that a minimum variance unbiased estimator of $\Theta$ is $\bar{\Theta}$, where

$$(11.9.14)\quad \bar{\Theta} = \frac{T_{(1)} + \cdots + T_{(i)} + T_{(i)}(n - i)}{i} .$$

Since the hazard, $\lambda(t) = 1/\Theta$, we propose the estimator $Z_n(t_i)$,

$$(11.9.15)\qquad Z_n(t_i) = \frac{1}{\bar{\Theta}} .$$

Preliminary investigation of this estimate under different survivorships is not encouraging, as the estimator exhibits severe bias.

Murthy [152] applies a method of estimating densities by using "windows" to hazard rate estimation. A window, $K(w)$, is a function satisfying the conditions

1. $K(w) = K(-w)$ ;

2. $K(w) \geq 0$ ;

3. $\int_{-\infty}^{\infty} k(w) = 1$ ;

and

4. $$\lim_{|w| \to \infty} w\,K(w) = 0 .$$

In [152] it is shown that the estimator (called the window estimator)

(11.9.16) $$Z_n(t_i) = \frac{f_n^*(t_i)}{R_n^*(t_i)}$$

is a consistent estimator for $\lambda(t)$ and where

(11.9.17) $$f_n^*(t) = \frac{\ln n}{n} \sum_{j=1}^{n} k(\ln n(t_j - t_i))$$

and

(11.9.18) $$R_n^*(t) = \int_t^\infty f_n^*(x)dx .$$

For a rectangular window

(11.9.19) $$K(w) = \begin{cases} \frac{1}{2h}, & -h \le w \le h \\ 0, & \text{otherwise} \end{cases} ,$$

we have the "rectangular window" estimator

(11.9.20) $$Z_n(t) = \frac{\frac{1}{n\,2h_1} \# \left\{ j : t - h_1 \le t_j \le t + h_1 \right\}}{\frac{1}{n}\left[ \# \left\{ j : t_j \ge t - h_1 \right\} + \sum_{j \epsilon A} \left( \frac{(t_j - t)}{2h} + \frac{1}{2} \right) \right]}$$

where, Set $A = \{j : t - h_1 \leq t_j \leq t + h_1\}$ and $h_i = h/(\ln n)$.

The expression is derived in the following way. Let

$$D(w) = \ln nK(\ln n - w) \quad .$$

Then

$$(11.9.21) \qquad D(w) = \begin{cases} \frac{1}{2h_1}, & -h_1 \leq w \leq h_1 \\ 0, & \text{otherwise} \end{cases} ,$$

hence

$$(11.9.22) \qquad f_n^*(t) = \frac{1}{n} \sum_{j=1}^{n} D(t_j - t) \quad .$$

since $D(t_j - t)$ is $1/2h_1$ when $|t_j - t| \leq h_1$, the sum counts the number of elements in Set A. The estimate of $R(t)$ is given by (11.9.18), which, upon substituting $w = t_j - x$, becomes

$$(11.9.23) \int_t^{\infty} f_n^*(x)dx = \int_{-\infty}^{t_j - t} D(w)dw$$

$$= \begin{cases} 1 & , t_j - t \geq h_1 \\ \frac{t_j - t + h_1}{2h_1} & , -h_1 \leq t_j - t \leq h_1 \\ 0 & , \text{otherwise} \end{cases}$$

and we have obtained the denominator of $Z_n(t)$.

A computational simplification of the window estimators was suggested by Watson and Leadbetter [211]. The denominator of the window estimator was replaced by the estimator, $R_n(t_k) = 1 - i/(n+1)$. Using the density expressed in Equation (11.9.17), we now consider the window estimator

$$(11.9.24) \qquad Z_n(t_i) = \frac{f_n^*(t_i)}{\frac{n+1-i}{n+1}} .$$

Since the denominator is not a random variable, we can write the expected value of this as

(11.9.25)

$$E\,Z_n(t_i) = \frac{n+1}{n+1-i} \ln n\, E \sum_{j=1}^{n} K(\ln n(T_j - t_i))$$

$$= \frac{n+1}{n+1-i} \ln n \sum_{j=1}^{n} \int_0^\infty K(\ln n(t - t_i)\, f_j(t)dt$$

where $f_j(t)$ is the density of the $j^{th}$ order statistic

$$(11.9.26) \qquad f_j(t) = j \binom{n-1}{j-1} F^{j-1}(t)\, R^{n-j-1}(t)\, f(t) .$$

This is applied for rectangular and triangular windows to the three sets of data.

A triangular window estimator is obtained when

$$(11.9.27) \qquad K(w) = \begin{cases} 0 & , \ w < -h \\ \frac{w}{h^2} + \frac{1}{h} & , \ -h \le w \le 0 \\ -\frac{w}{h^2} + \frac{1}{h} & , \ 0 < w \le h \\ 0 & , \ h < w \end{cases} .$$

Let $D(w) = \ln nK(w \ln n)$, then

$$(11.9.28) \qquad D(w) = \begin{cases} 0 & , \ w < h_1 \\ \frac{w}{h_1^2} + \frac{1}{h_1} & , \ -h_1 \le w \le 0 \\ -\frac{w}{h_1^2} + \frac{1}{h_1} & , \ 0 < w \le h_1 \\ 0 & , \ h_1 < w \end{cases}$$

where $h_1 = h/(\ln n)$.

The density estimator is

$$(11.9.29) \qquad f_n^*(t) = \sum_{j=1}^{n} D(t_j - t)$$

and

$$(11.9.30) \qquad f_n^*(t_i) = \frac{1}{n\, h_1} \sum_{j \in A_i} \left( 1 - \frac{t_j - t_i}{h_1} \right)$$

where Set $A_i = \{j: |t_j - t_i| \le h_1\}$.

The reliability estimator is

$$(11.9.31) \quad R_n^*(t) = \int_t^{\infty} f_n^*(x)dx = \frac{1}{n} \sum_{j=1}^{n} \int_t^{\infty} D(t_j - x)dx$$

$$= \frac{1}{n} \sum_{j=1}^{n} \int_{-\infty}^{t_j - t} D(u)du \quad ,$$

where

(11.9.32)

$$\int_{-\infty}^{t_j-t} D(u)du = \begin{cases} 0 & , \; t_j - t < -h_1 \\ \dfrac{(t_j - t)^2}{2h_1} + \dfrac{(t_j - t)}{h_1} + \dfrac{1}{2} & , \; -h_1 \le t_j - t \le 0 \\ -\dfrac{(t_j - t)^2}{2h_1} + \dfrac{(t_j - t)}{h_1} + \dfrac{1}{2}, & 0 < t_j - t \le h_1 \\ 0 & , \; h_1 < t_j - t \end{cases}$$

The hazard rate estimator is

(11.9.33)

$$Z_n(t_i) = \frac{\dfrac{1}{n\,h_1} \displaystyle\sum_{j \epsilon A_i} \left(1 - \dfrac{t_j - t_i}{h_1}\right)}{\left[\dfrac{1}{n}\left[\#\{j: t_j > t_i + h_1\} + \displaystyle\sum_{j \epsilon A_i}\left(\dfrac{1}{2} + \dfrac{|t_j - t_i|}{h_1} + SGN(t_j - t_i)\dfrac{(t_j - t_i)^2}{2h_p}\right)\right]\right]}$$

where $SGN(x) = x/|x|$ (the sign of $x$).

The simplified triangular-window estimator is

$$(11.9.34) \qquad Z_n(t_i) = \frac{\frac{1}{n h_1} \sum_{j \in A_i} 1 - \frac{t_j - t_i}{h_1}}{1 - \frac{i}{n+1}} .$$

11.10 Test Results

The empirical estimator, given in (11.9.6), the simple rectangular window estimator of (11.9.24) and the simple triangular window estimator of (11.9.34) were used on a set of randomly generated data from a known truncated exponential distribution and on a set of 200 times-to-death of people from the Los Angeles area. The time-to-death of people was obtained from the Los Angeles Public Health Cooperative Data File. The date of birth and month and day of death, in the year 1970, was received from cards. If the year of birth was not given, the age at death was subtracted from 1970 and used for the year of birth. The birth date and death date were converted to days and subtracted to give time-to-death in days. A FORTRAN subroutine, CALL DATE(I YEAR, JMONTH, KYEAR, NDAYS), was used to make the conversion and account for leap years.

The 200 exponential random numbers were generated by a FORTRAN subroutine, CALL RGAMMA (1.,15000.,200,V), developed by Frane and Murthy [75]. The mean was 15000 days and the variables were truncated at 43800 days. The hazard is constant at $\lambda = 6.7.10^{-5}$, with a spike at 120 years.

A sort routine, CALL SORT (A,1,200) was used to put the data in ascending order.

Programs for the estimators were tested for numerical correctness by using uniformly generated data with

$$t_i = 182(i - 1), \quad 1 \leq i \leq 200 .$$

The hazard is

$$\frac{1}{c - t}, \quad 0 \leq t \leq c ,$$

with $c = 36218$ days and $\lambda(0) = 2.75.10^{-5}$.

The results of the three estimators are shown in Figures 30 - 36. The time-to-death, in days, was divided by 365 to give time-to-death in years and the hazard was multiplied by $10^5$ to provide clarity in the presentation.

ious window widths, h, were used. The effect of h on estimate is shown in Figure 29.

The hazard rate estimates, determined by the least square method, are fit to the three models, using BMDP3R as shown in Figures 26 - 28.

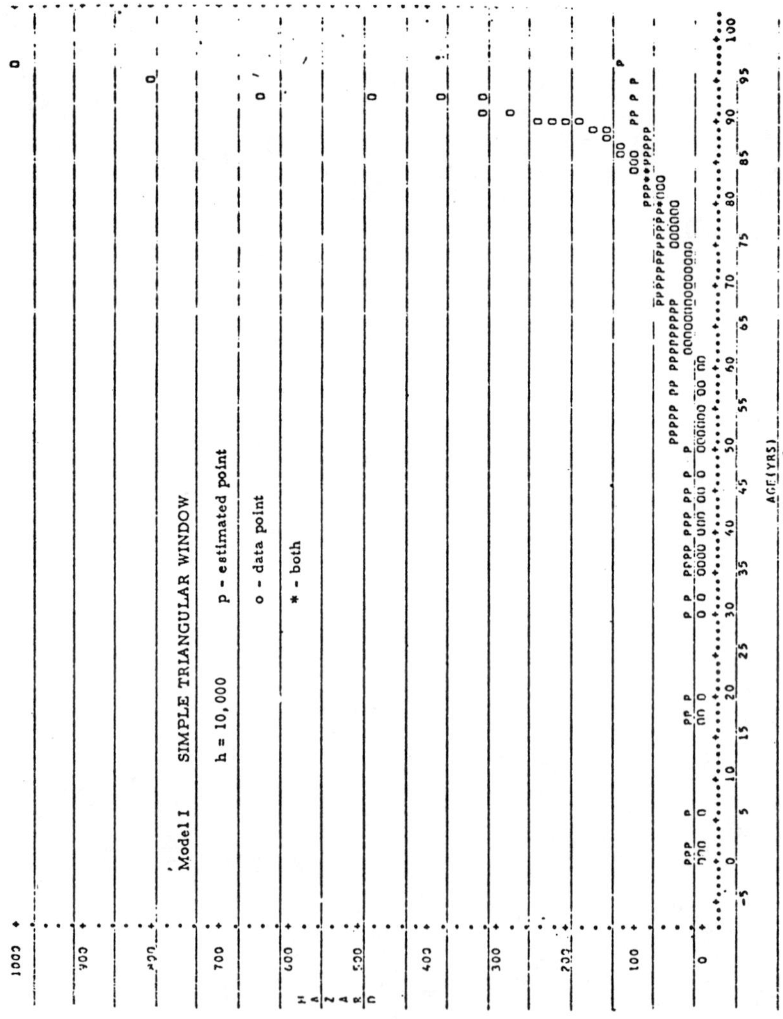
Model I SIMPLE TRIANGULAR WINDOW
h = 10,000
p - estimated point
o - data point
* - both
HAZARD
AGE (YRS)

FIGURE 26

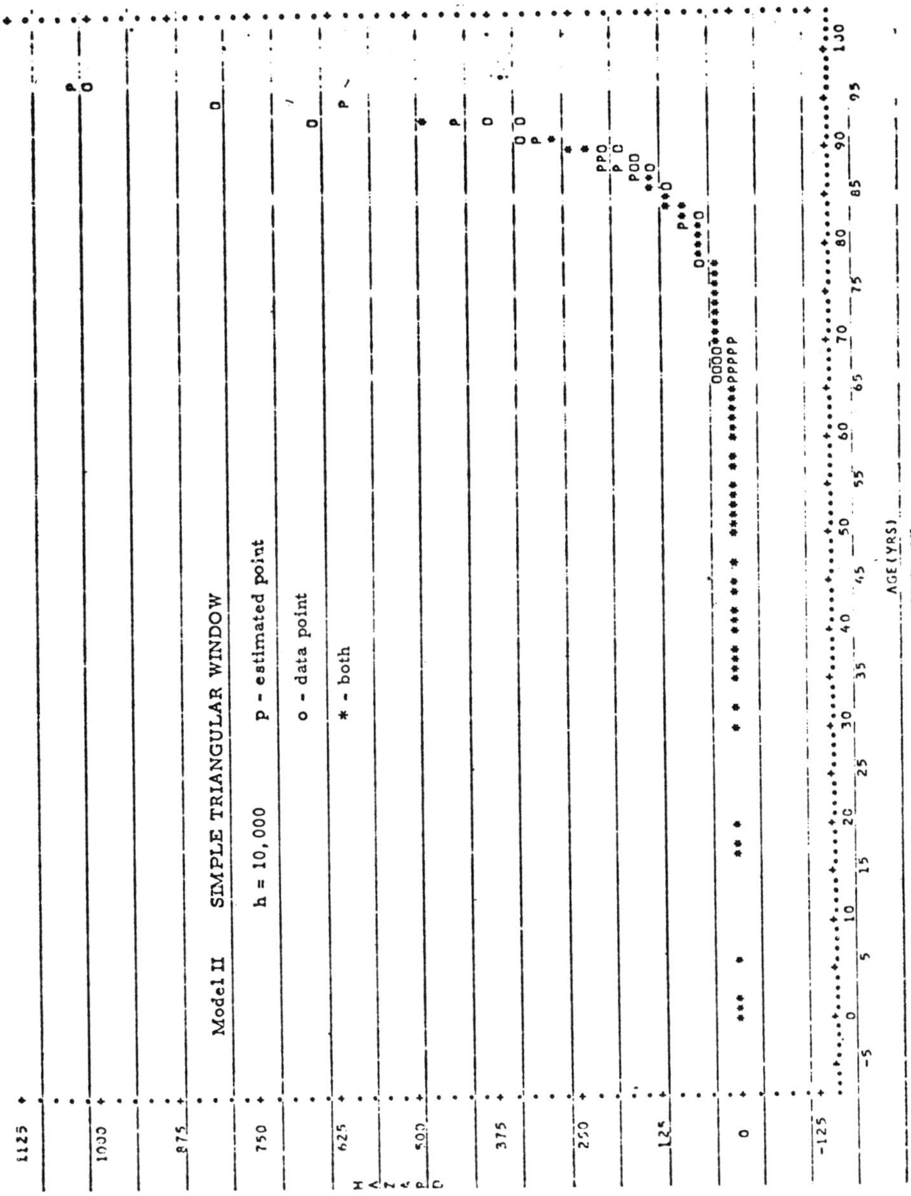
Model II SIMPLE TRIANGULAR WINDOW
h = 10,000
p - estimated point
o - data point
* - both
HAZARD
1125
1000
875
750
625
500
375
250
125
0
-125
-5
0
5
10
15
20
25
30
35
40
45
50
55
60
65
70
75
80
85
90
95
100
AGE (YRS)

FIGURE 27

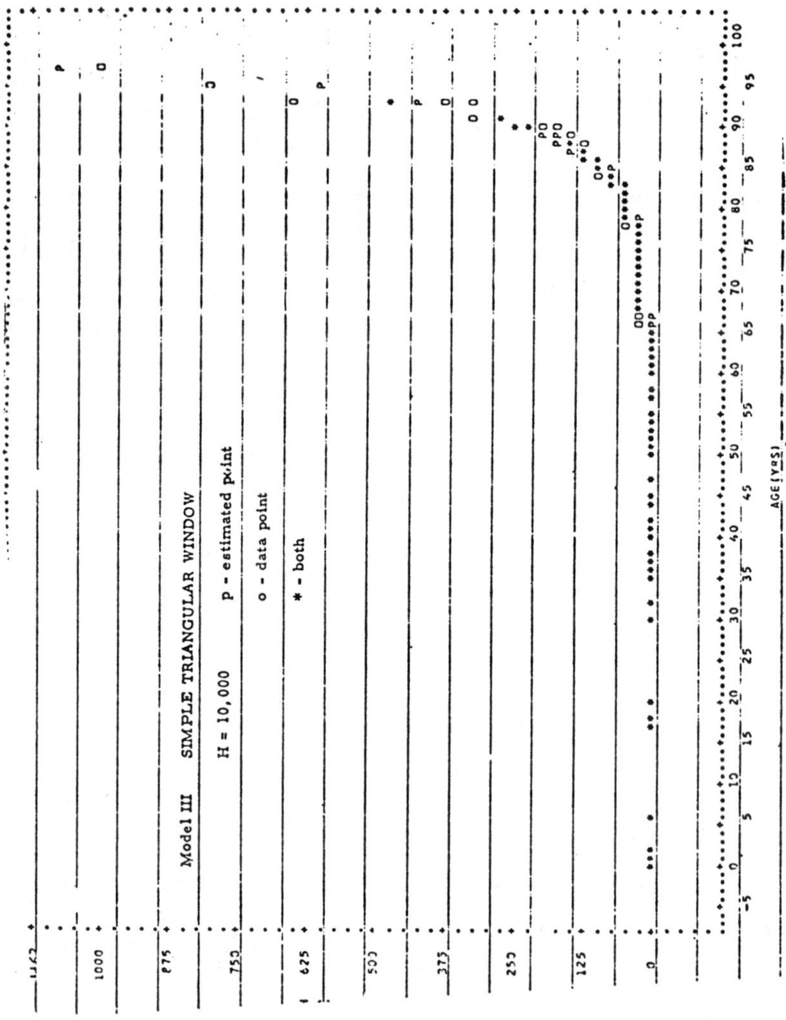
Model III SIMPLE TRIANGULAR WINDOW
H = 10,000
p - estimated point
o - data point
* - both
1000
750
625
375
250
125
0
-5
0
5
10
15
20
25
30
35
40
45
50
55
60
65
70
75
80
85
90
95
100
AGE (YRS)

FIGURE 28

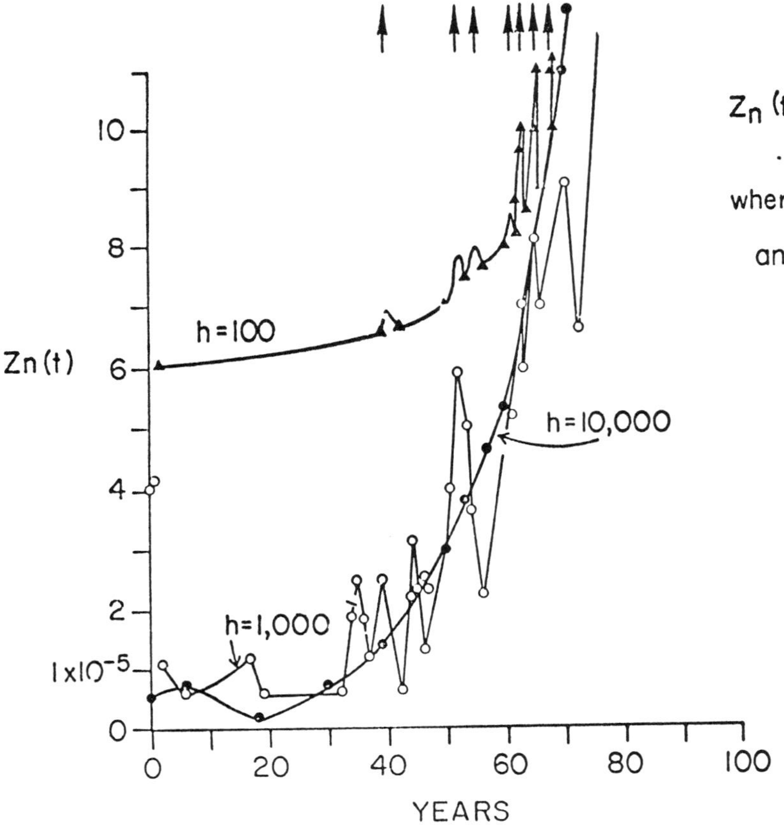


$$Z_n(t_i) = \frac{\frac{1}{2h_{,n}} \sum_{j \in A_i} 1}{1 - \frac{i}{n+1}}$$

where $A_i = \{ j: /t_j - t_i/ \leq h_1 \}$

and $h_1 = h/\log_{10} n$

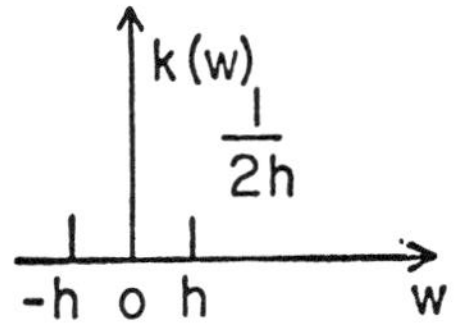


TIME-TO-DEATH IN LOS ANGELES

FIGURE 29

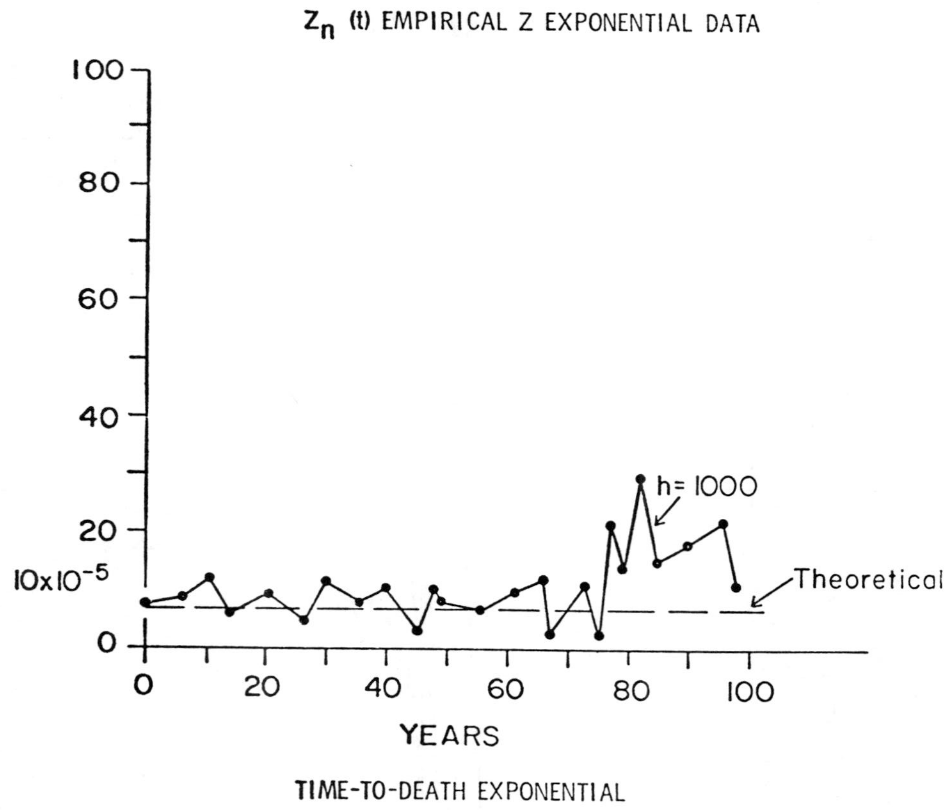
Z_n (t) EMPIRICAL Z EXPONENTIAL DATA
100
80
60
40
20
10x10^-5
0
h= 1000
Theoretical
0
20
40
60
80
100
YEARS
TIME-TO-DEATH EXPONENTIAL

FIGURE 30

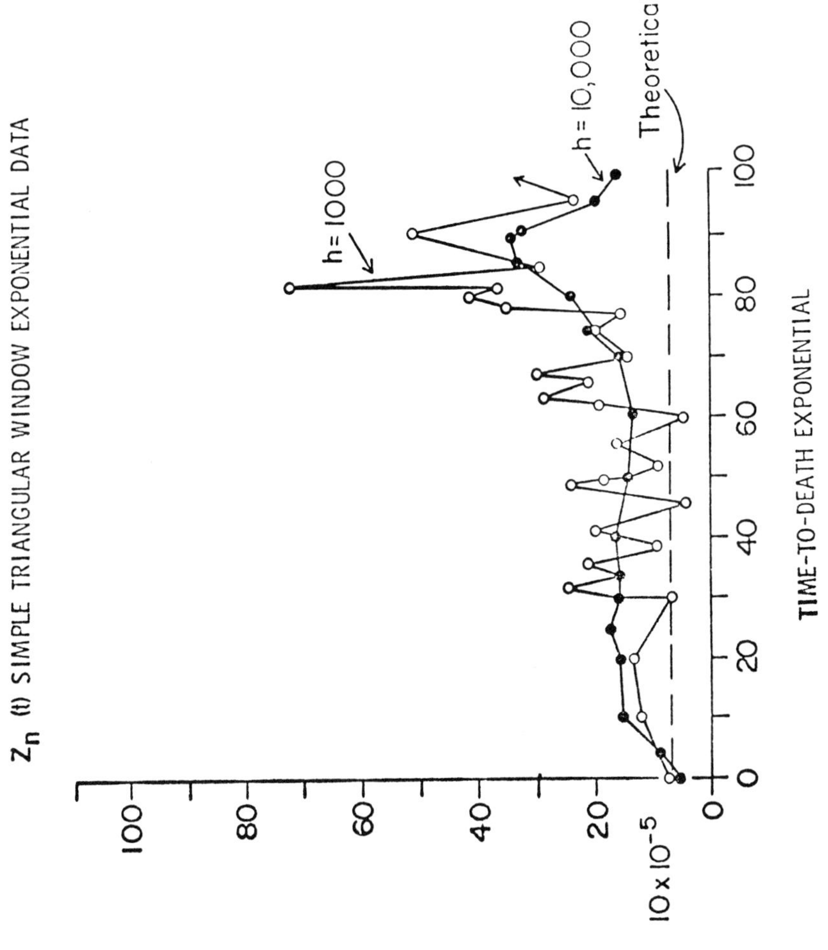
$Z_n$ (t) SIMPLE TRIANGULAR WINDOW EXPONENTIAL DATA
100
80
60
40
20
$10 \times 10^{-5}$
0
h = 1000
h = 10,000
Theoretical
0
20
40
60
80
100
TIME-TO-DEATH EXPONENTIAL

FIGURE 31

$Z_n$ (t) SIMPLE RECTANGULAR WINDOW

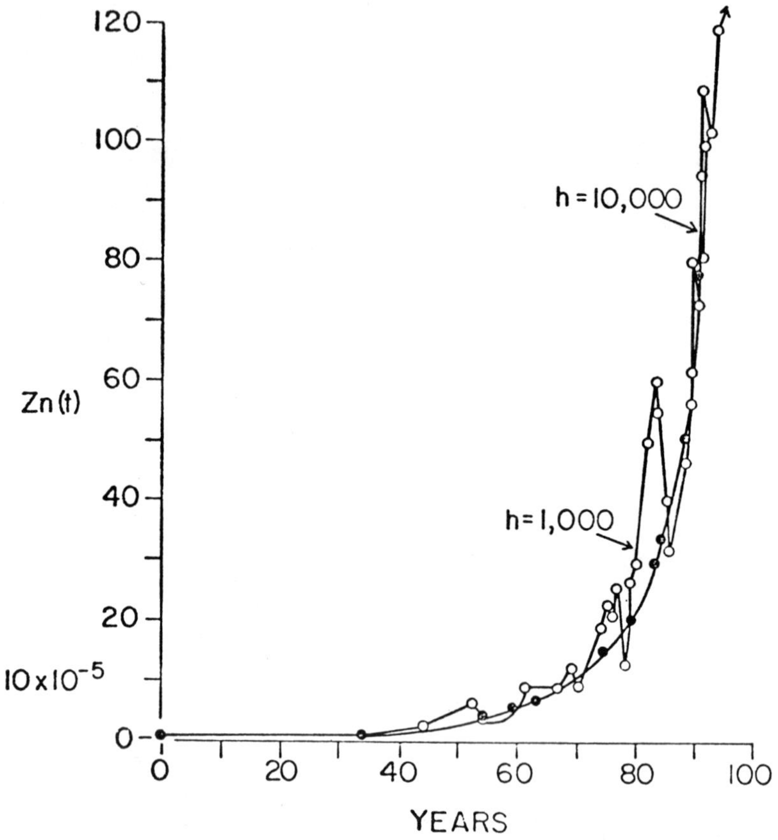


TIME-TO-DEATH IN LOS ANGELES

FIGURE 32

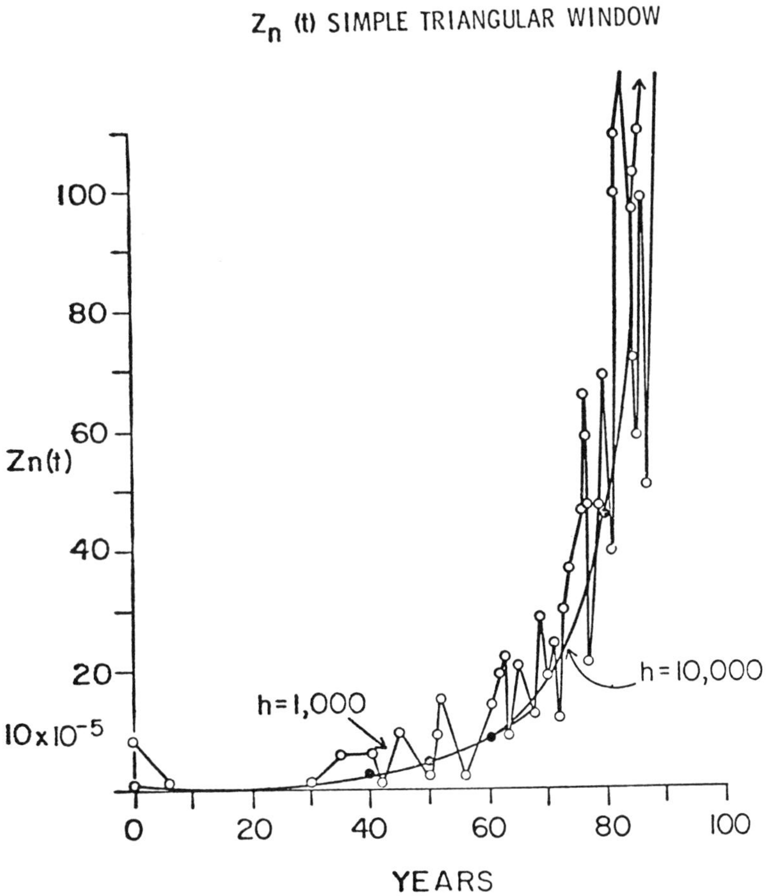


TIME-TO-DEATH IN LOS ANGELES, n=200

FIGURE 33

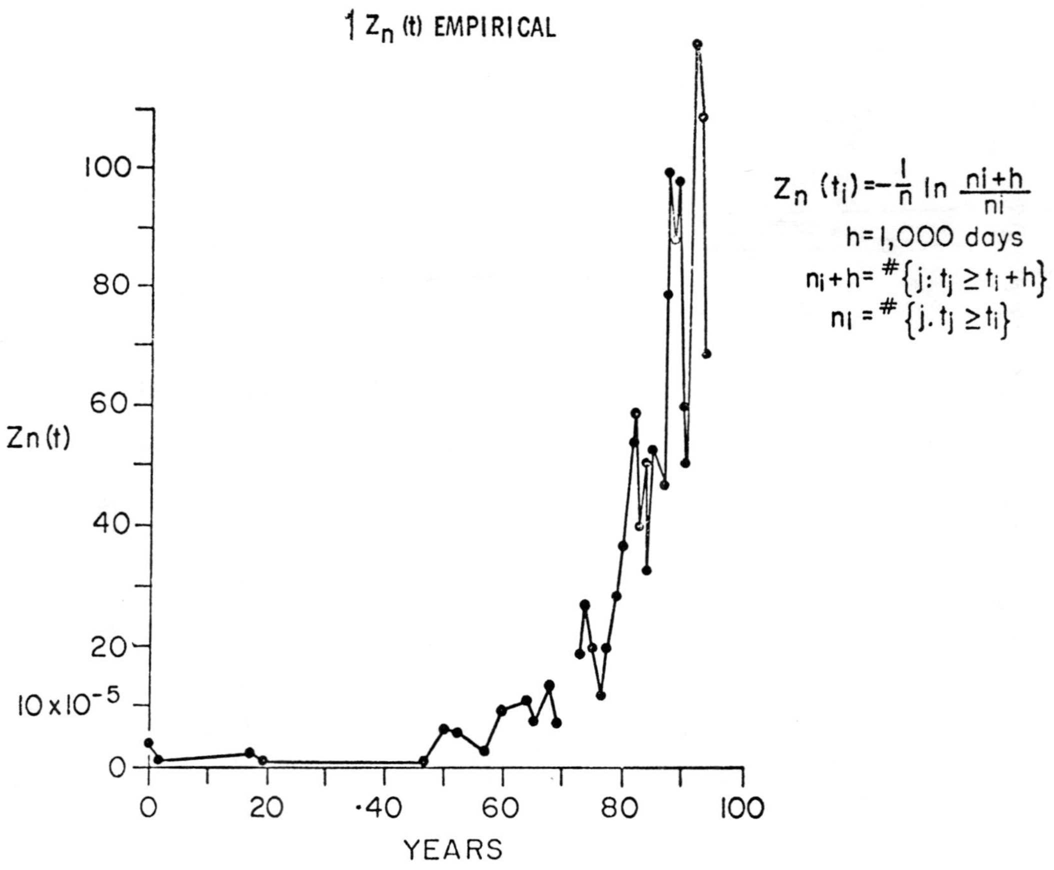


TIME-TO-DEATH DATA

FIGURE 34

$Z_n$ (t) SIMPLE TRIANGULAR WINDOW

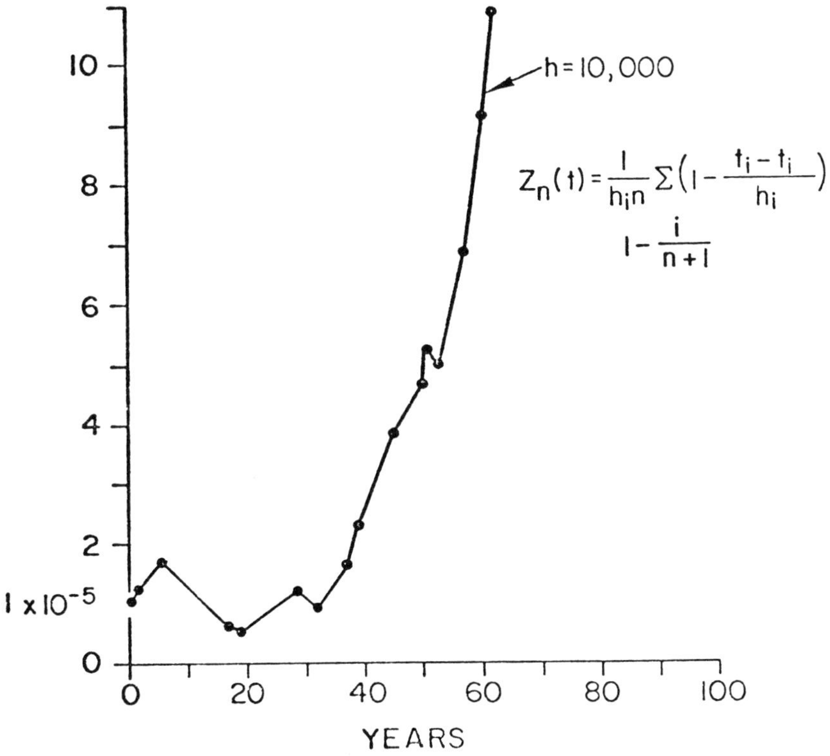


TIME-TO-DEATH IN LOS ANGELES

FIGURE 35

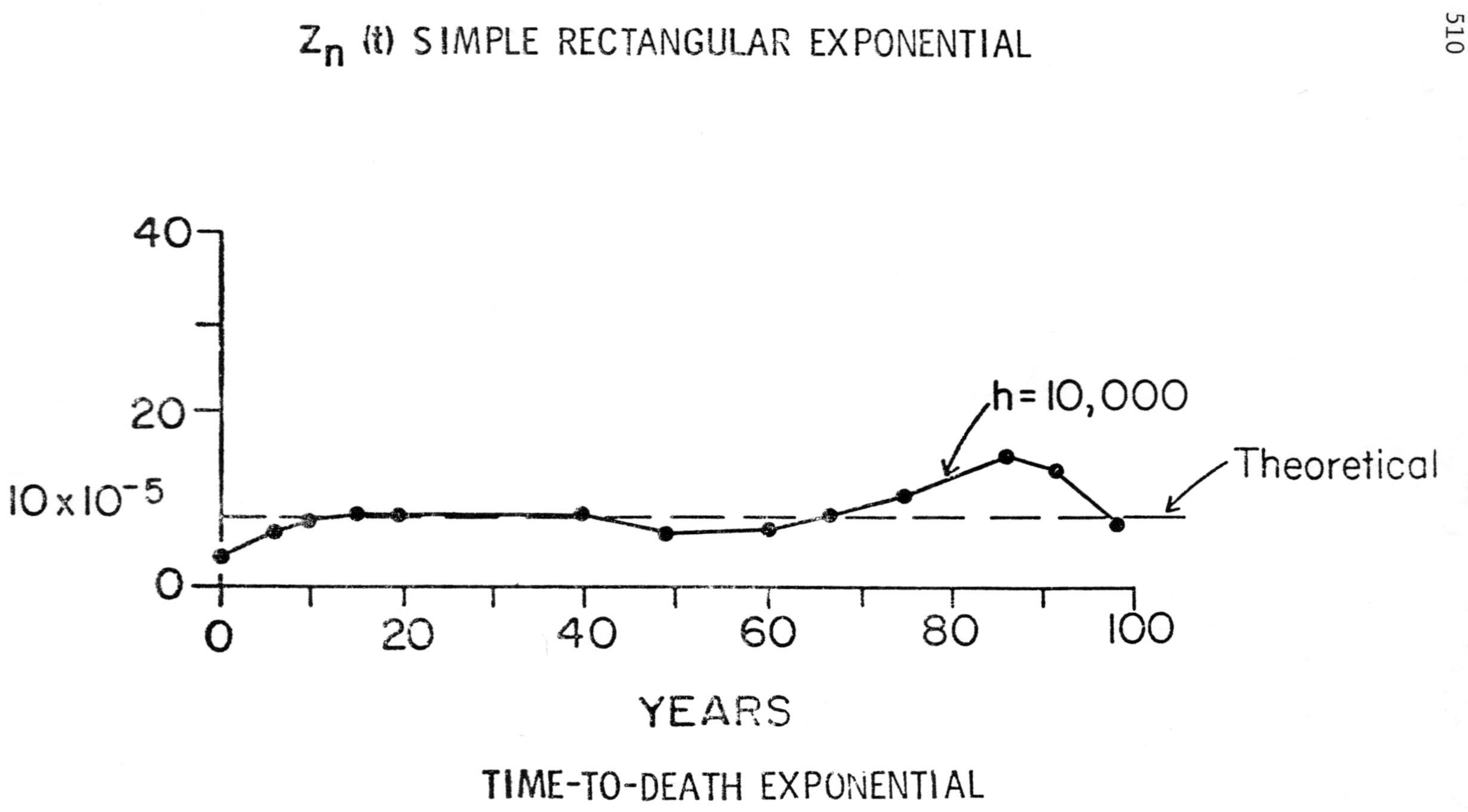
$Z_n$ (t) SIMPLE RECTANGULAR EXPONENTIAL
40
20
10x10^-5
0
h=10,000
Theoretical
0
20
40
60
80
100
YEARS
TIME-TO-DEATH EXPONENTIAL

FIGURE 36

## 11.11 Applications of the Models to Survival Data

In this section, the mathematical models as advanced in the previous sections, which (for specific values of the parameters) represent throughout the life span, not only the three basic types of mortality rates = constant, increasing and decreasing, but also, many combinations of these properties in consecutive segments of life span will be applied to data. Since the bath-tub shaped mortality rate curves are special cases of these models, we call these models with the bath-tub (B-1) property. With the use of a graphics program on our IBM 2250, the versatility of these models is demonstrated. The corresponding probability distributions and survivorship functions are obtained in closed forms. Also, the number of parameters on which these families of distributions depend are kept at a minimum. Several biological applications of these models are mentioned. Approaches to the problem of estimating the parameters are discussed.

Observed failure data can be used to estimate the event rate function (the terms mortality rate, or risk will be used interchangeably) which can then be translated into the estimation of a survivorship function. The estimation of the event rate function, therefore, assumes an important role in the estimation, as well as prediction, of survivorship. Nonparametric methods for estimating hazard rates were considered by Murthy [152] and Grenander [90]. However, the most they can do is to throw light on the shape of the underlying event rate function and, hence, cannot be used for decision making and prediction since the estimation of a continuous infinity of parameters is implicit in all those procedures. Thus, parametric procedures, based on realistic models for the event rate function, are the only suitable approaches for efficient estimation and prediction. It is generally accepted, based on both deductive reasoning and extensive empirical evidence, that the ideal event rate curve consists of an early decreasing phase, followed by a phase of useful life, where it remains approximately constant, before climbing to failure due to wearout (refer to Figure 15 of Chapter 10). However, there have been no models for the event rate advanced so far, that depend on as few parameters as possible and which also contain all the three phases mentioned earlier and which, at the same time, give rise to the survivorship function in a closed form.

We, therefore, propose herein, families of distributions that contain those corresponding to increasing hazard rate (HR), decreasing hazard rate (DHR) and, finally, the constant hazard rate (exponential distributions) and combinations thereof, giving rise to the classical bath-tub shape hazard curves which are characterized in a closed form.

## Theory

Denoting by $\lambda(t)$ the mortality rate at time $t$, the probability of death occuring within the time interval $(t, t+dt)$ is given by $\lambda(t)dt$. The probability $F(\cdot)$ of death before time $t+dt$ may then be expressed by the following differential equation

$$(11.11.1) \qquad F(t+dt) = F(t) + (1 - F(t))\,\lambda(t)dt$$

which means that the probability of death before time $t+dt$ is the sum of the probabilities of two mutually exclusive events; i.e.,

1. death before time $t$, and
2. no death before time $t$ and death in $(t, t+dt)$.

The differential Equation (11.11.1) may be written as

$$(11.11.2) \qquad F'(t) + \lambda(t)\,F(t) = \lambda(t) \quad ,$$

which may be solved by ordinary methods with the boundary

condition

$$F(0) = 0 . \tag{11.11.3}$$

By putting

$$y(t) = \int_0^t \lambda(u)du \tag{11.11.4}$$

the solution may be written as

$$F(t) = 1 - e^{y(0)-y(t)} \tag{11.11.5}$$

where $F(t)$ is called the distribution function associated with the mortality rate $\lambda(t)$ and

$$S(t) = 1 - F(t) = e^{y(0)-y(t)} \tag{11.11.6}$$

is called the survivorship function. The density function corresponding to (11.11.5) is given by

$$f(t) = \frac{dF(t)}{dt} . \tag{11.11.7}$$

It is clear from Equations (11.11.5) and (11.11.6) that there is a one-to-one correspondence between the mortality rate on the one hand and the distribution and survivorship function on the other. If we can discover mortality functions, $\lambda(t)$, with the bath-tub property and obtain the integral

$$y(t) = \int_0^t \lambda(t)dt$$

in a closed form, Equations (11.11.5) and (11.11.6) will give the corresponding distribution and survivorship functions, respectively, in closed forms.

Using the derivations of Models I, II and II as outlined in Section 11.8 of this chapter, we obtain statistical models with the bath-tub property. In Model I, when $a = 0$, $d = 1$ then $\lambda(t) = c$ and when $c = 0$, $b = 0$ then $\lambda(t) = a$.

## 11.12 Real Life Examples That the Model Can Be Applied To

The mortality rates corresponding to many real life situations fall within the domain of our models. From the practical point of view, we distinguish among three different categories of mortality rates, namely A, B and C, depending on the shape. Category A is marked by a decreasing risk function, followed by an increasing one. Category B is purely decreasing; while Category C is increasing.

In the biological field, the classical example of a

bath-tub hazard curve -- Category A -- is the survival data of humans (as well as other animals). It is characterized by: high infant mortality during the first year of life, slowly decreasing risk from ages 1 - 4, the lowest mortality rate starting from age 5 to around 35, and increasing risk for older ages (Figure 15, Chapter 10).

The Category A model can also be used for survival data of many other diseases, as long as they have this same general pattern. For example, Gehan [82] observed from data on the survival of males with angina pectoris that the death rate, per year, is highest in the first year after diagnosis. For the next nine years, the hazard function remains fairly constant and increases somewhat later.

Category B curves characterize situations where there is an initial high risk which decreases slowly, as time progresses. Survival data on patients after surgery, transplant operations, or other medical treatments that would improve the chances of survival, belong to this category.

## 11.13 Maximum Likelihood Procedure for Estimations

The method of maximum likelihood is discussed here. Since similar techniques are applied to all three models, more detailed explanations will be given for Model I, while only brief summaries of equations will be given for Models II and III.

MODEL I: Let $t_1, t_2, \ldots, t_n$ be a random sample of size N from the distribution F(t) given by (11.8.18). The likelihood of the observed sample is

$$(11.13.1)\quad L = \prod_{i=1}^{N} \frac{1}{(1+bti)^{a/b}} e^{-cti^{d}} \left[ c\, dti^{d-1} + \frac{a}{1+bti} \right]$$

and

$$(11.13.2)\quad \ln L = -\frac{a}{b} \sum_{i=1}^{N} \ln(1+bti) - c \sum_{i=1}^{N} ti^{d}$$

$$+ \sum_{1}^{N} \ln\left[ c\, dti^{d-1} + \frac{1}{1+bti} \right]$$

where the $\hat{a}, \hat{b}, \hat{c}$ and $\hat{d}$ that will maximize (11.13.2) can be obtained by solving the following equations; the second partial derivatives are given by:

$$\frac{\partial^2 \ln L}{\partial a^2} = -b^2 \sum_{1}^{N} \frac{t_i^{2(b-1)}}{[\lambda(t_i)]^2}$$

$$\frac{\partial^2 \ln L}{\partial a\, \partial c} = -\sum_{1}^{N} t_i^{b} \ln t_i + \sum_{1}^{N} \frac{t_i^{b-1}(1 + b \ln t_i)}{\lambda(t_i)} +$$

$$- ab \sum_{1}^{N} \frac{t_i^{2(b-1)}}{[\lambda(t_i)]^2} \left[1 + b \ln t_i\right]$$

$$\frac{\partial^2 \ln L}{\partial a \, \partial c} = bd \sum_{1}^{N} \frac{t_i^b}{[\lambda(t_i)]^2 (1 + ct_i)^2}$$

$$\frac{\partial^2 \ln L}{\partial a \, \partial d} = - b \sum_{1}^{N} \frac{t_i^{(b-1)}}{[\lambda(t_i)]^2 (1 + ct_i)}$$

$$\frac{\partial^2 \ln L}{\partial b^2} = - a \sum_{1}^{N} t_i^b (\ln t_i)^2$$

$$+ a \sum_{1}^{N} \frac{t_i^{b-1} \ln t_i (2 + b \ln t_i)}{\lambda(t_i)}$$

$$- a^2 \sum_{1}^{N} \frac{t_i^{2(b-1)} (1 + b \ln t_i)^2}{[\lambda(t_i)]^2}$$

$$\frac{\partial^2 \ln L}{\partial b \, \partial c} = ad \sum_{1}^{N} \frac{t_i^b (1 + b \ln t_i)}{[\lambda(t_i)]^2 (1 + ct_i)^2}$$

$$\frac{\partial^2 \ln L}{\partial b \, \partial d} = - a \sum_{1}^{N} \frac{t_i^{b-1} (1 + b \ln t_i)}{[\lambda(t_i)]^2 (1 + ct_i)}$$

$$\frac{\partial^2 \ln L}{\partial c^2} = \frac{\partial d}{c} \sum_1^N \frac{t_i}{1 + ct_i} - \frac{2d}{c^3} \sum_1^N \ln(1 + ct_i)$$

$$+ \frac{d}{c} \sum_1^N \frac{t_i^2}{(1 + ct_i)^2} + 2d \sum_1^N \frac{t_i^2}{\lambda(t_i)(1 + ct_i)^3}$$

$$- d^2 \sum_1^N \frac{t_i^2}{[\lambda(t_i)]^2 (1 + ct_i)^4}$$

$$\frac{\partial^2 \ln L}{\partial c \, \partial d} = \frac{1}{c^2} \sum_1^N \ln(1 + ct_i) - \frac{1}{c} \sum_1^N \frac{t_i}{1 + ct_i}$$

$$- \sum_1^N \frac{t_i}{\lambda(t_i)(1 + ct_i)^2}$$

$$+ d \sum_1^N \frac{t_i}{[\lambda(t_i)]^2 (1 + ct_i)^3}$$

$$\frac{\partial^2 \ln L}{\partial d^2} = - \sum_1^N \frac{1}{[\lambda(t_i)]^2 (1 + ct_i)^2}$$

$$\frac{\partial \ln L}{\partial a} = - \frac{1}{b} \sum_1^N \ln(1 + bt_i) + \sum_1^N \frac{1}{\lambda(t_i)(1 + bt_i)} = 0$$

$$\frac{\partial \ln L}{\partial b} = \frac{a}{b^2}\sum_{1}^{N} \ln(1 + bt_i) - \frac{a}{b}\sum_{1}^{N} \frac{t_i}{1 + bt_i}$$

$$- a\sum_{1}^{N} \frac{t_i}{\lambda(t_i)(1 + bt_i)} = 0$$

$$\frac{\partial \ln L}{\partial c} = - \sum_{1}^{N} t_i^d + d \sum_{1}^{N} \frac{t_i^{d-1}}{\lambda(t_i)} = 0$$

$$\frac{\partial \ln L}{\partial d} = - c \sum_{1}^{N} t_i^d \ln t_i + c \sum_{1}^{N} \frac{t_i^{d-1}(1 + d \ln t_i)}{\lambda(t_i)}$$

$$= 0 \;,$$

where

$$\lambda(t_i) = c\, dt_i^{d-1} + \frac{a}{1 + bt_i} \;. \tag{11.13.3}$$

With the aid of a computer, these equations can be solved iteratively. Initial estimates can be obtained from non-linear least-squares fit to the empirical hazard function.

Estimates of the asymptotic variances and covariances of the maximum likelihood estimates may be obtained from the matrix:

(11.13.4)

$$M = \begin{bmatrix} \frac{-\partial^2 \ln L}{\partial a^2} & \frac{-\partial^2 \ln L}{\partial a \; \partial b} & \frac{-\partial^2 \ln L}{\partial a \; \partial c} & \frac{-\partial^2 \ln L}{\partial a \; \partial d} \\ \frac{-\partial^2 \ln L}{\partial a \; \partial c} & \frac{-\partial^2 \ln L}{\partial b^2} & \frac{-\partial^2 \ln L}{\partial b \; \partial c} & \frac{-\partial^2 \ln L}{\partial b \; \partial d} \\ \frac{-\partial^2 \ln L}{\partial a \; \partial c} & \frac{-\partial^2 \ln L}{\partial b \; \partial c} & \frac{-\partial^2 \ln L}{\partial c^2} & \frac{-\partial^2 \ln L}{\partial c \; \partial d} \\ \frac{-\partial^2 \ln L}{\partial a \; \partial d} & \frac{-\partial^2 \ln L}{\partial b \; \partial d} & \frac{-\partial^2 \ln L}{\partial c \; \partial d} & \frac{-\partial^2 \ln L}{\partial d^2} \end{bmatrix}^{-1}$$

evaluated at $a = a$, $b = b$, $c = c$ and $d = d$.

<u>MODEL II</u>: The equations involved in solving are, briefly:

$$(11.13.5) \quad \ln L = \sum_{1}^{N} \ln(abe^{-bt_i} + cdt_i^{d-1}) - \sum_{1}^{N} a(1 - e^{-bt_i}) - \sum_{1}^{N} ct_i^d$$

with partial derivatives

$$\frac{\partial \ln L}{\partial a} = b \sum_{1}^{N} \frac{e^{-bt_i}}{abe^{-bt_i} + cdt_i^{d-1}} - \sum_{1}^{N} (1 - e^{-bt_i}) = 0$$

$$\frac{\partial \ln L}{\partial b} = a \sum_{1}^{N} \frac{e^{-bt_i}(1 - bt_i)}{abe^{-bt_i} + cdt_i^{d-1}} - a \sum_{1}^{N} t_i\, e^{-bt_i} = 0$$

$$\frac{\partial \ln L}{\partial c} = d \sum_{1}^{N} \frac{t_i^{d-1}}{abe^{-bt_i} + cdt_i^{d-1}} - \sum_{1}^{N} t_i^{d} = 0$$

$$\frac{\partial \ln L}{\partial d} = c \sum_{1}^{N} \frac{t_i^{d-1}(1 + d \ln t_i)}{abe^{-bt_i} + cdt_i^{d-1}} - c \sum_{1}^{N} t_i^{d} \ln t_i = 0.$$

MODEL III: For this model we have

$$\text{(11.13.6)} \qquad \ln L = \sum_{1}^{N} \ln \left( \frac{a}{1 + bt_i} + cde^{dt_i} \right) - \frac{a}{b} \sum_{1}^{N} \ln (1 + bt_i) - c \sum_{1}^{N} (e^{dt_i} - 1)$$

and the partial derivatives are

$$\frac{\partial \ln L}{\partial a} = \sum_{1}^{N} \frac{1}{\left( \frac{a}{1 + bt_i} + cde^{dt_i} \right) \left( 1 + bt_i \right)} - \sum_{1}^{N} \frac{\ln (1 + bt_i)}{b} = 0$$

$$\frac{\partial \ln L}{\partial b} = - \sum_{1}^{N} \frac{at_i}{\left(\frac{a}{1+bt_i} + cde^{dt_i}\right)\left(1 + bt_i\right)^2}$$

$$+ \frac{a}{b^2} \sum_{1}^{N} \ln (1 + bt_i) - \frac{a}{b} \sum_{1}^{N} \frac{t_i}{1 + bt_i} = 0$$

$$\frac{\partial \ln L}{\partial c} = \sum_{1}^{N} \frac{de^{dt_i}}{\frac{a}{1 + bt_i} + cde^{dt_i}} - \sum_{1}^{N} (e^{dt_i} - 1) = 0$$

$$\frac{\partial \ln L}{\partial d} = \sum_{1}^{N} \frac{ce^{dt_i}(1 + dt_i)}{\frac{a}{1 + bt_i} + cde^{dt_i}} - c \sum_{1}^{N} t_i e^{dt_i} = 0 .$$

## 11.14 Numerical Example

A hypothetical cohort of 1,000 people born in the United States in the year 1900 was made up, using information recorded in Vital Statistics of the United States. (The probability of dying, for ages $\geq 70$, was approximated using the values in the latest 1967 issue.) The survival data are presented in life-table form (see Table VII below) and the empirical event function was calculated using

$$\lambda(t_{mi}) = \frac{2q_i}{h_i(1 + p_i)}$$

where

$t_{mi}$ = the midpoint of the $i^{th}$ interval;

$h_i$ = the width of the $i^{th}$ interval;

$q_i$ = the conditional proportion of people dying in the $i^{th}$ interval; and

$p_i$ = the conditional proportion of people surviving in the $i^{th}$ interval;

as described by Kimball [122].

Nonlinear least-squares fits to the empirical event function were attempted for all three models and computations were performed using the BMDX85, Nonlinear Least Squares, a package program written at the Health Sciences Computing Facility of the University of California at Los Angeles. The estimated parameters and hazard functions are shown in Table IX.

Model I seems to feet the data best, so the method of maximum likelihood was performed, giving estimates as follows:

$$\left\{ \begin{array}{l} \hat{a} = 1.5942\text{ E01};\quad \hat{b} = 2.6120\text{ E02}; \\ \hat{c} = 8.6350\text{ E-11};\quad \hat{d} = 6.2990\text{ E00}. \end{array} \right. \tag{11.14.1}$$

The value of log likelihood (Eq. (11.13.2)) using maximum likelihood estimates is -0.4378E04 compared to -0.4413E04 using the least squares estimates.

TABLE VII

U. S. SURVIVAL DATA

| Age | N | Dead | q | p | pp | λ(t)* |
|---|---|---|---|---|---|---|
| 0- 0.99 | 1000 | 162 | 0.1620 | 0.8380 | 0.8380 | 0.176270 |
| 1- 4.99 | 838 | 39 | 0.0465 | 0.9535 | 0.79903 | 0.011900 |
| 5-14.99 | 799 | 23 | 0.0288 | 0.9712 | 0.77602 | 0.002922 |
| 15-24.99 | 776 | 38 | 0.0490 | 0.0951 | 0.73800 | 0.005023 |
| 25-34.99 | 738 | 35 | 0.0474 | 0.9526 | 0.70302 | 0.004855 |
| 35-44.99 | 703 | 37 | 0.0526 | 0.9474 | 0.66604 | 0.005402 |
| 45-54.99 | 666 | 57 | 0.0856 | 0.9144 | 0.60903 | 0.008942 |
| 55-64.99 | 609 | 106 | 0.1740 | 0.8260 | 0.50306 | 0.019058 |
| 65-74.99 | 503 | 189 | 0.3757 | 0.6243 | 0.31406 | 0.046259 |
| 75-84.99 | 314 | 248 | 0.7898 | 0.2102 | 0.06602 | 0.130534 |
| 85-94.99 | 66 | 66 | 1.0000 | 0.0000 | 0.00000 | 0.200000 |

* $$\lambda(t) = \frac{2q}{h(1 + p)}$$

where

h = the year interval, according to Kimball's method.

TABLE VIII

U. S. SURVIVAL DATA
(Hazard Function)*

| Midpoint Year | Observed | Model I | Model II | Model III |
|---|---|---|---|---|
| 0.5 | 0.17630 | 0.17307 | 0.17630 | 0.17453 |
| 3.0 | 0.01190 | 0.02906 | 0.01191 | 0.02922 |
| 10.0 | 0.00292 | 0.00873 | 0.00001 | 0.00877 |
| 20.0 | 0.00502 | 0.00445 | 0.00010 | 0.00439 |
| 30.0 | 0.00485 | 0.00360 | 0.00077 | 0.00292 |
| 40.0 | 0.00540 | 0.00524 | 0.00333 | 0.00219 |
| 50.0 | 0.00894 | 0.01147 | 0.01036 | 0.00175 |
| 60.0 | 0.01906 | 0.02649 | 0.02617 | 0.00146 |
| 70.0 | 0.04626 | 0.05693 | 0.05730 | 0.00126 |
| 80.0 | 0.13052 | 0.11237 | 0.11299 | 0.00244 |
| 90.0 | 0.20000 | 0.20591 | 0.20563 | 0.20087 |

| | | |
|---|---|---|
| a = 1.9872=01 | a = 2.8035E-01 | a = 3.2761E01 |
| b = 2.2764E02 | b = 1.0781E00 | b = 3.7340E02 |
| c = 2.4398E-12 | c = 3.9204E-12 | c = 1.1531E-20 |
| d = 6.1851E00 | d = 6.0841E00 | d = 4.9992E-01 |

*Least squares estimation on $\lambda(t)$.

## 11.15 Graphics Program

We shall now demonstrate the versatility of the models considered in this chapter with respect to their ability to describe the various mortality rates that one encounters in real life. To this end, an interactive graphics program was written in such a way that a person at the console can select one of the models at a time, and type in different values of the parameters through a keyboard. The corresponding event function will then be displayed on the screen. If desired, different increments of the parameters can also be typed in, and plots of these curves will be displayed one after the other as the parameters increase or decrease by the specified amount each time. Thus, the characteristics of each model can be fully illustrated easily. Pictures of these plots are shown in Figures 37, 38 and 39 for Models I, II and III, respectively.

# FIGURE 37

## MODEL I

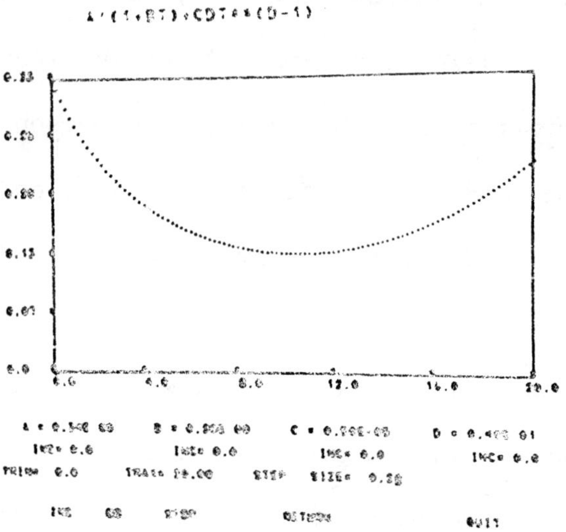


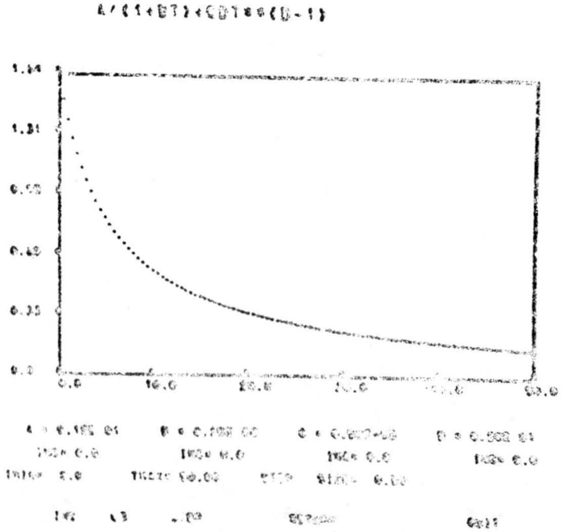

FIGURE 37

MODEL I

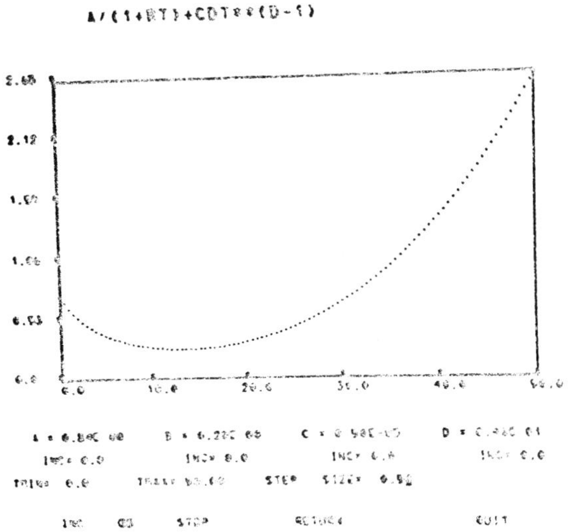


FIGURE 38

MODEL II

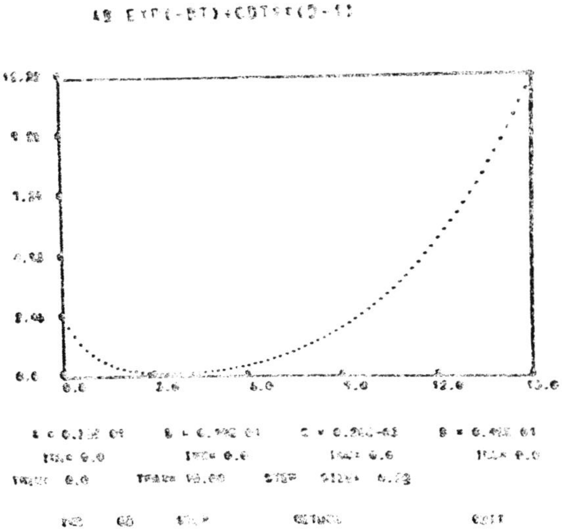

FIGURE 38

MODEL II

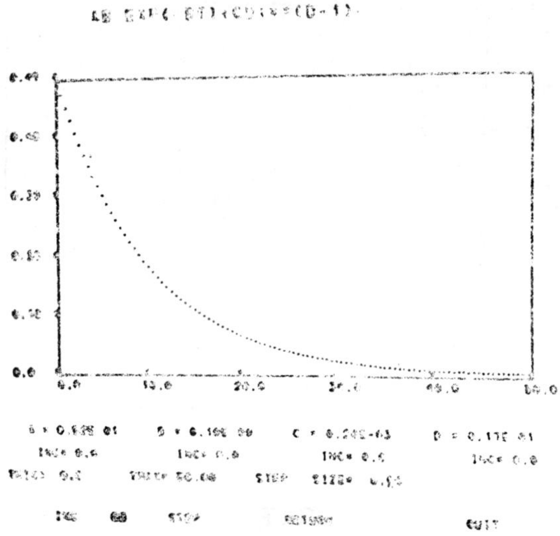

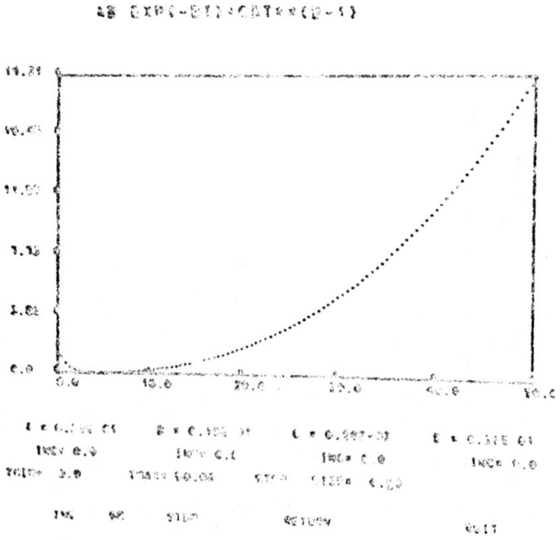

# FIGURE 38

## MODEL II

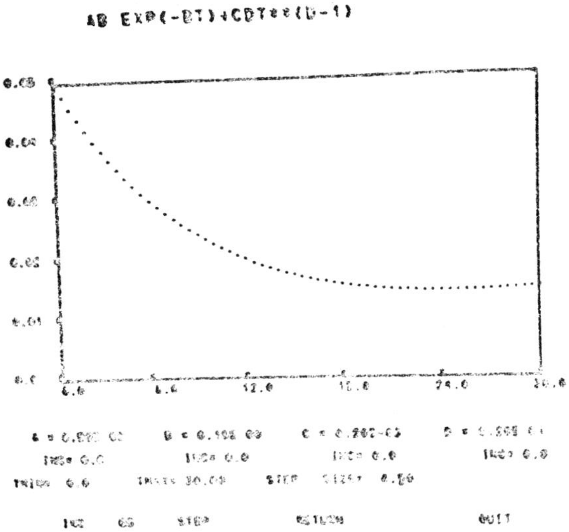


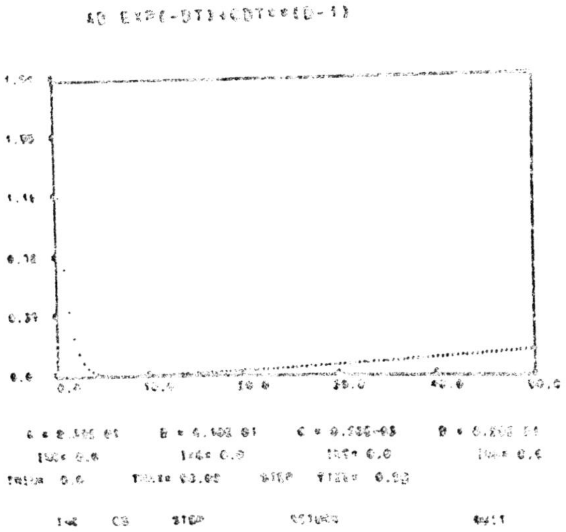

FIGURE 39

MODEL III

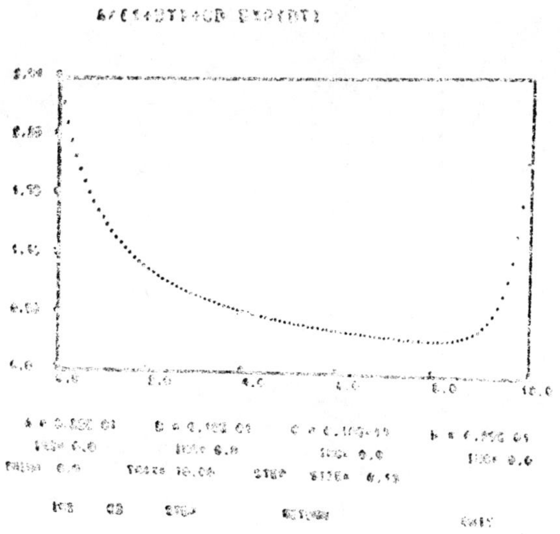

# CHAPTER 12. FURTHER APPLICATIONS TO BIOLOGICAL AND MEDICAL PROBLEMS

## 12.1 Introduction

An important equation in the study of stochastic point processes is

$$(12.1.1)\qquad F(t) = U(t) + \int_0^{\infty} U(y)\, K(t-y)dy, \quad t \geq 0 \quad ,$$

where, in the general case $F(t)$ and $U(t)$ are rectangular matrices and $K(t)$ is a rectangular matrix satisfying the relation

$$(12.1.2)\qquad K(-t) = K^T(t), \qquad t \geq 0 \ .$$

The above relation is significant in the study of neuronal networks. For simplicity, assume that all the functions involved in (12.1.1) are scalar and that

(i) $F(t)\Delta t$ = the probability that an event (apike) will occur in channel 2 (the output) between times $t$ and $t + \Delta t$, when an event occurs in channel 1 (the input) at $t = 0$ (crosscorrelation between channels 1 and 2);

(ii) $K(t)\Delta t$ = the probability that an event will

occur in channel 1 between times $t$ and $t + \Delta t$ when an event occurs in channel 1 at $t = 0$ (autocorrelation function of channel 1); and

(iii) $U(t)\Delta t$ = the probability that an event occurring in channel 1 will trigger a series of events leading to an event in channel 2 between $t$ and $t + \Delta t$ seconds later (delay function).

Then Equation (12.1.1) simply expresses in terms of probabilities the fact that one event, observed in channel 2, $t$ seconds after an event in channel 1 has occured may have been caused by that event triggering a process of duration $t$ which, in turn, results in an event in channel 2, $t$ seconds later. This is expressed in the first term in the right-hand side of (12.1.1). The second term in the right-hand side of this equation expresses the probability that the event observed may be the result of an event occurring at $t - y$ seconds in channel 1, triggering a process of duration $y$, whose final result is an event occurring $(t - y) + y = t$ seconds after the observed spike in channel 1. When several input channels and several output channels are used, the integral equation becomes the matrix integral equation given earlier.

Although several procedures might be suggested for

the solution of (12.1.1), we use herein the initial-value methods which are particularly interesting due to the feasibility of their use on modern digital computers. A solution of (12.1.1) is derived using invariant imbedding techniques and it is fairly self contained.

## 12.2 Derivation of the Initial-Value Problem [117], [118]

The equation considered is the matrix Fredholm integral equation of the second kind, Equation (12.1.1), where $F(t)$ and $U(t)$ are $M \times N$ matrices and $K(t)$ is an $N \times N$ matrix. Furthermore, the matrix $K(t)$ satisfies the relation (12.1.2) where the superscript on the right-hand side stands for matrix transporition. It will also be assumed that the matrices $F(t)$ and $K(t)$ admit the following representations:

$$F(t) = \int_0^\infty e^{-tz} Q(z)dz, \qquad t \geq 0 \quad , \tag{12.2.1}$$

$$K(t) = \int_0^\infty e^{-tz} W(z)dz, \qquad t \geq 0 \quad , \tag{12.2.2}$$

where $Q(z)$ is an $M \times N$ matrix and $W(z)$ is an $N \times N$. Let the $N \times N$ square matrix $J$ be defined by the equation

$$(12.2.3) \qquad e^{-tz} I = J(t,z) + \int_0^\infty J(y,z)\, K(t-y)dy \quad ,$$

$t \geq 0$, $z \geq 0$, where $I$ is the $N \times N$ unit matrix. The following representation formula is derived from (12.1.1), (12.1.2) and (12.2.1) and the superposition principle for solutions of linear systems:

$$(12.2.4) \qquad U(t) = \int_0^\infty Q(z)\, J(t,z)dz, \qquad t \geq 0 \ .$$

At this step in the derivation, it is convenient to rewrite (12.2.3) in the form

$$(12.2.4) \quad e^{-tz} I = J(t,z) + \int_0^t J(y,z)\, K(t-y)dy$$

$$+ \int_t^\infty J(y,z)\, K^T(y-t)dy, \quad t \geq 0, \ z \geq 0 \ .$$

In the last relation, use has been made of (12.1.2). Differentiating (12.2.5) we obtain

(12.2.6)

$$-ze^{-tz} I = J_t(t,z) + J(t,z)\, K(0) + \int_0^t J(y,z)\, K'(t-y)dy$$

$$- J(t,z)\, K^T(0) - \int_t^\infty J(y,z)\, K^{T'}(y-y)dy =$$

$$= J_t(t,z) + \int_0^t J(y,z)\, K'(t - y)dy$$

$$- \int_t^\infty j(y,z)\, K^{T'}(y - t)dy \quad ,$$

since $K(0) = K^T(0)$.

Integration by parts shows that

$$(12.2.7) \int_0^t J(y,z)\, K'(t - y)dy = - J(t,z)\, K(0) + J(0,z)\, D(t)$$

$$+ \int_0^t J_t(y,z)\, K(t - y)dy \quad ,$$

and assuming that

$$\lim_{t \to \infty} J(t,z)\, K^T(t) = 0, \qquad z \geq 0 \quad ,$$

it also shows that

$$(12.2.9) \int_t^\infty J(y,z)\, K^{T'}(y - t)dy$$

$$= - J(t,z)\, K^T(0) - \int_t^\infty J_t(y,z)\, K^T(y - t)dy \quad .$$

Combining Equations (12.2.7), (12.2.8) and (12.2.9) we see that

$$(12.2.10) \quad - ze^{-tz} I = J_t(t,z) + J(0,z)\, K(t) + \int_0^t J_t(y,z)\, K(t-y)dy + \int_0^\infty J_t(y,z)\, K^T(y-t)dy \quad .$$

Rewriting the above equation and making use of (12.1.2) and (12.2.2), we find

$$(12.2.11) \quad - ze^{-tz} I - J(0,z) \int_0^\infty e^{-tz} W(z)dz = J_t(t,z) + \int_0^\infty J_t(y,z)\, K(t-y)dy, \quad t \geq 0 \quad .$$

Comparison of this relation with (12.2.3) and use of the superposition principle yields the basic equation

$$(12.2.12) \quad J_t(t,z) = - zJ(t,z) - J(0,z) \cdot \int_0^\infty W(z')\, J(t,z')dz', \quad t \geq 0 \quad .$$

For convenience, the following notation is introduced:

$$(12.2.13) \quad H(z) = J(0,z), \qquad z \geq 0 \quad .$$

An equation involving the function $H(z)$ is easily derived from (12.2.7). We begin by writing

$$(12.2.14)\quad I = H(z) + \int_0^\infty J(y,z)\,K(-y)dy$$

$$= H(z) + \int_0^\infty J(y,z)\,K^T(y)dy$$

$$= H(z) + \int_0^\infty \int_0^\infty e^{-yz'}\,J(y,z)\,W^T(z')dy\,dz' \quad ,$$

where (12.1.2) and (12.2.3) have been used to arrive at the final expression. Defining

$$(12.2.15)\quad R(z,z') = \int_0^\infty e^{-yz'}\,J(y,z)dy, \qquad z,z' \geq 0 \quad ,$$

then (12.2.14) can be rewritten as

$$(12.2.16)\qquad H(z) = I - \int_0^\infty R(z,z')\,W^T(z')dz' \quad .$$

Under the assumption that

$$(12.2.17)\qquad \lim_{t\to\infty} e^{-tz'}\,J(t,z) = 0, \qquad z,z' \geq 0 \quad ,$$

integration by parts of the right-hand side of (12.2.15) shows that

(12.2.18)

$$R(z,z') = \frac{H(z)}{z'} + \frac{1}{z'} \int_0^\infty e^{-yz'} \, J_t(y,z)dy$$

$$= \frac{H(z)}{z'} + \frac{1}{z'} \int_0^\infty$$

$$\cdot \; e^{-yz'} \left( -zJ(y,z) - H(z) \int_0^\infty W(z'') \, J(y,z'') \right) dy$$

$$= \frac{H(z)}{z'} - \frac{z}{z'} R(z,z')$$

$$- \frac{H(z)}{z'} \int_0^\infty W(z'') \, R(z'',z')dz'' \quad .$$

To arrive at the final expression in the right-hand side of the previous equation, use is made of (12.2.12), (12.2.13) and (12.2.15). Rewriting (12.2.3) in the forms

$$(12.2.19) \qquad J(t,z) \; E \; e^{-tz} \, I - \int_0^\infty J(y,z) \; K(t-y)dy$$

and

$$(12.2.20) \quad J^T(t,z') = e^{-tz'} \, I - \int_0^\infty K^T(t-y) \; J^T(y,z)dy \quad .$$

Cross-multiplying the sides of these equalities, the following equation is obtained:

$$(12.2.21) \; e^{-tz'} \; J(t,z) - J(t,z) \int_0^\infty K^T(t-y) \; J^T(y,z)dy \; =$$

$$= e^{-tz} J^T(t,z') - \int_0^\infty J(y,z)\, K(t-y)dy\, J^T(t,z') \quad .$$

Integration of both sides, with respect to the variable $t$, and use of the definition of the function $R(z,z')$ (see (12.2.15)) yields

$$(12.2.22)\quad R(z,z') - \int_0^\infty \int_0^\infty J(t,z)\, K^T(t-y)\, J^T(y,z)dt\, dy$$

$$= R^T(z',z) - \int_0^\infty \int_0^\infty J(y,z)\, K(t-y)\, J^T(t,z)dt\, dy \quad ,$$

but

$$(12.2.23)\quad \int_0^\infty \int_0^\infty J(t,z)\, K^T(t-y)\, J^T(y,z)dt\, dy$$

$$= \int_0^\infty \int_0^\infty J(y,z)\, K^T(y-t)\, J^T(t,z)dy\, dt$$

$$= \int_0^\infty \int_0^\infty J(y,z)\, K(t-y)\, J^T(t,z)dt\, dy \quad .$$

From the two previous relations, it is seen that

$$(12.2.24)\qquad R(z,z') = R^T(z',z) \quad .$$

Equation (12.2.16) can be rewritten as

$$(12.2.25) \qquad H^T(z) = I - \int_0^\infty W(z')\, R(z',z)dz' \;.$$

This relation can now be used to modify the right-hand side of (12.2.18),

$$(12.2.26) \qquad R(z,z') = \frac{H(z)}{z'} - \frac{z}{z'} R(z,z') - \frac{H(z)}{z'} (I - H^T(z')) \;.$$

From this relation, we establish the relation for $R(z,z')$ as

$$(12.2.27) \qquad R(z,z') = \frac{H(z)\, H^T(z')}{z + z'} \;,$$

and Equation (12.2.16) can be rewritten as

$$(12.2.28) \quad H(z) = I - \int_0^\infty (z + z')^{-1} H(z)\, H^T(z')\, W^T(z')dz' \;.$$

This is a nonlinear integral equation for $J(0,z) = H(z)$. Its solution provides the initial condition for the differential Equation (12.2.12). The method of successive approximations has worked will in certain applications [118].

## 12.3 The Initial-Value Problem

The results of the previous section can be summarized as follows:

(1) Solve the separate nonlinear integral equation (12.2.28), $z \geq 0$;

(2) Use the solution $H(z)$ to solve the differential system defined by the differential equation

$$J_t(t,z) = -zJ(t,z) - H(z)\int_0^\infty W(z')\,J(t,z')dz' \tag{12.3.1}$$

with $t \geq 0$, $z \geq 0$ and the initial condition

$$J(0,z) = H(z) . \tag{12.3.2}$$

(3) Obtain the solution of the integral Equation (12.1.1), using the relation

$$U(t) = \int_0^\infty Q(z)\,J(t,z)dz . \tag{12.3.3}$$

In doing these calculations, the method of lines [117] is employed and integrals on the interval $(0,\infty)$ are approximated by finite sums.

A simple example will serve to illustrate the above method. Let Equation (12.1.1) be considered for the particular case when

$$M = N = 1 \quad ; \tag{12.3.4}$$

that is, all quantities are scalars, and

$$F(t) = \lambda + e^{-t} \quad , \tag{12.3.5}$$

$$K(t) = \lambda \quad . \tag{12.3.6}$$

The function $Q(z)$, linked to the function $F(t)$ by the relation of Equation (12.2.1) is

$$Q(z) = \lambda\delta(z) + \delta(z - 1) \tag{12.3.7}$$

where $\delta$ stands for Dirac's delta function. Correspondingly, (12.3.3) becomes

$$U(t) = \lambda J(t,0) + J(t,1) \quad . \tag{12.3.8}$$

This demonstrates that knowledge of the function $J(t,z)$ for $z = 0$ and $z = 1$ is sufficient to compute the delay function $U(t)$.

The function $W(z)$ related to the kernel $K(t)$ by Equation (12.2.2) is

$$W(z) = \lambda\delta(z) \quad . \tag{12.3.9}$$

With this in mind, the nonlinear integral (12.2.28) may be rewritten as

(12.3.10) $$H(z) = 1 - \frac{\lambda H(z)\, H(0)}{z} .$$

From this last relation, it easily can be seen that

(3.3.11) $$H(0) = 0 \quad \text{and} \quad H(1) = 1 .$$

These initial conditions are complemented by the following differential equations, obtained by rewriting (12.3.1) for the special cases $z = 0$ and $z = 1$:

(12.3.12) $$J_t(t,0) = 0 ,$$

(12.3.13) $$J_t(t,1) = - J(t,1) - \lambda J(t,0) .$$

Equations (3.3.11) - (3.3.13) yield

(12.3.14) $$J(t,0) = 0 \quad \text{and} \quad J(t,1) = e^{-t} ,$$

and the desired delay function is

(12.3.15) $$U(t) = e^{-t}, \qquad t \geq 0 .$$

## 12.4 Relations to the Renewal Equation

Let the matrix $\Phi(t,z)$ be defined as the solution of the matrix integral equation

$$(12.4.1) \quad K(t) = \Phi(t) + \int_0^\infty \Phi(y)\, K(t-y)dy, \qquad t \geq 0 .$$

Comparison of this equation with (12.2.3) and use of the superposition principle for linear systems shows that

$$(12.4.2) \qquad \Phi(t) = \int_0^\infty W(z)\, J(t,z)dz, \qquad t \geq 0 .$$

Equation (12.3.1) can then be written as

$$(12.4.3) \qquad J_t(t,z) = - zJ(t,z) - H(z)\, \Phi(t) .$$

Integration of this equation, with the initial condition

$$(12.4.4) \qquad J(0,z) = H(z) ,$$

yields

$$(12.4.5) \; J(t,z) = H(z)\Big[ I \exp(-tz) + \int_0^t \cdot \exp[-(t-y)z]\, \Phi(y)dy \Big] .$$

Multiplying on the left by the matrix W and integrating, we find that the matrix $\Phi$ satisfies the Volterra integral equation

$$\Phi(t) = L(t) + \int_0^t L(t-y)\,\Phi(y)dy, \qquad t \geq 0 , \tag{12.4.6}$$

where

$$L(t) = \int_0^\infty e^{-tz}\,W(z)\,H(z)dz, \qquad t \geq 0 . \tag{12.4.7}$$

Equation (12.4.6) is the renewal equation.

In subsequent investigations researchers will apply multiple-spike trains. Much remains to be done mathematically and computationally. In particular, we must show that the solution of the Cauchy system provides a solution of the Fredholm integral equation and we must investigate the most efficient numerical methods for carrying out the operations required in Section 12.3. It would also be highly desirable to obtain detailed information about the behavior of the matrix $J$ for large values of the argument $t$.

## 12.5 Prediction of Arrythmias Via the Renewal Integral Equation

The digitized electrocardiogram is treated as a realization from a discrete point process. We will describe in the following sections the use of spectral methods which may be used in the analysis of the electrocardiogram (ECG). The spectral or frequency domain approach has a two-fold value. First, it lends a conceptual simplicity to the theoretical interpretation of time varying behavior, such as that of the ECG. This simplicity promotes an understanding of the implied behavior of time domain models, especially when linear transformations are involved. Second, the spectral approach has simpler sampling properties than does the more straightforward time domain approach. Spectral analysis enables us to acquire a detailed knowledge of the harmonic content of the sample data [154]. This new knowledge can be used to improve methods of recording data, to develop models that adequately account for the observed harmonic content, and finally, to assist in the removal (filtering) of unwanted (noisy) harmonic components.

### 12.5.1 Methods of Data Collection and Analysis

The patient ECG data is collected on FM tape and is then digitized at 256 samples/sec. The digitized tape is then organized into a sequential patient file for use in various monitoring and analysis programs, as developed in [49] at the UCLA Brain Research Institute. The power spectral density (psd) program has been designed to utilize an an IBM 2250 system, in-line to an IBM 360/91 computer, such as that of the University of California at Los Angeles Health Sciences Computing Facility. With this power spectral density program the user can view the power spectral density of a patient's ECG, based on any selected segment of the data. Furthermore, the user can remove any desired power from the frequency domain and retransform into the time domain, or he can remove segments from the time domain and transform into the frequency domain. In addition to the above, there are other options available that make it possible to obtain printed output of the selected time series, the psd of the selected series, and the reconstruction of the time series from the frequency to the time domain [156].

The transformation to the frequency domain is implemented with the Cooley-Tukey fast Fourier transform [49], [156]. The program allows for samples as large as 2048 or as small as 256 samples. The input time series is adjusted with a cosine taper, in order to avoid the undesirable effects of the rectangular window [49].

#### 12.5.2 Theoretical Basis for Power Spectral Density Analysis

The incoming ECG wave form is digitized at the rate of 256 points/sec. and the digitized electrocardiogram is considered as a realization from a discrete stationary process in the wide sense. More precisely, let the sequence $\{V(n)\}$, $n = 1,2,\ldots,$ be the stochastic process underlying the digitized ECG. Since it is assumed that $\{V(n)\}$ is stationary in the wide sense, we have for the covariance between $V(n)$ and $V(n+K)$

$$(12.5.1) \qquad \rho(K) = \operatorname{cov}\,(V(n), V(n+k))$$

$$= \int_{\pi}^{\pi} e^{iK\lambda}\, dF(\lambda)$$

where $F(\lambda)$ is the power spectrum of the stochastic process $\{V(n)\}$. If $F(\lambda)$ is absolutely continuous, we can write

$$(12.5.2) \qquad dF(\lambda) = f(\lambda)d\lambda$$

where $f(\lambda)$ is called the spectral density of the stochastic process $\{V(n)\}$. Combining (12.5.1) and (12.5.2), and using the Fourier inversion formula, we obtain, under general conditions, that

$$(12.5.3) \qquad f(\lambda) = \frac{1}{2\pi} \sum_{K=-\infty}^{\infty} \rho(k)e^{-ik\lambda} .$$

In the above equation, if we substitute for the covariances $\rho(k)$ their sample values, we obtain what is called the periodogram. Let $I_N(\lambda)$ denote the periodogram. It is well known that $I_N(\lambda)$ is not a consistent estimate of the true spectral density $f(\lambda)$ of the process $\{V(n)\}$ [150], [90]. The class of estimates, $f_N^*(\lambda)$, are therefore proposed where

$$(12.5.4) \qquad f_N^*(\lambda) = \int_{-\pi}^{\pi} I_N(\ell)\, W_\lambda(\ell) d\ell$$

where $W_\lambda(\ell)$ is a specified weight function, or so-called window function. It is then shown that $f_N^*(\lambda)$ is consistent for estimating $f(\lambda)$ [150], [90]. The rectangular window used in this section is as given in the power spectral density programs in [150], [90] and [49].

### 12.5.3 Presentation of Processed and Analyzed Data

Table IX below presents the vanishing of the low-frequency (noisy) component, as the sample size or length of the record progressively increases to 32 sec.

Tables X through XIII present the ordinates of the power spectral density function, the cumulative power at the low frequency and at the fundamental frequency, and its multiples for the entire PQRST, as well as the individual waves. At the bottom of each of these tables are given the values of the low frequency $\lambda_0$ and the fundamental frequency $\lambda_1$ for each patient.

TABLE IX

| Frequency $\lambda$ (cps) | 8 sec | | 16 sec | | 32 sec | |
|---|---|---|---|---|---|---|
| | $f(\lambda)$ | $F(\lambda)$ | $f(\lambda)$ | $F(\lambda)$ | $f(\lambda)$ | $F(\lambda)$ |
| 0.125 ($\lambda_0$) | 8.17 | 8.17 | 2.10 | 2.66 | 0.52 | 1.23 |
| 1.3125($\lambda_1$) | 9.55 | 39.59 | 17.05 | 28.91 | 20.80 | 31.00 |
| $2\lambda_1$ | | 48.20 | | 42.01 | | 39.42 |
| $3\lambda_1$ | | 52.06 | | | | 43.73 |
| $4\lambda_1$ | | 56.95 | | 50.35 | | 49.13 |
| $5\lambda_1$ | | 66.71 | | 59.85 | | 60.57 |
| $6\lambda_1$ | | 72.95 | | 67.71 | | 67.38 |
| $7\lambda_1$ | | 76.93 | | 72.29 | | 72.51 |
| $8\lambda_1$ | | 80.71 | | 76.65 | | 76.35 |
| $9\lambda_1$ | | 83.20 | | 79.96 | | 79.27 |
| $10\lambda_1$ | | 85.35 | | 83.30 | | 82.75 |
| $12\lambda_1$ | | 90.64 | | 89.29 | | 89.00 |

TABLE X

PQRST

| Frequency $\lambda$ (cps) | Cumulative psd $F(\lambda)$ for Patient | | | | | | |
|---|---|---|---|---|---|---|---|
| | 1[a] | 2[b] | 3[c] | 4[d] | 5[e] | 6[f] | 7[g] |
| $\lambda_0$ | 5.93 | 11.91 | 26.48 | | 18.21 | 3.36 | 17.85 |
| $\lambda_1$ | 24.41 | 22.41 | 52.19 | 16.87 | 36.44 | 14.63 | 26.11 |
| $2\lambda_1$ | 36.39 | 27.62 | 63.23 | 46.27 | 44.97 | 16.45 | 35.25 |
| $3\lambda_1$ | 50.49 | 29.12 | 66.10 | 58.01 | | 20.00 | 43.05 |
| $4\lambda_1$ | 55.04 | 34.24 | 72.22 | 68.21 | 47.88 | 27.43 | 48.06 |
| $5\lambda_1$ | 63.62 | 44.10 | 77.88 | 80.50 | 53.81 | | 58.19 |
| $6\lambda_1$ | 68.23 | 53.33 | 81.72 | 86.69 | 57.30 | | 69.14 |
| $7\lambda_1$ | 74.70 | 59.17 | 83.92 | 90.53 | 61.64 | | 76.80 |
| $8\lambda_1$ | 80.00 | 63.58 | 86.35 | 92.89 | | 52.86 | 83.21 |
| $9\lambda_1$ | 84.75 | 72.39 | 87.53 | 96.60 | | | 84.72 |
| $10\lambda_1$ | 86.83 | 78.11 | 89.57 | 97.72 | 70.53 | | 86.00 |
| $11\lambda_1$ | 88.97 | 82.04 | 91.48 | 98.01 | | | 89.58 |
| $12\lambda_1$ | 90.58 | 87.28 | 92.75 | 98.75 | | 68.42 | 91.00 |
| $13\lambda_1$ | 93.62 | | | 99.48 | 80.11 | | |
| $14\lambda_1$ | | | | | | | |
| $15\lambda_1$ | | | | | | 80.50 | |

[a] $\lambda_0 = 0.250;\ \lambda_1 = 1.4375$

[b] $\lambda_0 = 0.250;\ \lambda_1 = 1.6900$

[c] $\lambda_0 = 0.250;\ \lambda_1 = 1.6250$

[d] $\lambda_1 = 1.625$

[e] $\lambda_0 = 0.250;\ \lambda_1 = 1.0625$

[f] $\lambda_0 = 0.250;\ \lambda_1 = 0.9425$

[g] $\lambda_0 = 0.250;\ \lambda_1 = 1.0625$

TABLE XI

QRS

| Frequency $\lambda$ (cps) | Cumulative psd $F(\lambda)$ for Patient | | | | | | |
|---|---|---|---|---|---|---|---|
| | 1[a] | 2[b] | 3[c] | 4[d] | 5[e] | 6[f] | 7[g] |
| $\lambda_0$ | 6.91 | 17.41 | 15.66 | | 16.12 | 2.79 | 23.48 |
| $\lambda_1$ | 16.05 | 34.05 | 54.12 | 17.21 | 28.68 | 5.86 | 34.00 |
| $2\lambda_1$ | 30.40 | 37.96 | 62.55 | 31.51 | 33.05 | 10.75 | 43.42 |
| $3\lambda_1$ | 35.88 | 42.10 | 66.91 | 51.57 | 36.52 | | 51.11 |
| $4\lambda_1$ | 46.99 | 46.94 | 71.77 | 68.29 | 40.20 | | 57.00 |
| $5\lambda_1$ | 53.58 | 52.36 | 75.65 | 77.04 | 44.24 | | 66.35 |
| $6\lambda_1$ | 64.49 | 58.00 | 78.39 | 82.87 | 48.47 | | 72.96 |
| $7\lambda_1$ | 70.46 | 63.51 | 81.72 | 89.50 | 52.65 | | |
| $8\lambda_1$ | 77.59 | 68.70 | | 93.71 | | 40.00 | |
| $9\lambda_1$ | | 73.52 | | 85.93 | | | |
| $10\lambda_1$ | 85.97 | 77.94 | | 97.10 | 65.39 | | 90.92 |
| $11\lambda_1$ | 89.58 | | | 98.43 | | | |
| $12\lambda_1$ | 91.26 | | | | | 62.84 | 94.62 |
| $13\lambda_1$ | 94.13 | | 92.65 | | | | |
| $14\lambda_1$ | | | | | | | |
| $15\lambda_1$ | | 93.05 | | | 80.96 | 75.57 | |

[a] $\lambda_0 = 0.250$; $\lambda_1 = 1.4375$

[b] $\lambda_0 = 0.250$; $\lambda_1 = 1.7000$

[c] $\lambda_0 = 0.250$; $\lambda_1 = 1.625$

[d] $\lambda_1 = 1.625$

[e] $\lambda_0 = 0.375$; $\lambda_1 = 1.0625$

[f] $\lambda_0 = 0.250$; $\lambda_1 = 0.9425$

[g] $\lambda_0 = 0.250$; $\lambda_1 = 1.0625$

TABLE XII

T-WAVE

| Frequency $\lambda$ (cps) | Cumulative psd F( ) for Patient | | | | | | |
|---|---|---|---|---|---|---|---|
| | $1^a$ | $2^b$ | $3^c$ | $4^d$ | $5^e$ | $6^f$ | $7^g$ |
| $\lambda_0$ | 7.85 | 36.52 | 59.34 | 5.60 | 12.62 | 29.43 | 48.66 |
| $\lambda_1$ | 54.49 | 83.57 | 74.60 | 50.00 | 52.59 | 50.15 | 75.58 |
| $2\lambda_1$ | 73.27 | | 92.00 | 74.99 | 72.96 | | 90.45 |
| $3\lambda_1$ | 90.71 | 95.28 | 95.25 | 87.82 | 83.71 | | |
| $4\lambda_1$ | 94.68 | 96.95 | 98.20 | 95.63 | 88.00 | 82.66 | |
| $5\lambda_1$ | | | | | | | |
| $6\lambda_1$ | | | | | | 90.27 | |
| $7\lambda_1$ | | | | | | | |
| $8\lambda_1$ | | | | | | | |
| $9\lambda_1$ | | | | | | | |
| $10\lambda_1$ | | | | | | | |
| $11\lambda_1$ | | | | | | | |
| $12\lambda_1$ | | | | | | | |
| $13\lambda_1$ | | | | | | | |
| $14\lambda_1$ | | | | | | | |
| $15\lambda_1$ | | | | | | | |

[a] $\lambda_0 = 0.375$; $\lambda_1 = 1.4375$

[b] $\lambda_0 = 0.250$; $\lambda_1 = 1.7000$

[c] $\lambda_0 = 0.250$; $\lambda_1 = 1.625$

[d] $\lambda_0 = 0.500$; $\lambda_1 = 1.625$

[e] $\lambda_0 = 0.375$; $\lambda_1 = 1.6625$

[f] $\lambda_0 = 0.250$; $\lambda_1 = 0.9425$

[g] $\lambda_0 = 0.250$; $\lambda_1 = 1.0625$

TABLE XIII

P-WAVE

| Frequency $\lambda$ (cps) | Cumulative psd $F(\lambda)$ for Patient | | | | | | |
|---|---|---|---|---|---|---|---|
| | 1[a] | 2[b] | 3[c] | 4[d] | 5[e] | 6[f] | 7[g] |
| $\lambda_0$ | 14.32 | 60.96 | 51.54 | 28.77 | 15.94 | 44.77 | 52.98 |
| $\lambda_1$ | 30.65 | 90.00 | 69.40 | 44.89 | 42.04 | 59.77 | |
| $2\lambda_1$ | 41.80 | 92.24 | 75.03 | 52.31 | 50.72 | | |
| $3\lambda_1$ | 50.56 | 94.44 | 86.66 | 62.96 | 61.27 | | |
| $4\lambda_1$ | 61.45 | 96.00 | 87.75 | 68.09 | 67.55 | 74.75 | 80.00 |
| $5\lambda_1$ | 68.24 | | 92.37 | 70.70 | 71.48 | | |
| $6\lambda_1$ | 74.19 | | 94.50 | 73.74 | 74.17 | | 88.05 |
| $7\lambda_1$ | | | 95.88 | 76.80 | 77.65 | | |
| $8\lambda_1$ | 80.33 | | 97.27 | 81.17 | 80.44 | 88.53 | |
| $9\lambda_1$ | | | | 83.13 | | | |
| $10\lambda_1$ | | | | 85.03 | | 91.32 | |
| $11\lambda_1$ | | | | 86.46 | | | |
| $12\lambda_1$ | | | | 87.83 | | | |
| $13\lambda_1$ | | | | | | | |
| $14\lambda_1$ | | | | | | | |
| $15\lambda_1$ | | | | | | | |

[a] $\lambda_0 = 0.500$; $\lambda_1 = 1.4200$

[b] $\lambda_0 = 0.250$; $\lambda_1 = 1.7000$

[c] $\lambda_0 = 0.250$; $\lambda_1 = 1.625$

[d] $\lambda_0 = 0.375$; $\lambda_1 = 1.625$

[e] $\lambda_0 = 0.250$; $\lambda_1 = 1.0625$

[f] $\lambda_0 = 0.250$; $\lambda_1 = 0.9425$

[g] $\lambda_0 = 0.3125$; $\lambda_1 = 1.0625$

### 12.5.4 Reconstruction for the ECG Based on Frequencies Corresponding to the K-Largest Peaks.

The electrocardiograms were reconstructed using the frequencies and the corresponding harmonics, in the following way. If $h$ is the height of the largest peak (generally occurring at $\lambda$) and $0 < \alpha < 1$, the frequencies corresponding to peak heights greater than or equal to $\alpha h$ are chosen. The harmonics at all of these chosen frequencies areare added to reconstruct the ECG. Clearly, we expect that the smaller the value of $\alpha$, the more exact the corresponding reproduction will be. These relationships for a single ECG are illustrated in Figures 40 - 45. Figure 40 presents the observed ECG and the corresponding PSD. Figure 41 presents the reconstructed ECG, compared to the observed ECG, based on $\alpha = 1/20$ corresponding to eleven chosen frequencies. Figure 42 at $\alpha = 1/100$ corresponds to forty-seven frequencies, and finally, Figure 43, $\alpha = 1/10{,}000$ corresponds to one hundred and four chosen frequencies. It may be noted that the ECG reconstructed in this way is not exactly a periodic approximation to the observed ECG.

Our basic finding, that most of the power in the spectrum of the observed ECG is accounted for by the

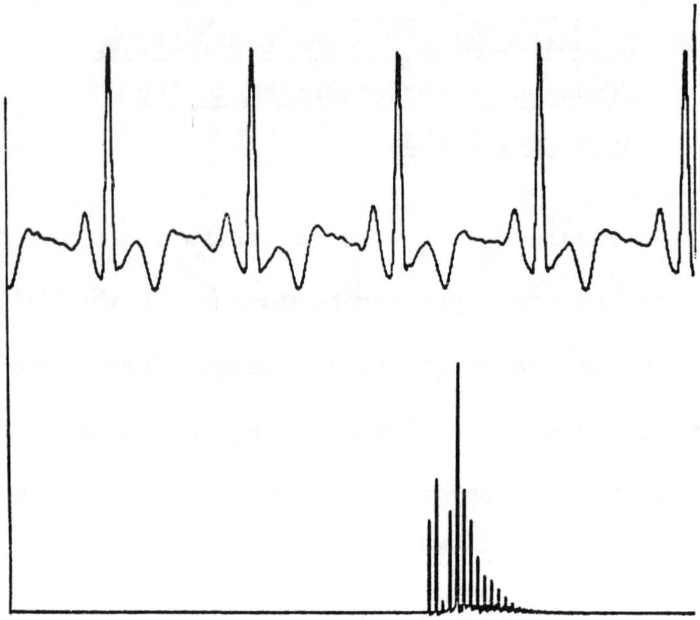

FIGURE 40

An ECG signal in sinus rhythm is shown at the top; the power spectral density for this signal is plotted in cycles per second at the bottom.

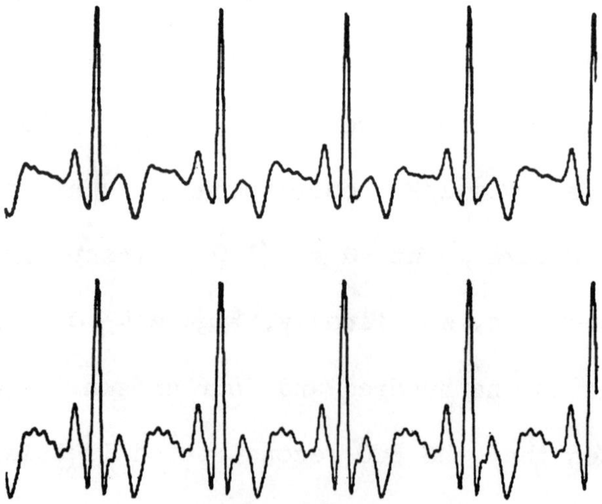

FIGURE 41

The ECG signal in sinus rhythm is shown at the top; at bottom the signal is reconstructed from 11 frequencies.

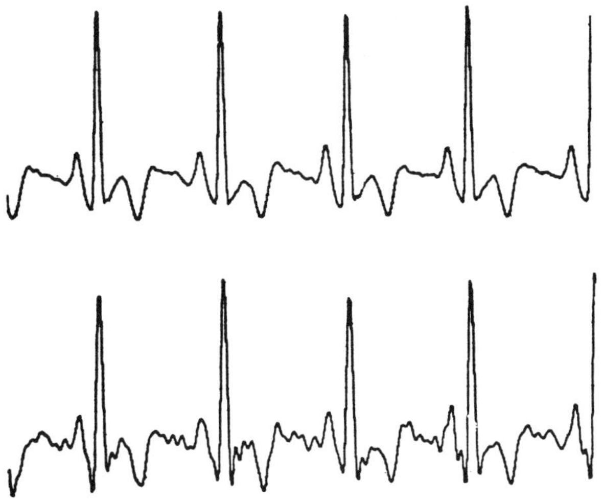

FIGURE 42

The same ECG is shown at the top and the reconstruction from 47 elements is shown at the bottom.

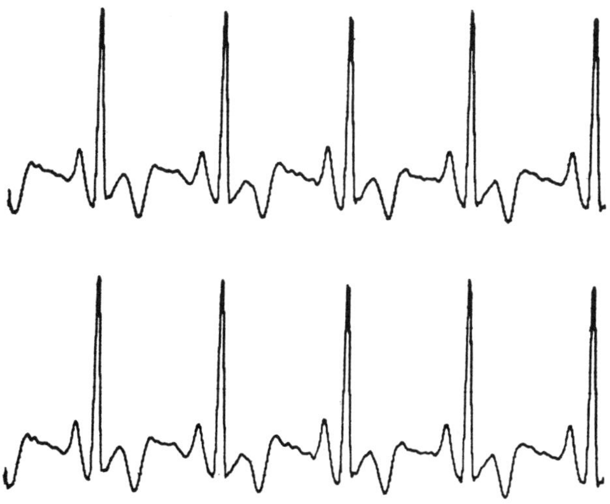

FIGURE 43

The reconstruction from 104 frequencies at bottom closely resembles the original signal shown at top.

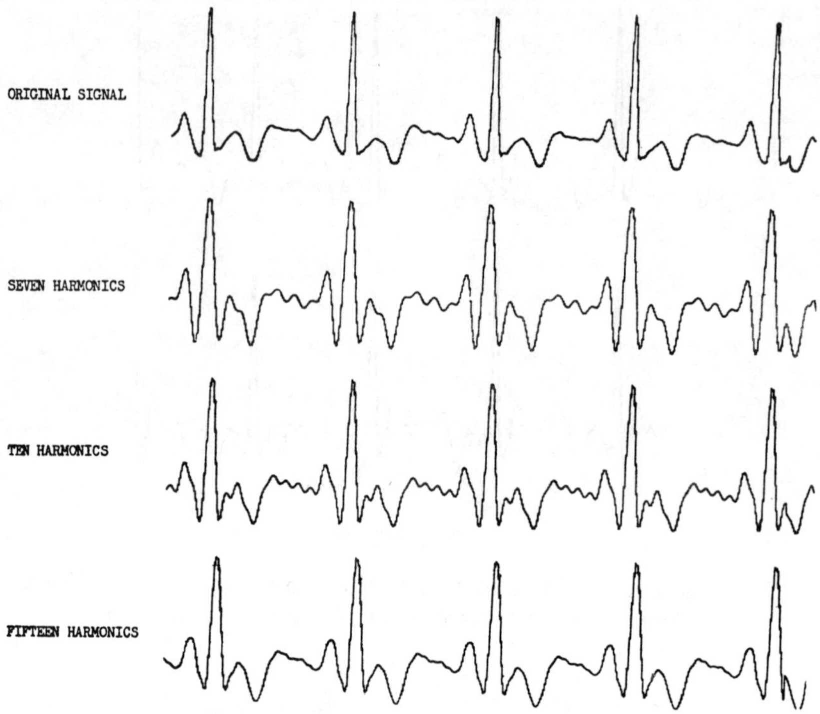


FIGURE 44

At top the ECG signal in sinus rhythm is shown; reconstruction based on 7, 10 and 15 harmonics are shown in sequence with progressive improvement in similarity to the original signal.

fifteenth multiple of the fundamental frequency (heart rate of the patient) naturally suggested the periodic model:

$$V(t) = \sum_{i=1}^{K} (A_i \cos 2\pi i\lambda t + B_i \sin 2\pi i\lambda t)$$

where $\lambda$ is the fundamental frequency (in cycles per second) and $k$ is the variable parameter [156]. Figure 44 above and Figure 45 below illustrate the original signal, compared to the periodic approximations corresponding to K values, equal to 7, 10 and 15, respectively.

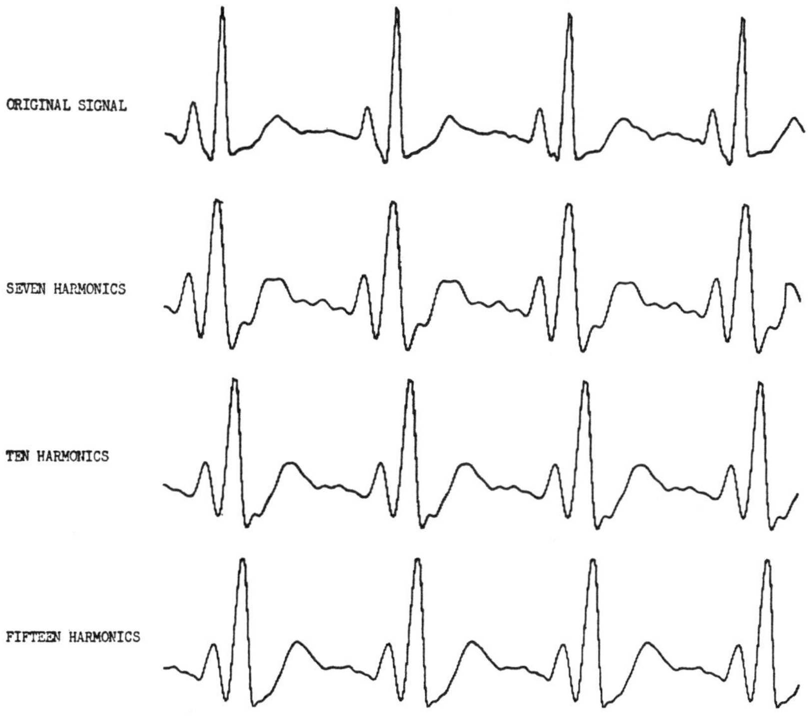


FIGURE 45

An ECG signal from a patient with a slower heart rate is shown at the top; reconstructions based on 7, 10 and 15 harmonics are shown in sequence with progressive improvement in similarity to the original signal.

12.5.5 Summary

The results of the analysis of the power spectral densities of seven patients in a coronary care unit have been presented in this section. The following are the salient features of the analysis.

1. At a sampling rate of 256 points/sec., the psd's based on 8, 16 and 32 sec. of record are compared, and it is discovered that the low-frequency component present in psd's based on the 8 sec. record, progressively vanished when the record length was increased to 32 sec. The fundamental frequency (heart rate) is the only periodic component of the phenomenon underlying the electrocardiogram.

2. In psd's of patients in sinus rhythm, the underlying periodic phenomenon consists of only the fundamental frequency, in addition to an unimportant low-frequency component. Most of the power (up to 90 percent) is explained by the fifteenth multiple of the fundamental frequency.

3. The psd of the QRS complex bears a marked resemblance to the psd of the entire PQRST.

4. By the second or third multiple of the fundamental frequency most of the power (in excess of 90 percent)

is explained in the T wave, whereas it takes exactly twice the multiple (i.e., the fourth or the sixth multiple of the fundamental frequency) to explain power in excess of 90 percent in the P wave.

5. When the ECG is reconstructed, based on harmonics corresponding to frequencies whose psd ordinates are greater than or equal to a designated fraction of the psd ordinate at the fundamental frequency, the smaller the value of $\alpha$, the closer the reconstructed ECG to the actual observed ECG.

6. When the ECG is reconstructed for patients in sinus rhythm, based on the first 15 multiples of the fundamental frequency (heart rate), an almost identical fit to the observed ECG is obtained. The fits based on frequencies up to the seventh and tenth multiple of the fundamental frequency are "good."

7. In order to obtain a reconstruction comparable to the 15-element periodic approximation, the frequencies corresponding to the largest 104 peaks are required in the power spectral density.

## 12.6 Statistical Analysis of Brain Waves from Randomly Interconnected Neural Nets

In the past, work has been done on formulating a model of the dynamics of a large number of interconnected neurons, proceeding from isolated netlets to the treatment of interacting ones [ 5 ], [ 6 ]. A number of other investigators have studied the dynamical behavior of unstructured probabilistic neural nets under a variety of assumptions, and several reviews have appeared in the literature [97], [99]. However, unlike most of the other investigations in this field, we are involved, in this section, in studying the properties of large neuronal populations as a function of the parameters of the individual neurons. Thus, we will attempt a model exploring the behavior of the brain in terms of the capabilities and limitations of individual neurons. In the dynamics of neural nets, the activity of any single neuron is, in principle, observable. On the other hand, the simultaneous monitoring of more than a few neurons presents a very difficult problem as far as the observability of the individual neuron firing pattern is concerned. These firing records of a large number of neurons, during a time interval, were taken to be the microstates of the system. However, the electroencephalogram (EEG), which can be considered as the sum of all potentials in the cell population at any instant of time [61], [96], could, in principle, be taken to define a set of macrostates. Therefore, it may be said that EEG patterns are good candidates for describing the overall macroscopic picture of the pattern of brain function [148]. The object of this section, then, is to test the hypothesis that certain periodicities apparent in the EEG can be produced by particular mathematical models of neural nets.

### 12.6.1 Assumptions and Biological Evidence for the Model

The model is based on the following five assumptions:

1. Neuronal organization in the sensory and motor portions of the cortex is described as a collection of many small, discrete nets of neurons. These will be referred to as <u>netlets</u>.
2. Such netlets form dynamical units. Neuronal activity within a netlet may be endogenous or triggered by afferent fibers. Such activity may be transient or self-sustained.
3. Neuronal connectivity is assumed to be probabilistic in the small, but subject to design in the

large. This means that connections within a netlet are chosen at random. Likewise, the distribution of afferent fibers within a netlet is assumed to be random.

4. We define a level of activity within a netlet as the fractional number of neurons firing at a particular instant. It is assumed that this is the only dynamical variable of interest. Details of the spatial distribution of the activity within a netlet will be disregarded.

5. Netlets can be labeled according to the particular motor function they control, or the particular sensory event which constitutes the chief afferent.

In the model outlined above, homogenous probabilistic nets are used as building blocks to simulate known design in the large and presumed randomness in the small. The dynamics of such systems is difficult but tractable. Some very simple systems have already been investigated [5], [6]. From these studies it has been determined that there exist some mechanisms which, potentially, may play an important role in neuronal function. In particular, it was found that under certain conditions, control exerted by afferent excitatory or inhibitory biases produce hysteresis effects in the form of reverberating circuits which may represent a type of short-term memory. Such control has been attributed for some time to neural centers located in the brain stem reticular formation. This is a structure which shows a great deal of homogeneity, great proliferation of dendritic processes, and apparent randomness [198]. More studies have been done with reverberatory activity and the results have appeared elsewhere [ 7 ].

It is believed that the neural netlet model is a useful description of at least certain portions of the cortex, also in view of some neurophysiological and anatomical factors concerning the discrete colonies of neurons in the motor-sensory cortex of the cat [ 8 ], [61], the columnar structures in the visual cortex of the cat [179] and the elementary units of organization in the somatosensory cortex [198]. More details may be found in [ 5 ], [109].

### 12.6.2 Mathematical Formalism for the Model

Unit properties: We make use of the neural net model developed in previous research by [ 5 ], [ 6 ]. It is assumed that if a neuron fires at time $t$, it produces the appropriate postsynaptic potential (PSP), after a fixed time interval called synaptic delay, $\tau$. All PSP's arriving at a neuron are summed instantly and if they exceed the specified threshold, will cause the neuron to fire. After firing, neurons are insensitive to further stimulation for a period of time called the "refractory period." For our purposes, we assume that the refractory period is greater than the synaptic delay, but less than twice the synaptic delay. Temporal summation occurs with decrements which depend on the time constant $\lambda_E$ and $\lambda_I$ of the excitatory and inhibitory PSP's, respectively. Following the absolute refractory period, the threshold of the neuron is immediately restored to normal. Thus, a neuron which fires at $t = n\tau$ will be insensitive at $t = (n+1)\tau$, and will be fully recovered at $t = (n+2)\tau$.

We define the activity, $\alpha_n$, of a netlet to be the fractional number of neurons firing at time $t = n\tau$. The activity is a scalar and does not specify which neurons in the netlet were firing.

The <u>parameters of the model</u> are defined to be the following:

$\tau$ synaptic delay;

A total number of neurons in the netlet;

$h$ fraction of inhibitory neurons in the netlet;

$\mu^+$ average number of axon branches emanating from an excitatory neuron;

$\mu^-$ average number of axon branches emanating from an inhibitory neuron;

$K^+$ the average EPSP produced by an excitatory neuron in arbitrary units;

$K^-$ the average IPSP produced by an inhibitory neuron in arbitrary units;

$\Theta$ firing threshold of the neurons in the netlet;

$\eta$ the minimum number of EPSP's necessary to trigger a neuron; and

$\alpha_n$ the activity, i.e., the function of active neurons in the netlet at $t = n\tau$.

Expectation value of the activity and the EEG: The expectation value $\langle\alpha_{n+1}\rangle$ of the activity at $t = (n+1)\tau$, i.e., the average value of $\alpha_{n+1}$ generated at the above time is given by:

(12.6.1) $$\langle\alpha_{n+1}\rangle = (1 - \alpha_n) P(\alpha_n)$$

where $P(\alpha_n)$ is the probability that a neuron receives PSP's exceeding its threshold at $t = (n+1)$ [ 5 ]. This quantity is a function of the activity at $t = n\tau$, and is given by

$$(12.6.2) \qquad P(\alpha_n) = \sum_{m=0}^{M\,max} \sum_{\ell \geq \eta}^{\ell\,max} P_\ell Q_m$$

where $P_\ell$ and $Q_m$ are the a priori probabilities that a neuron receives $\ell$ and $m$ excitatory and inhibitory inputs respectively, i.e.:

$$(12.6.3) \qquad P_\ell = e^{-\alpha_n \mu^+(1-h)} \frac{[\alpha_n(1-h)\mu^+]^\ell}{\ell!}$$

$$(12.6.4) \qquad Q_m = e^{-\alpha_n h\mu^-} \frac{(\alpha_n h\mu^-)^m}{m}$$

and

$$(12.6.5) \qquad \ell\,max = A\alpha_n(1-h)\mu^+ ,$$

$$(12.6.6) \qquad M\,max = A\alpha_n h\mu^- .$$

If in (12.6.1) we superimpose with the signal a level of white noise $R$ with zero mean and standard deviation $\delta$, then our original equation can be adequately written as:

$$(12.6.7) \qquad \langle\alpha_{n+1}\rangle = (1-\alpha_n)\, P(\alpha_n) + R .$$

From this equation we can get the variation of the membrane potential for one neuron, as well as for the whole neural net population in time, i.e., the EEG [62]. That is, if we know the activity at time $t = n\tau$, say $\alpha_n$, and we recall that at this time we have, for the population of neurons $[A\alpha_n \mu^+(1 - h) - A\alpha_n \mu^- h]$ PSP's, then the voltage is given by [96]:

$$V(t_0) = A\alpha_n \mu^{\alpha}(1 - h) - A\alpha_n \mu^- h \quad . \tag{12.6.8}$$

If we assume also that the PSP's decay with time and we call $\lambda_E$ and $\lambda_I$ the time constants for the EPSP.s and IPSP's, respectively, then the potential at subsequent times will be given by

$$\begin{aligned} V(t) = {} & e^{-\lambda_e t} V_E(t_0) - e^{-\lambda_I t} V_I(t_0) \\ & + A\alpha_n(t)\mu^+(1-h) - A\alpha_n(t)\mu^- h \end{aligned} \tag{12.6.9}$$

where

$$\begin{aligned} V_E(t_0) &= A\alpha_n(t_0)\, \mu^+(1-h) \quad , \\ V_I(t_0) &= A\alpha_n(t_0)\, \mu^- h \quad . \end{aligned} \tag{12.6.10}$$

### 12.6.3 Autocorrelation and Spectral Analysis of the EEG

In order to analyze the data further, any possible existence of a rhythmic activity, characteristic for a particular brain function, is made visible by an autocorrelation method. The first parameter in this time-series data is of an autocorrelation between values of the variate $X_i$ and the same variate at a constant interval or lag of time $X_{i+p}$. The autocorrelation coefficient for a particular lag P is then given by the following equation:

$$(12.6.11)\quad r_p = \frac{(N-P)\Sigma X_i X_{i+p} - (\Sigma X_i)(\Sigma X_{i+p})}{\sqrt{(N-P)\Sigma(X_i^2) - (\Sigma X_i)^2}\sqrt{(N-P)\Sigma(X_{i+p}^2) - (\Sigma X_{i+p})^2}}$$

The summations extend over the range $i = 1$ to $i = N - P$, or, as is sometimes done, the upper limit is fixed at $N - M$, where M is the maximum value assigned to the lag. Here, N is the total number of observations. An examination of r, calculated as a function of p, indicates those lags or periods over which the data of the time series seem to be correlated. Fifty successive values, each representing the number of neurons discharging per unit time, are correlated with a similar series of fifty successive values, the time lag between the two series being varied between 0 and

20 units of time, corresponding to the periods of the preponderant rhythmic activities. Subsequently, the latter series of fifty values is correlated with another similar series, using the same time lag from 0 - 20 units of time, etc. In this manner, an autocorrelation coefficient is obtained for each period from 0 - 20 units of time and are plotted, as seen in Figures 46 through 51. The autocorrelation calculations give an estimate of the degree of correlation between values which are apart by 0 - 20 units of time. It is, therefore, a measure of the regularity of the rhythmic activity of the model. In order to obtain an estimate of the power, or total amount of the rhythmic activity in the different regions of the time series and for the range of 0 - 20 units of time, a computer program is written in such a way as to calculate the power spectrum, often called the spectral density of the process.

Denoting by $\rho(n)$ the true, or population autocovariance of lag n, we have the following spectral representation for $\rho(n)$, given by

$$\rho(n) = \int e^{in\lambda}\, df(\lambda) \tag{12.6.12}$$

where $F(x)$ is the so-called spectral distribution and the

limits of integration in (12.6.12) are $(-\pi,\pi)$ or $(-\infty,\infty)$, according as the process is discrete or continuous. If $F(\lambda)$ is absolutely continuous, it is then necessary and sufficient for $F(\lambda)$ to have the representation

$$F(\lambda) = \int_{-\infty}^{\lambda} f(t)dt \tag{12.6.13}$$

and $f(t)$ is called the power spectral density (psd) function. In the discrete case, which is the case one deals with in practical application, one obtained for $f(x)$, the following formula by inverting (12.6.13):

$$f(\lambda) = \frac{1}{2\pi} \sum_{-\infty}^{\infty} e^{-in\lambda} \rho(n) \quad . \tag{12.6.14}$$

In actual computation we use the Biomedical (BMD) Package of programs of the University of California at Los Angeles Health Science Computing Facility for obtaining the power spectral densities. This program, of course, is based on the Fast Fourier Transform (FFT) approach which results in higher accuracy and a substantial saving in CPU time. Such calculations are used throughout this section for all time series analyzed and the results may be found in the following subsection.

### 12.6.4 Results

The most definite conclusion to be drawn from this type of work is that several simulated neural networks have the ability to create periods of spontaneous rhythmic activity, as can be seen in Figures 46 - 51. These figures give the frequency spectrum analysis under different network parameters. These periods are very similar to those periods of spontaneous activity that can be recorded from the animal and human thalamus, cerebral cortex and hippocampus. To assure that the observed rhythimic activity is, indeed, a special feature of the neural network, one may run several cases in which the parameters of the network are varied and the noise characteristics are kept constant. As may be expected, the results change according to the parameters, which suggests that we are dealing with a model which is a very realistic approximation to the underlying phenomenon of rhythmicity.

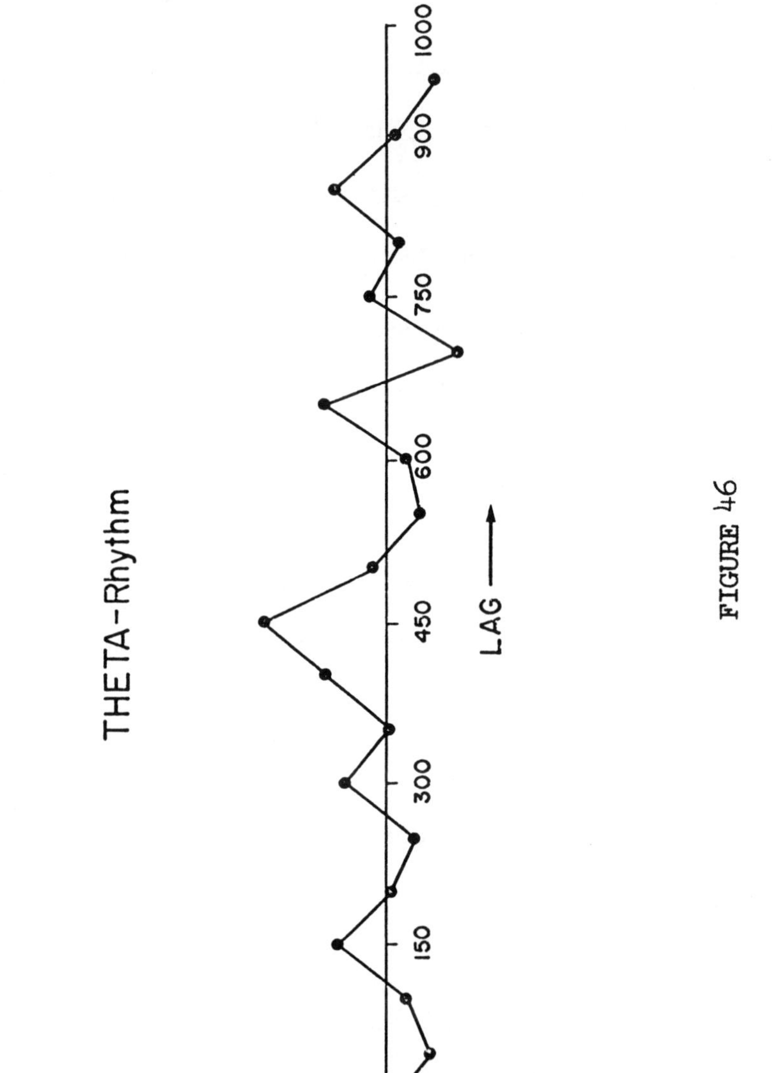
THETA-Rhythm
LAG
0
150
300
450
600
750
900
1000
1.0
0.8
0.6
0.4
0.2
0.0
-0.2
-0.4
-0.6
-0.8
-1.0
CORRELATION COEFFICIENT

FIGURE 46

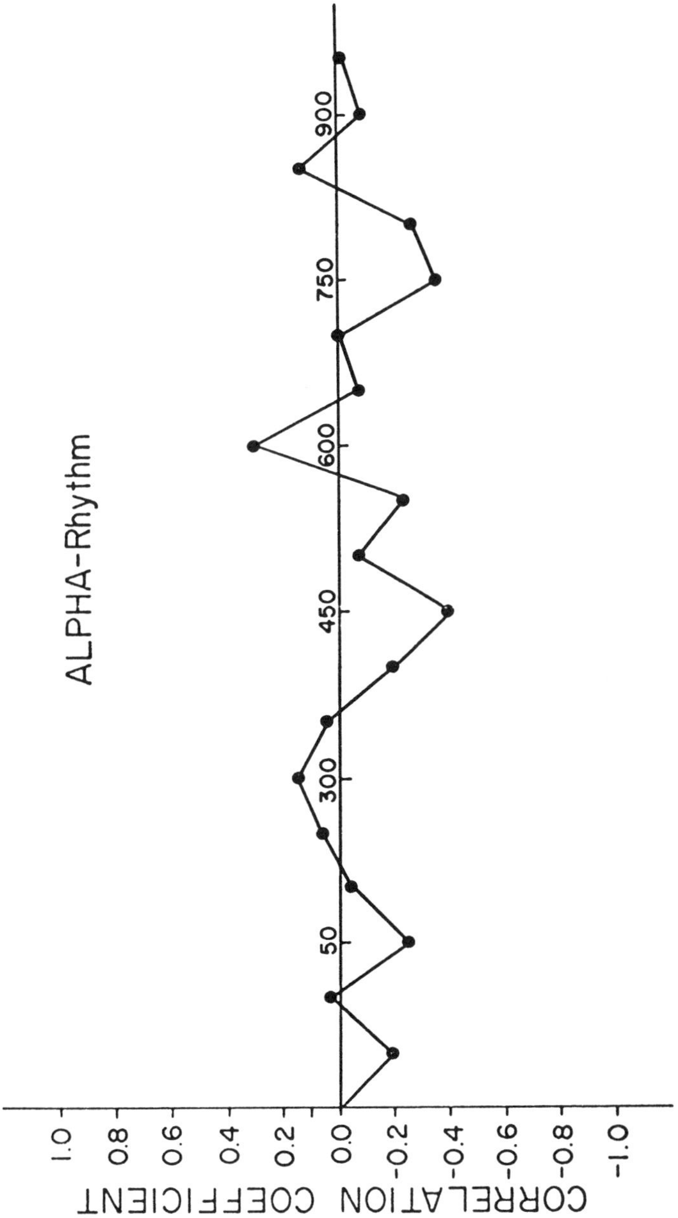
ALPHA-Rhythm
CORRELATION COEFFICIENT
1.0
0.8
0.6
0.4
0.2
0.0
-0.2
-0.4
-0.6
-0.8
-1.0
50
300
450
600
750
900

FIGURE 47

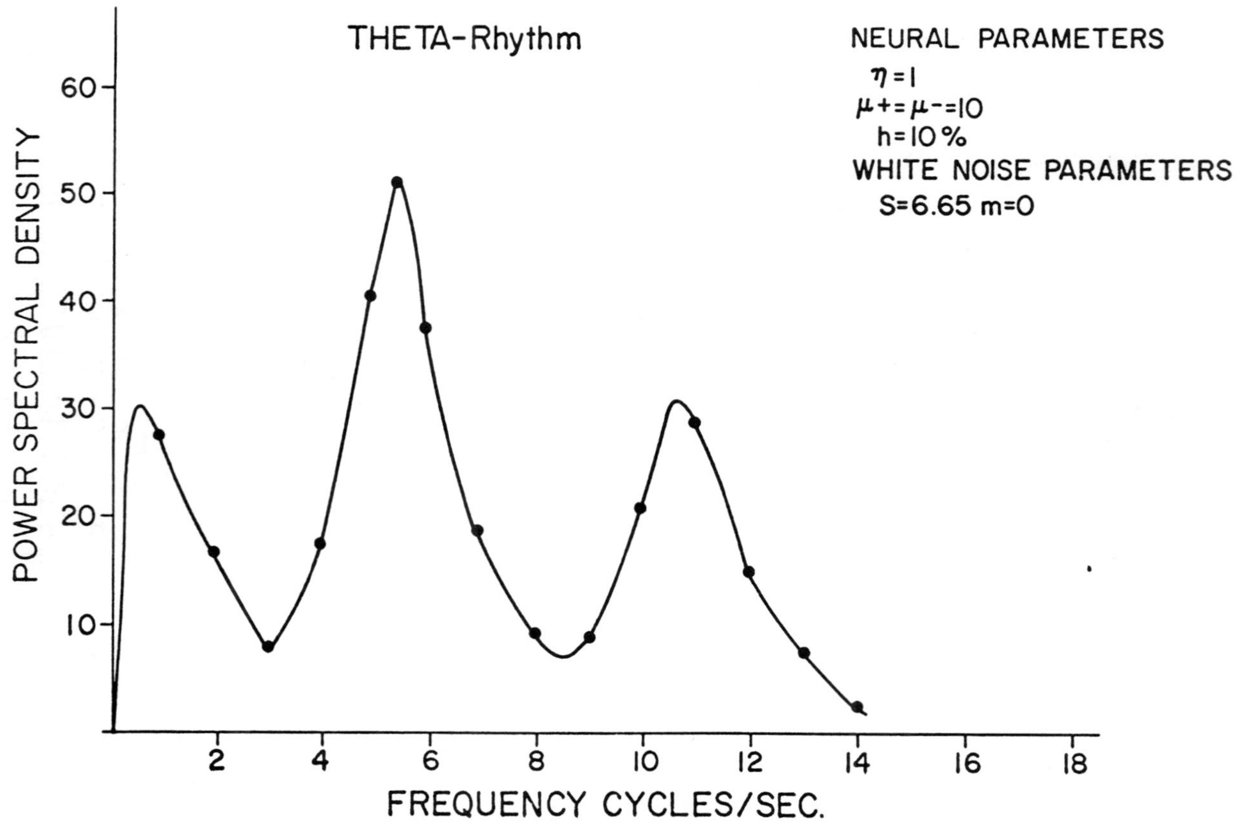
THETA-Rhythm
NEURAL PARAMETERS
η=1
μ+=μ-=10
h=10%
WHITE NOISE PARAMETERS
S=6.65 m=0
POWER SPECTRAL DENSITY
60
50
40
30
20
10
2
4
6
8
10
12
14
16
18
FREQUENCY CYCLES/SEC.

FIGURE 48

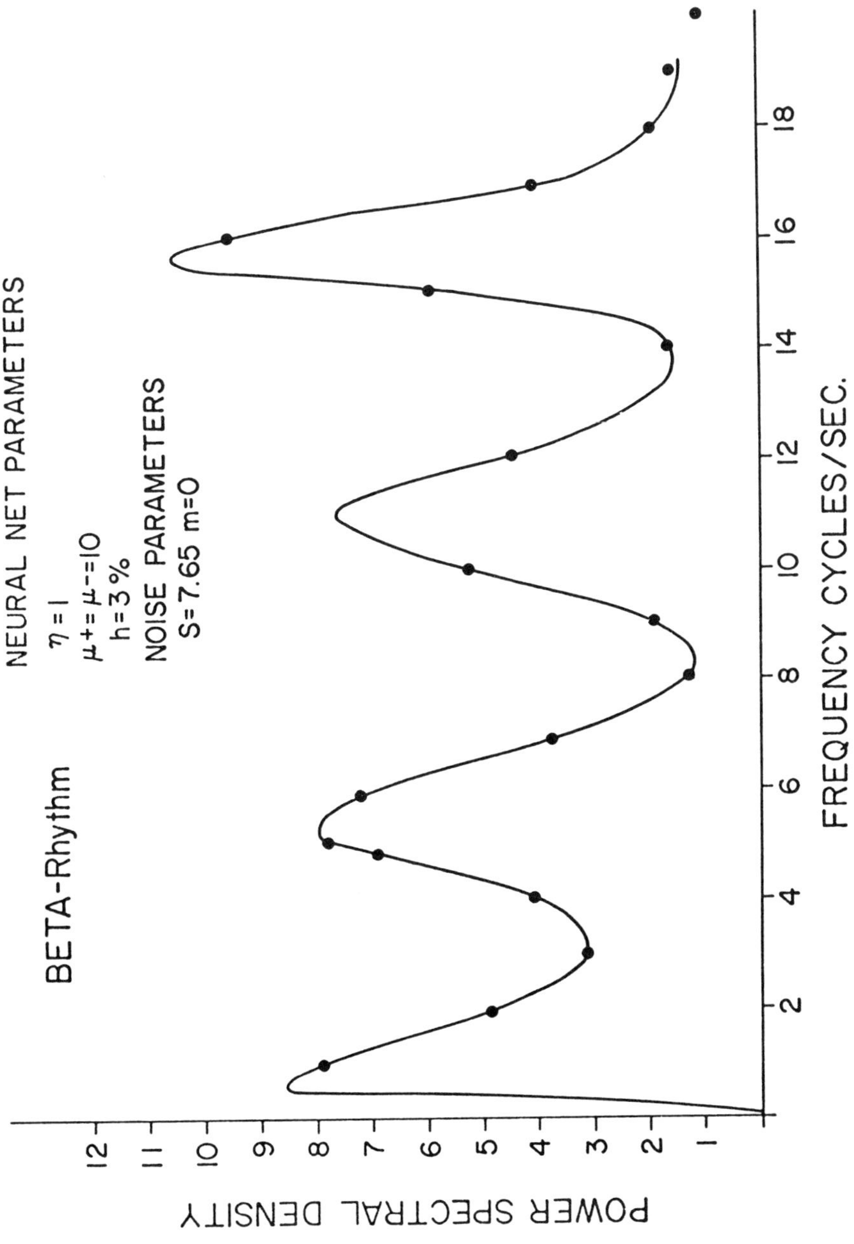

BETA-Rhythm
NEURAL NET PARAMETERS
η = 1
μ+ = μ− = 10
h = 3 %
NOISE PARAMETERS
S = 7.65 m = 0
POWER SPECTRAL DENSITY
FREQUENCY CYCLES/SEC.


FIGURE 49

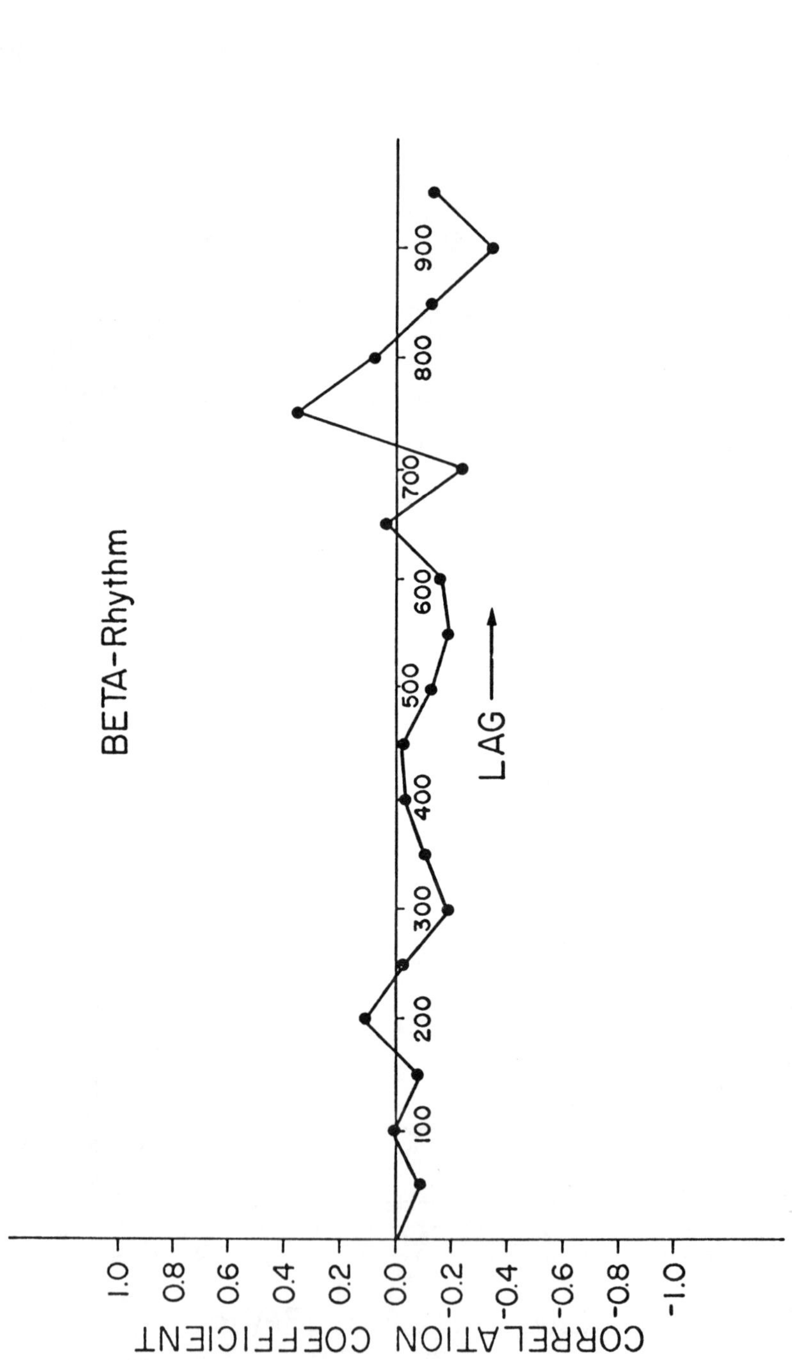
BETA-Rhythm
LAG
CORRELATION COEFFICIENT
1.0
0.8
0.6
0.4
0.2
0.0
-0.2
-0.4
-0.6
-0.8
-1.0
100
200
300
400
500
600
700
800
900

FIGURE 50

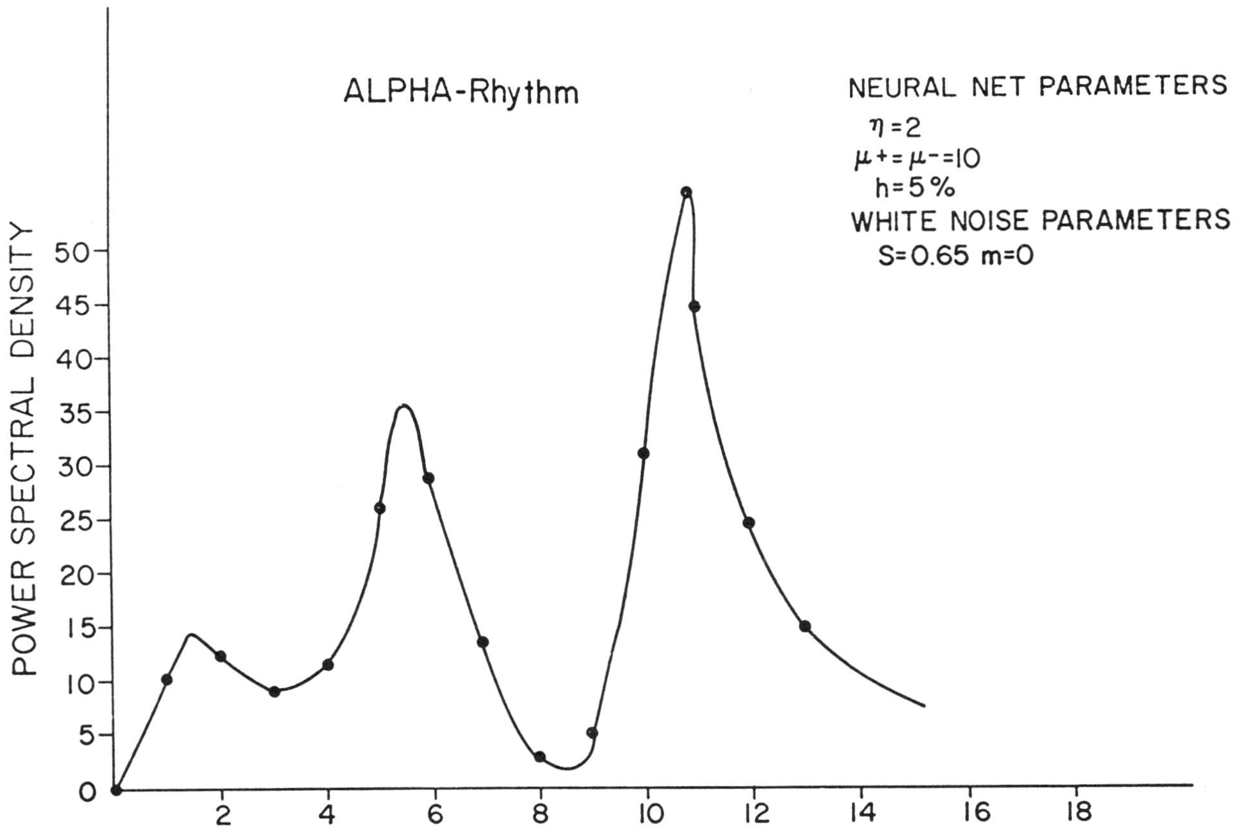
ALPHA-Rhythm
NEURAL NET PARAMETERS
η=2
μ+=μ-=10
h=5%
WHITE NOISE PARAMETERS
S=0.65 m=0
POWER SPECTRAL DENSITY
0
5
10
15
20
25
30
35
40
45
50
2
4
6
8
10
12
14
16
18
FREQUENCY CYCLES/SEC.

**FIGURE 51**

# BIBLIOGRAPHY

[1] Aitchison, J. and Brown, J.A.C. The Lognormal Distribution. London: Cambridge University Press, 1957. Second edition, 1966.

[2] Albrecht, Carl O. "Statistical Evaluation of a Limited Number of Fatigue Test Specimens Including a Factor of Safety Approach," Symposium on Fatigue Tests of Aircraft Structures: Low-cycle, Full-scale and Helicopters. Los Angeles: Fourth Pacific Area National Meeting of the American Society for Testing Materials, 1962.

[3] Albrecht, Carl O. "Statistical Evaluation of a Limited Number of Fatgiue Test Specimens Including a Factor of Safety Approach." Proceedings of a symposium on Aircraft Structures, 1963, pp. 150-166.

[4] American Society for Testing Materials. A Tentative Guide for Fatigue Testing and the Statistical Analysis of Fatigue Data. Special Technical Publication, No. 91-A. N.D.

[5] Aninos, P.A. Dynamics and Function of Neural Structures. Ph.D. Dissertation, 1969, Syracuse University. Ann Arbor, Michigan: University Microfilms, 1970.

[6] Anninos, P.A.; Beck, B.; Csermely, T.J.; Harth, E.M. and Pertile, G. "Dynamics of Neural Structures," J. Theor. Biol. **26** (1970), p. 121.

[7] Anninos, P.A. "Cyclic Modes in Probabalistic Neural Nets," Kybernetik **11** (1972), p. 5.

[8] Asonuma, H.; Stoney, S.D., Jr. and Abzug, C. "Relationship Between Afferent Input and Motor Outflow in Cat Motor Sensory Cortex," J. Neurophysiol. **31** (1968), p. 670.

[ 9] Barer, R.D. and Peters, B.S. Why Metals Fail. New York: Gordon and Breach Sciences, 1970.

[10] Barlow, R.E.; Proschan, F. and Hunter, L.C. Mathematical Theory of Reliability. New York: John Wiley and Sons, 1965.

[11] Barlow, R.E. and Proschan, F. "Tolerance and Confidence Limits for Classes of Distributions Based on Failure Rate," Annals of Math. Stat. **37** (1966), p. 1594.

[12] Barrois, W. "The Philosophy of Fatigue Tests on Large Dimension Aircraft Structures," in Full Scale Testing of Aircraft Structures. Proceedings of a symposium held in Amsterdam, June 1959.

[13] Bartholomew, D.J. "A Problem in Life Testing," American Statistical Association Journal **52** (1957), pp. 350-355.

[14] Bartlett, M.S. "Some Evolutionary Stochastic Processes," J. Roy. Statist. Soc. B, **11** (1949), p. 211.

[15] Bartlett, M.S. "Recurrence and First Passage Times," Proc. Cambridge Phil. Soc. **25** (1953), p. 263.

[16] Bastenaire, F. "A Study of the Scatter of Fatigue Test Results by Statistical and Physical Methods," in Fatigue of Aircraft Structures. Proceedings of a symposium held in Paris, 1961.

[17] Berg, J.W. and Robbins, G.F. "The Failure of a Model to Predict Cancer Survival," Journal of Chronic Diseases **20** (1967), p. 809.

[18] Birnbaum, Z.W. and Saunders, S.C. "A Statistical Model for Life-Length of Materials," JASA **53** (1958), pp. 151-160.

[19] Birnbaum, Z.W. and Saunders, S.C. "A Probabilistic Interpretation of Miner's Rule," Journal of Applied Mathematics **16** (1968), pp. 637-652.

[20] Birnbaum, Z.W. and Saunders, S.C. "A New Family of Life Distributions," Journal of Applied Probability 6, No. 2 (1969), p. 385.

[21] Blackwell, D. and Girshick, M.A. Theory of Games and Statistical Decisions. New York: John Wiley and Sons, 1954.

[22] Boag, J.W. "Maximum Likelihood Estimates of the Proportion of Patients Cured by Cancer Therapy," Journal of the Royal Statistical Society B, 11 (1949), pp. 15-53.

[23] Bowker, A.H. and Lieberman, G.J. Engineering Statistics. Englewood Cliffs, N.J.: Prentice-Hall, 1959.

[24] Brass, W. "Models of Birth Distributions in Human Populations," Biometrika (1958), p. 59.

[25] Broadbent, S. "Simple Mortality Rates," Applied Statistics 7 (1958), pp. 86-95.

[26] Buckland, W.R. "Statistical Assessment of the Life Characteristic," Griffin's Statistical Monograph No. 13. New York: Hafner, 1964.

[27] Buxbaum, Dr. Otto. "Extreme Value Analysis and its Application to C.G. Vertical Accelerations Measured on Transport Airplanes of Type C-130. AGARD-R-579-71, NATO, March 1971.

[28] Chavez, O.A.R. "Stochastic Models to Fatigue," Journal of the Engineering Mechanics Division, ASCE, EM 3 5293, 93 (June 1967), pp. 147-155.

[29] Christensen, R.H. "Growth of Fracture in Metal Under Random Cyclic Loading," Proceedings of the First International Conference on Fracture, edited by T. Yokobori. Japanese Society for Strength and Fracture of Material. Tokyo, 1965, p. 1502.

[30] Cioclor, D.D. "Cumulative Fatigue Damage Under Repeated Loadings With Periodical Variation of Stress Amplitude," in Essaid des Matieres Metalliques, 1971, pp. 104-112.

[31] Cohen, A.C., Jr. "Progressively Censored Samples in Life Testing," Technometrics 5 (August 1963), pp. 327-339.

[32] Cohen, A.C., Jr. "Maximum Likelihood Estimation in the Weibull Distribution Based on Complete and on Censored Samples," Technometrics 7 (1965), pp. 579-588.

[33] Coleman, Bernard D. "Statistics and Time Dependence of Mechanical Breakdown in Fibers," Journal of Applied Physics, 29, No. 6 (June 1958), pp. 968-983.

[34] Coleman, Bernard D. "Time Dependence of Mechanical Breakdown in Bundles of Fibers. IV. Infinite Ideal Bundle Under Oscillating Loads," Journal of Applied Physics 29, No. 7 (July 1958), pp. 1091-1099.

[35] Coleman, Bernard D. and Marquardt, D.W. "Time Dependence of Mechanical Breakdown in Bundles of Fibers. IV. Infinite Ideal Bundle Under Oscillating Loads," Journal of Applied Physics 29, No. 7 (July 1958), pp. 1091-1099.

[36] Coleman, R. and Gastwirth, J.L. "Some Models for Interaction of Renewal Processes Related to Neuron Firing," Journal Applied Probability 6 (1969), pp. 38-58.

[37] Combs, C.A. and Wujek, J.H. "Concerning Reliability Prediction," IEEE Proceedings (September 1963), p. 1248.

[38] Connor, J.A. "Electronic Part Failure Rates in Space Environments," IEEE Transactions on Reliability R-12 (1963), pp. 5-10.

[39] Cooley, J.W. and Tukey, J.W. "An Algorithm for the Machine Calculation of Complex Fourier Series," Math. Comput. 19 (January 1965), pp. 297-301.

[40] Cox, D.R. Renewal Theory. New York: John Wiley and Sons, 1962.

[41] Cox, D.R. Renewal Theory. London: Methuen, 1967.

[42] Cox, D.R. and Smith, W.L. "The Superposition of Several Strictly Periodic Sequences of Events," Biometrika 40 (1953), pp. 1-11.

[43] Cox, D.R. and Smith, W.L. "A Direct Proof of a Fundamental Theorem of Renewal Theory," Skand. Aktuar. 36 (1953), p. 139.

[44] Cox, D.R. and Smith, W.L. "On the Superposition of Renewal Processes," Biometrika 41 (1954), pp. 91-99.

[45] Cramér, H. Mathematical Methods of Statistics. Princeton, N.J.: Princeton University Press, 1946.

[46] Dandekar, V.M. "Certain Modified Forms of Binomial and Poisson Distributions," Sankhya 15, N.D., pp. 237-250.

[47] Davis, D.J. "An Analysis of Some Failure Data," Journal of the American Statistical Association 47 (1952), pp. 113-149.

[48] Desu, M.M. "A Characterization of the Exponential Distribution by Order Statistics," Annals of Math. Stat. 42 (1971), pp. 837-838.

[49] Dixon, W.J. "Biomedical Computer Programs, BMD × 92," Health Sciences Computing Facility. Los Angeles: University of California, 1969.

[50] Dmitrichenko, S.S. "Empirical Stress-Amplitude Distributions for Calculating Cumulative Damage," Russian Engineering Journal XLIX No. 5 (May 1969), pp. 8-10.

[51] Dodson, C.T.J. "Nature of Bonds in Paper and Behavior Under Mechanical Strain," Reports on Progress in Physics, 33, Part I (1970), pp. 1-43.

[52] Doob, J.L. "Renewal Theory From the Point of View of Probability," Trans. Amer. Math. Soc. 63 (1948), pp. 422-438.

[53] Dougherty, James E. and Spicer, Herbert C., Jr. "Helicopter Fatigue Substantiation Procedures for Civil Aircraft.' Proceedings of a symposium on Fatigue Tests of Aircraft Structures: Low-cycle, Full-scale and Helicopters. Fourth Pacific National Meeting of the American Society for Testing Materials, Los Angeles, 1963.

[54] Drenick, R.F. "Failure Law of Complex Equipment," SIAM Journal of Applied Mathematics **8** (1960), pp. 680-690.

[55] Dronkers, J.J. "Approximate Formulae for the Statistical Distributions of Extreme Values," Biometrika **45** (1954), pp. 447-470.

[56] Dubey, S.D. "Some Percentile Estimators for Weibull Parameters," Technometrics **9** (1967), pp. 119-129.

[57] Eaton, J.R. "Mechanical and Thermal Properties of Solids," in Electrons, Neutrons and Protons in Engineering. New York: Pergammon Press, 1966, Chapter 16.

[58] Eggwertz, Sigge. "Inspection Periods Determined from Data of Crack Development and Strength Reduction of an Aircraft Structure Using Statistical Analysis," in Fatigue of Aircraft Structures. Proceedings of a symposium held in Paris, 1961.

[59] Eiler, W. and Goeldner, K. "Performance and Evaluation of Fatigue Tests Under Statistical Load, Part I," Maschinenbautechnik **11**, No. 11, (1962), pp. 590-593. A NASA Technical Translation, National Aeronautics and Space Administration, Washington, D.C., October 1970, pp. 1-11.

[60] Elderton, W.P. Frequency Curves and Correlation. Cambridge: Cambridge University Press, 1938.

[61] Elul, R. Synchronization of EEG Activity in Epilepsies. Edited by Petsche and Brazier. Wien, N.Y.: Springer-Verlag, 1972.

[62] Elul, R. "Thesenisis of the EEG," Intern. Rev. Neurobiol. **15** (1972).

[63] Epstein, B. "Application of the Theory of Extreme Values in Fracture Problems," American Statistical Association Journal **43** (September 1948), pp. 403-412.

[64] Epstein, B. "Statistical Aspects of Fracture Problems," Journal of Applied Physics **19** (February 1948), pp. 140-147.

[65] Epstein, B. "Estimation From Life Test Data," Technometrics **2** (November 1960), pp. 447-454.

[66] Epstein, B. and Sobel, M. "Life Testing," Journal of the American Statistical Association **48** (September 1953), pp. 486-502.

[67] Fatt, D. and Katz, B. "Spontaneous Sub-threshold Activity at Motor Nerve Endings," J. Physiology **117** (1952), pp. 109-128.

[68] Feller, W. "On the Integral Equation of Renewal Theory," Annals of Math. Statist. **12** (1941), pp. 243-267.

[69] Feller, W. "On Probability Problems in the Theory of Counters," in Courant Anniversary Volume. Interscience Publishers, 1948, pp. 105-115.

[70] Feller, W. An Introduction to Probability Theory and Its Applications, Second edition. New York: John Wiley and Sons, 1957.

[71] Feller, W. An Introduction to Probability Theory and Its Applications, Vol II. New York: John Wiley and Sons, 1966.

[72] Ford, D.G.; Graff, D.G. and Payne, A.O. "Some Statistical Aspects of Fatigue Life Variation," in Fatigue of Aircraft Structures. Proceedings of a symposium held in Paris, 1961.

[73] Ford, D.G.; Graff, D.G. and Payne, A.O. "Some Statistical Aspects of Fatigue Life Variation," Proceedings of a symposium on Aircraft Structures held in Paris, 1963, pp. 179-208.

[74] Forsyth, P.J.E. "Fatigue Damage and Crack Growth in Aluminum Alloys," Acta Metallurgica **11** (July 1963), pp. 703-715.

[75] Frame, J. and Murthy, V.K. "A Gamma Random Number Generator," accepted for publication in the Journal of the American Statistical Society. To appear.

[76] French, F.E. and Bierman, J.M. "Probabilities of Fetal Mortality," Public Health Reports **77** (1962), pp. 835-847.

[77] Freudenthal, A.M. The Expected Time to First Failure. Ohio State University Research Foundation report for the Air Force Materials Laboratory, Research and Technology Division, Wright-Patterson Air Force Base, Ohio, under USAF Contract AF 33(657)-8741, 1958.

[78] Freudenthal, A.M. "The Material Aspect of Reliability," in Structural Fatigue in Aircraft. Proceedings of a symposium at the Fifth Pacific Area National Meeting, American Society for Testing Materials, Seattle, Washington, 1965.

[79] Freudenthal, A.M. and Heller, R.A. "Accumulation of Fatigue Damage," in Fatigue in Aircraft Structures. New York: Academic Press, 1956, pp. 146-177.

[80] Garg, R.C. "Dependability of a Complex System with General Waiting Time Distributions," IEEE Transactions on Reliability **R-12** (1963), pp. 17-21.

[81] Garg, M.; Rao, B. and Redmond, C. "Maximum Likelihood Estimation of the Parameters of the Gompertz Survival Function," Journal of the Royal Statistical Society, Applied Statistics, **19** (1970), p. 152.

[82] Gehan, E. "Estimating Survival Functions from the Life Table," J. Chron. Dis., 21 (1969), p. 629.

[83] Geller, Sheldon. An Approximation to the Distribution of the Number of Failures and Applications to Life-Test Data. M.S. in Engineering. Los Angeles: University of California, 1964.

[84] Ghare, P.M. and Kim, Y.H. "An Approximating Function for the Hazard Rate Curve," Proceedings of the 1970 Technical Conference, Transactions of ASQC, pp. 367-371.

[85] Gibson, J.R. and McKeown, Thomas. "Observations on All Births (23,970) in Birmingham, 1947, Duration of Gestation," British Journal of Social Medicine 4 (1950), pp. 221-238.

[86] Gnedenko, B.V. "Normal Distribution in Processing of Experimental Information," Russian Engineering Journal XLIX (February 1969), pp. 11-13.

[87] Gompertz, B. "On the Nature of the Function Expressive of the Law of Human Mortality and on the New Mode of Determining the Value of Life Contingencies," Phil. Trans. Royal Soc. A 115 (1925), p. 513.

[88] Greenwood, M. and Yule, G.U. "An Inquiry Into the Nature and Frequency Distributions Representative of Multiple Happenings with Particular Reference to the Occurrence of Multiple Attacks of Diseased or of Repeated Accidents," Journal of the Royal Statistical Society 83 (1920), pp. 255-279.

[89] Grenander, Ulf. "On Empirical Spectral Analysis of Stochastic Processes," Ark. Math. 1 (1951), pp. 503-531.

[90] Grenander, Ulf. "On the Theory of Mortality Measurement," Skand. Akturarietidskrift 39 (1956), p. 1.

[91] Griffith, A.A. "The Phenomenon of Rupture and Flow in Solids," Philos. Trans. Royal Society London A, 221 (1920), pp. 161-198.

[92] Grigor'ev, E.T. "Errors in Determining the Natural Frequency of Vibrations in Machines," Russian Engineering Journal XLIX (March 1969), pp. 23-26.

[93] Gumbel, E.J. Statistical Theory of Extreme Values and Some Practical Applications: A Series of Lectures. U.S. Department of Commerce, National Bureau of Standards, Applied Mathematics Series No. 33. Washington, D.C.: U.S. Government Printing Office, February 1954.

[94] Hammersley, J.M. "Discussion," in "The Superposition of Several Strictly Periodic Sequences of Events," by Cox, D.R. and Smith, W.L., Biometrika 40 (1953), pp. 1-11.

[95] Hammersley, J.M. "On Counters with Random Deadtime, I," Proceedings of the Cambridge Philosophical Society 49 (1953), pp. 623-637.

[96] Harmon, L.D. "Problems in Neural Modeling," in Neural Theory and Modeling. Edited by Reiss, R.F. Stanford, Calif.: Stanford University Press, 1964.

[97] Harmon, L.D. and Lewis, E.F. "Neural Modeling," Physiol. Rev. 46 (1966), p. 513.

[98] Harris, C. and Singpurwalla, N.D. "Life Distributions Derived from Stochastic Functions," IEEE Transactions on Reliability R-17 (June 1968), pp. 70-79.

[99] Harter, M.L. and Moore, A.H. "Maximum Likelihood Estimation of the Parameters of Gamma and Weibull Populations from Complete and from Censored Samples," Technometrics 7 (1965), pp. 639-643.

[100] Harth, E.M.; Csermely, T.J.; Beck, B. and Lindsey, R.D. "Brain Functions and Neural Dynamics," J. Theor. Biol. 26 (1970), pp. 93-120.

[101] Hartman, C.G. Science and the Safe Period. Baltimore, Md.: Williams and Wilkins, 1962.

[102] Heller, R.A. and Donat, R.C. "Fatigue Failure of a Redundant Structure," in Structural Fatigue in Aircraft. A symposium of the Fifth Pacific Area National Meeting, American Society for Testing Materials, Seattle, Washington, 1965.

[103] Henry, L. "Fécondité et Famille, Modèles Mathematiques," Population, **3** (1957), pp. 413-444.

[104] Henry, L. "Some Data on Natural Fertility," Eugenics Quarterly 8 (1961), pp. 81-91.

[105] Henry, L. "Fécondité et Famille, Modèles Mathematiques, II," Population **16** (1961), pp. 27-48 and 261-282.

[106] Henry, L. "La Fécondité Naturelle, Observation Theorie, Resultats," Population **16** (1961), pp. 625-636.

[107] Herwald, S.W. "Evaluation and Reliability," Electrical Engineering **81** (1962), pp. 614-617.

[108] Hubbard, Ralph B., Jr. "Fatigue Failure of Metal Due to Narrow Band Random Loading," Ph.D. Dissertation, Department of Engineering Mechanics, University of Wisconsin, September 1966.

[109] Hubel, D.H. and Weisel, T.N. "Receptive Field and Functional Architecture in Two Visual Areas (18 and 19) of the Cat," J. Neurophysiology **28** (1965), p. 229.

[110] Impellizzeri, L.F. "Development of a Scatter Factor Applicable to Aircraft Fatigue Life," in Structural Fatigue in Aircraft. Proceedings of a symposium of the Fifth Pacific Area National Meeting, American Society for Testing Materials, Seattle, Washington, 1965.

[111] Jacoby, G., et. al. "Random Load Fatigue," C. E. Trans. VDI-Z, III, No. 21, in German, pp. 1479.

[112] James, W.H. "On the Possibility of Segregation in the Propensity to Spontaneous Abortion in the Human Female," Annals of Human Genetics 25 (1961), pp. 207-213.

[113] Jennrich, R.I. "FAST - A Subroutine to Compute Finite Fourier Transforms by the Cooley-Tukey Algorithm," Los Angeles: Health Sciences Computing Facility, University of California, 1970.

[114] Johnson, Leonard G. "The Effect of Inclusions of the Fatigue Life of Steel," Industrial Mathematics 11, Part I (1961), pp. 57-63.

[115] Ju, F.D.; Yao, J.T.P and Liu, T.T. "A Criterion for Dynamic Low-Cycle Shear Fracture," AFOSR Report AFOSR-69-0999TR. Albuquerque, New Mexico: Bureau of Engineering Research, University of New Mexico, March 1962.

[116] Kagiwada, H.; Kalaba, R. and Vereeke, B. "Invariant Imbedding and Fredholm Integral Equations with Displacement Kernels on an Infinite Interval," International J. Computer Math. 2 (1970), pp. 221-229.

[117] Kalaba, R. "Reduction of Matrix Integral Equations with Displacement Kernels on the Half-Line to Cauchy Systems," Proceedings of the 1970 Summer Workshop on Invariant Imbedding. New York: Springer-Verlag, 1971.

[118] Kalaba, R. and Ruspini, Enrique H. "Invariant Imbedding and a Matrix Integral Equation of Neuronal Networks," Mathematical Biosciences 12 (1971), pp. 273-280.

[119] Kausch von Schmelling, H.H.; Moghe, S.R. and Hsiao, C.C. "Influence of Reforming Processes on the Fracture Strength of Solids," Journal of Applied Physics, **38**, No. 1 (January 1967), pp. 201-204.

[120] Kendall, M.G. The Advanced Theory of Statistics, Volume I. London: Charles Griffin, 1958.

[121] Khazanov, I.I. "Estimating the Life Variability of Large Components," Russian Engineering Journal **XLVI**, No. 6 (June 1966), pp. 5-10.

[122] Kimball, A.W. "Estimation of Mortality Intensities in Animal Experiments," Biometrics **16** (1960), pp. 505-521.

[123] Kodlin, D. "A New Response Time Distribution," Biometrics **23** (1967), p. 239.

[124] Kowalewski, J. "On the Relation Between Fatigue Lives Under Random Loading and Under Corresponding Program Loading," in Full Scale Fatigue Testing of Aircraft Structures. Proceedings of a symposium held in Amsterdam, June 1959.

[125] Kugel, R.V. and Getselevich, V.B. "Life Factor Distribution Laws for Machines and Components," Russian Engineering Journal **XLVI**, No. 5 (January 1966), pp. 7-11.

[126] Kulikov, N.K. "Mechanical Engineering and Mathematics," Russian Engineering Journal **XLVI**, No. 1 (January 1966), pp. 82-85.

[127] Lieblein, J. "On the Exact Evaluation of the Variances and Covariances of Order Statistics in Samples from the Extreme-Value Distribution," Annals of Math. Stat. **24** (1953), pp. 282-287.

[128] Lieblien, J. "A New Method of Analyzing Extreme-Value Data," National Advisory Committee for Aeronautics, Technical Note 3053 (1954), p. 73.

[129] Leikin, A.S. "Increasing the Strength of Machine Parts by Optimum Stress Distribution," Russian Engineering Journal XLVI, No. 11 (november 1966), pp. 5-8.

[130] Levy, P. "Systèmes Semi-Markoviena à su plus une Infinité Denombrable D'états Possibles," Proceedings of the International Congress of Math, 2 (1954), p. 293.

[131] Lotka, A. "Théorie Analytique des Associations Biologiques," Act. Scientifiques et Industrielles 2 (1939), pp. 123-136.

[132] Lundberg, Bo K.O. and Eggwertz, S. "The Relationship Between Load Spectra and Fatigue Life," in Fatigue in Aircraft Structures. Edited by Freudenthal, A.M. New York: Academic Press, 1956, pp. 255-278.

[133] Madayag, Angel F. (Ed.) Metal Fatigue: Theory and Design. New York: John Wiley and Sons, Inc., 1969.

[134] Mann, H.B. and Wald, A. "On Stochastic Limit and Order Relationships," Annals of Math. Stat. 14 (1943), pp. 217-226.

[135] Mann, N.R. "Point and Interval Estimates for Reliability Parameters When Failure Times Have the Two-Parameter Weibull Distribution," Ph.D. Dissertation. Ann Arbor, Michigan: University Microfilms, 1965.

[136] Mann, N.R. "Results on Location and Scale Parameter Estimation with Application to the Extreme-Value Distribution," Aerospace Research Laboratories, Report ARL 67-0023, Office of Aerospace Research, United States Air Force, Wright-Patterson Air Force Base, Ohio, 1967.

[137] McMillan, J.C. and Pellow, R.M. "Fatigue Crack Propagation Under Programmed Loads and Crack Tip Opening Displacements," Engineering Fracture Mechanics 2 (1970), pp. 81-84.

[138] Mendenhall, W. "A Bibliography on Life Testing and Related Topics," Biometrika **45** (December 1958), pp. 512-543.

[139] Menon, M.V. "Estimation of the Shape and Scale Parameters of the Weibull Distribution," Technometrics **5** (1963), pp. 175-182.

[140] Mikhlin, S. and Smolitskiy, K. Approximate Methods for the Solution of Differential and Integral Equations. New York: American Elsevier, 1967.

[141] Miner, Milton A. "Cumulative Damage in Fatigue," Journal of Applied Mechanics **12** (1945), pp. A159-A164.

[142] Mittenbergs, A.A. "Empirical Analysis of Fatigue Strength of Pin-Loaded Lug Joints," in Fatigue Tests of Aircraft Structures: Low-cycle, Full-scale and Helicopters. A symposium of the Fourth Pacific Area National Meeting, American Society for Testing Materials, Los Angeles, Cal., 1962.

[143] Mohan, C.; Garg, R.C. and Singal, P.P. "Dependability of a Complex System," Operations Research **10** (1962), pp. 310-313.

[144] Mood, A. Introduction to the Theory of Statistics. New York: McGraw Hill Book Co., 1950.

[145] Moore, C.P.; Perkel, D.H. and Segundo, J.P. "Statistical Analysis and Functional Interpretation of Neuronal Spike Data," Ann. Rev. Psychology **28** (1966), pp. 493-522.

[146] Morozov, B.A. "Fatigue of Large Components Under Pulsating Compressive Stresses," Russian Engineering Journal **XLIX**, No. 2 (February 1969), pp. 17-18.

[147] Morrison, D.V. and David, H.A. "The Life Distribution and Reliability of a System with Spare Components," Annals of Math. Stat. **31** (1960), pp. 1084-1094.

[148] Mountcastle, V.B. "Modality and Topographic Properties of Single Neurons of Cat's Somatic Sensory Cortex," J. Neurophysiol. 20 (1957), p. 408.

[149] Murthy, V.K. "On the General Renewal Process," Ph. D. Dissertation. Chapel Hill, No. Carolina: University of North Carolina Institute of Statistics, Mimeo Series No. 293, 1961.

[150] Murthy, V.K. "Estimation of the Spectrum," Ann. Math. Statist. 32 (1961), pp. 730-738.

[151] Murthy, V.K. "Notes on the Parametric Approach in Reliability," Douglas Aircraft Co., Inc., Douglas Paper No. 1906, December 1963.

[152] Murthy, V.K. "Estimation of Jumps, Reliability and Hazard Rate," Annals of Math. Stat. 36 (1965), pp. 1032-1040.

[153] Murthy, V.K. "Study of Nonparametric Techniques for Estimating Reliability and Other Quality Parameters," NASA Contract Final Report, McDonnel-Douglas Corporation, 1968.

[154] Murthy, V.K., et. al. "Statistical Analysis of the Electrocardiogram," Proceedings of the Third Asilomar Conference on Circuits and Systems, December 1969, pp. 14-19.

[155] Murthy, V.K., et. al. "Mathematical Model for Electrocardiogram Abnormality Detection," in Proceedings of the Fourth Asilomar Conference on Circuits and Systems, November 1970, pp. 687-689.

[156] Murthy, V.K., et. al. "Analysis of Power Spectral Densities of Electrocardiograms," Math. Biosci. 12 (1971), pp. 41-51.

[157] Murthy, V.K. and Swartz, Boyd. Annotated Biblio-Graphy on Cumulative Fatigue Damage and Structural Reliability Models. ARL Report, ARL 72-0161, United States Air Force, Wright-Patterson Air Force Base, Ohio, December 1972.

[158] Nesbitt, Robert E.L., Jr. Perinatal Loss. Philadelphia, Pa.: F.A. Davis, Co., 1957.

[159] Neyman, J. "Contribution to the Theory of the Chi-Square Test," Proceedings of the First Berkeley Symposium held at Berkeley, California on August 13-18, 1945 and January 27-29, 1946. Berkeley, Calif.: University of California Press, pp. 239-273.

[160] Owen, A.R.G. "The Theory of Genetical Recombination," Proc. Royal Philosophical Society of London, B, **136** (1949), p. 67.

[161] Papoulis, A. "The Abused Concept of Conditional Failure Rates," IEEE Transactions on Reliability, in Letter to the Editor, **R-13** (June 1964), pp. 62-63.

[162] Pearson, K. Tables for Statisticians and Biometricians, Part I. Cambridge: Cambridge University Press, 1924.

[163] Perrin, E.B. and Sheps, M.C. "Stochastic Models for Human Fertility," Abstract in Biometrics **18**, p. 624.

[164] Perrin, E.B. and Sheps, M.C. "Human Reproduction: A Stochastic Process," Biometrics **20** (March 1964), pp. 28-45.

[165] Portman, V.T. "Assessment of Machine Component Life From Observational Rate," Russian Engineering Journal **XLIX**, No. 4 (April 1969), pp. 10-14.

[166] Potter, R.G., Jr. "Some Relationships Between Short Range and Long Range Risks of Unwanted Pregnancy," Milbank Memorial Fund Quarterly **38** (1960), pp. 255-263.

[167] Potter, R.G., Jr. "Some Physical Correlates of Fertility Control in the United States," Proceedings of the Conference of International Population Union, VII (1967), p. 294.

[168] Prevorsek, D. and Lyons, W.J. "Fatigue Fracture in Fibrous Polymers as a Brittle, Crack-Nucleation Process," Journal of Applied Physics 35, No. 11 (November 1964), pp. 3152-3164.

[169] Pyke, R. "Markov Renewal Process: Definitions and Preliminary Properties," Annals of Math. Stat. 32 (1961), pp. 1231-1242.

[170] Pyke, R. "Markov Renewal Processes of Zero Order and Their Applications to Counter Theory," in Studies in Applied Probability and Management Science. Edited by Karlin, et. al. Stanford, Calif.: Stanford University Press, 1962, pp. 173-183.

[171] Rabinowicz, E.; McIntire, I. and Shiralkar, B. "Life Testing Using Continuous Acceleration," in Space Simulation. Edited by Richmond, Joseph C. Proceedings of the Conference of the Institute for Basic Standards of the National Bureau of Standards at Gaithersburg, Maryland. Washington, D.C.: U.S. Government Printing Office, October 1970, pp. 457-471.

[172] Raithby, K.D. "A Comparison of Predicted and Achieved Fatigue Lives of Aircraft Structures," in Fatigue Life of Aircraft Structures. Proceedings of the symposium held in Paris, 1961, pp. 249-261.

[173] Rao, C.R. Advanced Statistical Methods in Biometric Research. New York: John Wiley and Sons, 1952.

[174] Ravishankar, T.J. "Simulation of Random Load Fatigue in Laboratory Testing," UTIAS Review 29 (March 1970).

[175] Rosenfeld, M.S. "Aircraft Structural Fatigue Research in the Navy," in Fatigue Tests of Aircraft Structures: Low-cycle, Full-scale and Helicoptors. Proceedings of a symposium of the Fourth Pacific Area National Meeting, American Society for Testing Materials, Los Angeles, 1962.

[176] Salt, T.L. "A Designer's Approach to the Fatigue Failure Mechanism." Proceedings of the 1973 Annual Reliability and Maintainability Symposium of the Institute of Electrical and Electronics Engineers, Inc., held at Philadelphia, Pa., 1973.

[177] Saltzberg, S., et. al. "ECG Monitoring and Waveform Analysis Utilizing Interactive Computer Graphics," J. Assoc. Advan. Med. Instrument 5 (1971), pp. 91-96.

[178] Saunders, S.C. "A Probabilistic Interpretation of Miner's Rule, II," SIAM J. Appl. Math. 19, No. 1 (July 1970), pp. 251-265.

[179] Scheibel, M.E. and Scheibel, A.B. "Anatomical Basis of Attention," in The Neurosciences. Newton, N.Y.: Rockefeller Press, 1968.

[180] Schijve, J. "The Endurance Under Program-Fatigue Testing," in Full-Scale Testing of Aircraft Structures, Proceedings of a symposium held in Amsterdam, June, 1959.

[181] Schijve, J. "Estimation of Fatigue Performance of Aircraft Structures," in Fatigue Tests of Aircraft Structures: Low-cycle, Full-scale and Helicoptors. Proceedings of a symposium of the Fourth Pacific Area National Meeting, American Society for Testing Materials, Los Angeles, 1962.

[182] Serenson, S.V. and Kogaev, V.P. "Life of Machine Components and the Porbability of Failure," Russian Engineering Journal XLVI, No. 1, (January 1966), pp. 6-11.

[183] Sheps, M.C. "Pregnancy Wastage as a Factor in the Analysis of Fertility Data," Abstract in Population Index 2 (1963), p. 225.

[184] Sheps, M.C. and Perrin, E.B. "Changes in Birth Rates as a Function of Contraceptive Effectiveness: Some Applications of a Stochastic Model," J. Amer. Public Health Assoc. 53

(1963), pp. 1031-1046.

[185] Sheps, M.C. and Perrin, E.B. "The Distribution of Birth Intervals Under a Class of Stochastic Fertility Models," Abstract in Biometrics 20, No. 991 (1964), p. 395.

[186] Singpurwalla, N.D. "Statistical Fatigue Models: A Survey," IEEE Transactions on Reliability R-20, No. 3 (August 1971), pp. 185-189.

[187] Slobin, B.Z. and Trofimov, O.R. "Statistical Analysis of Random Load Variations," Russian Engineering Journal XLVI, No. 10 (October 1966), pp. 4-8.

[188] Smith, Clarence R. "Small Specimen Data for Predicting Life of Full-Scale Structures," in Fatigue Tests of Aircraft Structures: Low-cycle, Full-scale and Helicoptors. Proceeding of the Fourth Pacific Area National Meeting, American Society for Testing Materials, Los Angeles, 1962.

[189] Smith, S.H. "Random-Loading Fatigue Crack Growth Behavior of Some Aluminum and Titanium Alloys," in Structural Fatigue in Aircraft. Proceedings of the Fifth Pacific Area National Meeting, American Society for Testing Materials, Seattle, Washington, 1965.

[190] Smith, W.L. "Asymptotic Renewal Theorems," Proc. Royal Society of Edinburgh, A, 64 (1953), pp. 9-48.

[191] Smith, W.L. "Asymptotic Renewal Theorems," Proc. Royal Society of Edinburgh, A, 62 (1954), pp. 9-48.

[192] Smith, W.L. "Extensions of a Renewal Theorem," Proc. of the Cambridge Philosophical Society 51 (1955), pp. 629-638.

[193] Smith, W.L. "Regenerative Stochastic Processes," Proc. of the Royal Society of Edinburgh, A, 232 (1955), pp. 6-31.

[194] Smith, W.L. "On Renewal Theory, Counter Problems and Quasi-Poisson Processes," Proc. Cambridge Philosophical Society 53 (1957), pp. 175-193.

[195] Smith, W.L. "Renewal Theory and Its Ramifications," Journal of the Royal Statistical Society, B, 20 (1958), pp. 243-302.

[196] Smith, W.L. "On the Cumulants of Renewal Processes," Biometrika 46 (1959), pp. 1-29.

[197] Sorenson, Arthur, Jr. "Product Reliability and Random Fatigue," IEEE Transactions on Reliability R-20, No. 4 (November 1971), pp. 244-248.

[198] Southworth, R.W. In Mathematical Methods for Digital Computers. Edited by Ralston, A. and Wilf, H., 1960.

[199] Srinivasan, S.K. and Rajamannar, G. "Counter Models and Dependent Renewal Point Processes Related to Neuronal Firing," Math. Biosci. 7 (1970), pp. 27-39.

[200] Srinivasan, S.K. and Rajamannar, G. "Renewal Point Processes and Neuronal Spike Trains," Math. Biosci. 6 (1970), pp. 331-335.

[201] Srinivasan, S.K. and Rajamannar, G. "Selective Interaction Between Two Independent Stationary Recurrent Point Processes," Journal of Applied Probability 7 (1970), pp. 476-482.

[202] Stevensen, J. and Moses. F. "Reliability Analysis of Frame Structures," Journal of the Structural Division, Proceedings of the ASCE 96, No. ST11 (November 1970), pp. 2409-2425.

[203] Tacklind, S. "Fourieranalytische Behandlung vom Erneuerungsproblem," Skand. Aktuar. 28 (1945), p. 68.

[204] Tartakovskii, I.B. "Predicting the Wear on Railway Wheels," Russian Engineering Journal XLIX

No. 4 (April 1969), pp. 17-20.

[205] Thoman, D.R.; Bain, L.J. and Antle, C.E. "Inferences on the Parameters of the Weibull Distribution," Technometrics 11 (1969), pp. 445-460.

[206] Thompson, N. and Wadsworth, N.J. "Metal Fatigue," Advances in Physics 7, No. 25 (January 1958), pp. 72-169.

[207] Tietze, C. "The Effect of Breatfeeding on the Rate of Conception," Proceedings of the Conference of the International Population Union, 1961.

[208] U.S. Government. Vital Statistics of the United States, 1900. Washington, D.C.: U.S. Government Printing Office.

[209] Wagner, G.R. and Mischke, C.R. "Cycles-to-Failure and Stress-to-Failure Weibull Distributions in Steel Wire Fatigue," Proceedings of the 1973 Annual Reliability and Maintainability Symposium of the Institute of Electrical Engineers, at Philadelphia, Pa., 1973.

[210] Warren, William. On Two-Dimensional Satellite Processes. Ph.D. Dissertation. Chapel Hill, North Carolina: University of North Carolina, 1962.

[211] Watson, G.S. and Leadbetter, M.R. "Hazard Analysis, I," Biometrika 51 (1964), pp. 175-184.

[212] Weertman, J. "Rate of Growth of Fatigue Cracks Calculated from the Theory of Infinitesimal Dislocations Distributed on a Plane," Proceedings of the First International Conference on Fracture, Japanese Society for Strength and Fracture of Materials, edited by Yokobori, T. in Tokyo, 1965, p. 153.

[213] Weibull. W. "A Statistical Distribution Function of Wide Applicability," Journal of Applied Mechanics 18 (1951), pp. 292-297.

[214] Weiss, G. and Zelen, M. "A Stochastic Model for Clinical Trials," Abstract in Biometrics, 1962, p. 627.

[215] Wirsching, P.H. and Yao, T.P. "Statistical Methods in Structural Fatigue," Journal of Structural Division, Proceedings of the ASCE (1970), pp. 1201-1219.

[216] Wolfowitz, J. "The Efficienty of Sequential Estimates and Wald's Equation for Sequential Processes," Annals of Math. Stat. **18** (1947), p. 215.

[217] Wood, W.A. "Mechanism of Fatigue," in Fatigue in Aircraft Structures. Edited by Freudenthal, A.M. New York: Academic Press, 1956, pp. 1-19.

[218] Yang, J.N. and Heer, E. "Reliability of Randomly Excited Structures," AIAA Journal **9**, No. 7 (July 1971), pp. 1262-1268.

[219] Yokobori, Takeo. The Strength, Fracture and Fatigue of Materials. Original in Japanese. Groningen, The Netherlands: P. Noordhoff., 1955. Translated, 1964.

[220] Zaitsev, G.Z. and Fardzhov, G.Z. "Fatigue Strength of Steel in Biharmonic Vibration," Russian Engineering Journal **XLIX**, No. 4 (April 1969), pp. 8-10.

[221] Zelen, M. "Application of Exponential Models to Problems in Cancer Research," Royal Statistical Society Journal, Series A, **129** (1966), pp. 368-398.

**V.K. Murthy**
is affiliated with both the University of California, Los Angeles, and the University of Southern California. Dr. Murthy's undergraduate work was completed at Andhra University (B.Sc., Honours) and at the University of Bombay (M.Sc.); the Ph.D. was granted by the University of North Carolina, Chapel Hill.

The American Statistical Association elected Dr. Murthy as Fellow in 1973. The author is also a Fellow of the Royal Statistical Society, of Sigma Xi, and a member of the Institute of Mathematical Statistics. Government and industry frequently call upon Dr. Murthy for consulting services.

**The General Point Process:** Applications to Structural Fatigue, Bioscience, and Medical Research (No. 5 of the Series)

concerns itself with the theory and applications of that process of events which occurs in succession, in time and in space, such as a straight line, a plane, and the three-dimensional space in which we live. As noted in the Preface, "the word 'event' or 'point' stands for the happening of a situation." Examples of such events include an airplane experiencing sudden acceleration due to turbulence or maneuvering procedures, or a person suffering an acute myocardial infarction. The lapses in time between points or events, when time is counted arbitrarily, i.e., not at the beginning of the happening of an event, is called a General Point Process.

The author's two prime objectives are

* to develop the theory involving the distribution of events by any specified time for a General Point Process
* to review the many fields of applications of this theory and to formulate their interrelations.

**Engineering applications** mainly are centered around the spreading of a dominant crack by the structure suffering "events" of stress at random epochs. The corresponding strain is a cumulative process with an imbedded equilibrium point process. The details of the computations relating to the probability that the cumulative damage exceeds a critical level (or the structure fails) are given.

**Biological applications** include the General Point Process associated with the sequence of occurrence of nerve pulses, as well as the process of human reproduction.

**Medical applications** include the number of events such as premature ventricular contractions and premature atricular contractions that occurred by a designated time *t* in one-line, red-time monitoring patients acutely ill in a coronary care unit with, say, heart attack. Similar situations occur in electroencephalography and the so-called "crib death" of babies.

Finally, the situations where one simultaneously analyzes several General Point Processes are considered, and the results are given.